Everyday Mathematics®

The University of Chicago School Mathematics Project

Math Masters

The McGraw·Hill Companies

The University of Chicago School Mathematics Project (UCSMP)

Max Bell, Director, UCSMP Elementary Materials Component; Director, *Everyday Mathematics* First Edition; James McBride, Director, *Everyday Mathematics* Second Edition
Andy Isaacs, Director, *Everyday Mathematics* Third Edition
Amy Dillard, Associate Director, *Everyday Mathematics* Third Edition

Authors
Max Bell, Jean Bell, John Bretzlauf, Mary Ellen Dairyko*, Amy Dillard, Robert Hartfield, Andy Isaacs, James McBride, Kathleen Pitvorec, Peter Saecker

**Third Edition only*

Technical Art
Diana Barrie

Teachers in Residence
Lisa Bernstein, Carole Skalinder

Editorial Assistant
Jamie Montague Callister

Contributors
Carol Arkin, Robert Balfanz, Sharlean Brooks, James Flanders, David Garcia, Rita Gronbach, Deborah Arron Leslie, Curtis Lieneck, Diana Marino, Mary Moley, William D. Pattison, William Salvato, Jean Marie Sweigart, Leeann Wille

Photo Credits
©C Squared Studios/Getty Images, p. 203; ©Tim Flach/Getty Images, cover; Getty Images, cover, *bottom left;* ©JupiterImages/Comstock, p. 82; ©Ken O'Donoghue, pp. 233, 234; Royalty-free/Corbis, pp. 315, 357.

---

www.WrightGroup.com

Copyright © 2007 by Wright Group/McGraw-Hill

All rights reserved. Permission is granted to reproduce the material contained herein on the condition that such material be reproduced only for classroom use; be provided to students, teachers, or families without charge; and be used solely in conjunction with Everyday Mathematics. Any other reproduction, for use or sale, is prohibited without prior written permission from the publisher.

Printed in the United States of America.

Send all inquiries to:
Wright Group/McGraw-Hill
P.O. Box 812960
Chicago, IL 60681

ISBN 0-07-604572-2

3 4 5 6 7 8 9 POH 12 11 10 09 08 07 06

Contents

Teaching Masters 

Home Link Masters 

Unit 1

Unit 2

Copyright © Wright Group/McGraw-Hill

Unit 3

Unit 4

Copyright © Wright Group/McGraw-Hill

Unit 5

Copyright © Wright Group/McGraw-Hill

Unit 6

Unit 7

Copyright © Wright Group/McGraw-Hill

Unit 8

Copyright © Wright Group/McGraw-Hill

Unit 9

Copyright © Wright Group/McGraw-Hill

Project Masters

Teaching Aid Masters

Copyright © Wright Group/McGraw-Hill

Game Masters

Copyright © Wright Group/McGraw-Hill

Teaching Masters and Home Link Masters

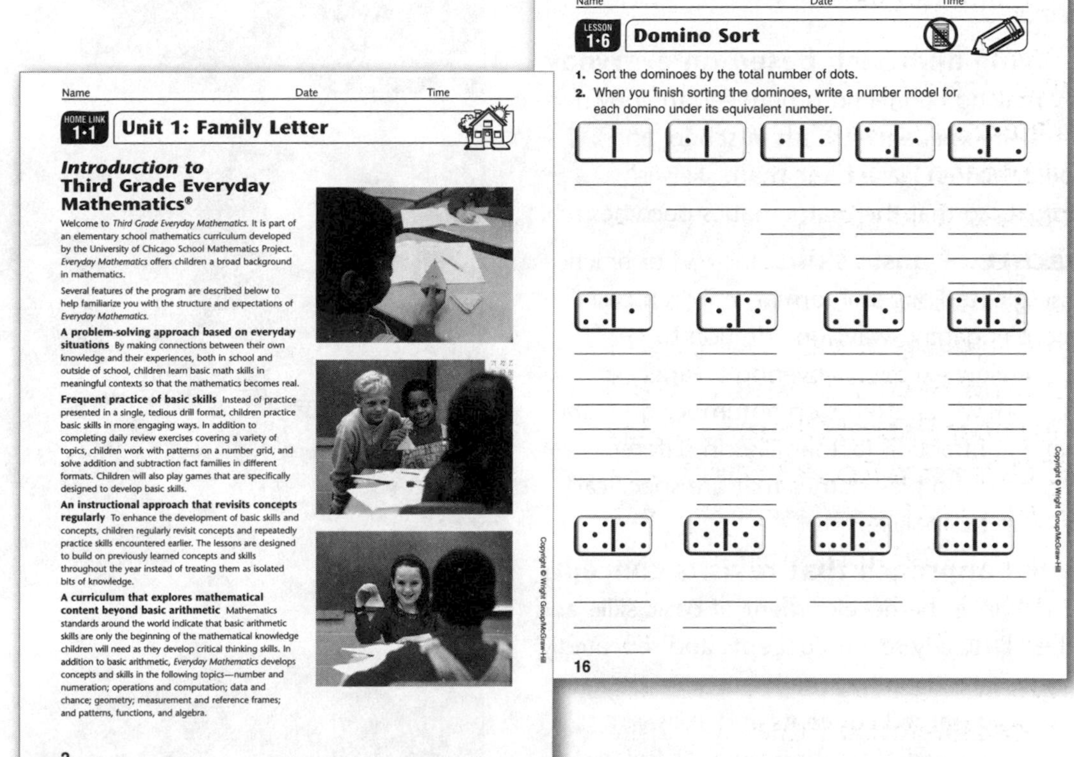

Name Date Time

HOME LINK 1·1 **Unit 1: Family Letter**

Introduction to Third Grade Everyday Mathematics®

Welcome to *Third Grade Everyday Mathematics.* It is part of an elementary school mathematics curriculum developed by the University of Chicago School Mathematics Project. *Everyday Mathematics* offers children a broad background in mathematics.

Several features of the program are described below to help familiarize you with the structure and expectations of *Everyday Mathematics.*

A problem-solving approach based on everyday situations By making connections between their own knowledge and their experiences, both in school and outside of school, children learn basic math skills in meaningful contexts so that the mathematics becomes real.

Frequent practice of basic skills Instead of practice presented in a single, tedious drill format, children practice basic skills in more engaging ways. In addition to completing daily review exercises covering a variety of topics, children work with patterns on a number grid, and solve addition and subtraction fact families in different formats. Children will also play games that are specifically designed to develop basic skills.

An instructional approach that revisits concepts regularly To enhance the development of basic skills and concepts, children regularly revisit concepts and repeatedly practice skills encountered earlier. The lessons are designed to build on previously learned concepts and skills throughout the year instead of treating them as isolated bits of knowledge.

A curriculum that explores mathematical content beyond basic arithmetic Mathematics standards around the world indicate that basic arithmetic skills are only the beginning of the mathematical knowledge children will need as they develop critical thinking skills. In addition to basic arithmetic, *Everyday Mathematics* develops concepts and skills in the following topics—number and numeration; operations and computation; data and chance; geometry; measurement and reference frames; and patterns, functions, and algebra.

Copyright © Wright Group/McGraw-Hill

2

Name Date Time

LESSON 1·6 **Domino Sort**

1. Sort the dominoes by the total number of dots.
2. When you finish sorting the dominoes, write a number model for each domino under its equivalent number.

Copyright © Wright Group/McGraw-Hill

16

Copyright © Wright Group/McGraw-Hill

Name Date Time

HOME LINK 1•1

Unit 1: Family Letter

Introduction to Third Grade Everyday Mathematics®

Welcome to *Third Grade Everyday Mathematics.* It is part of an elementary school mathematics curriculum developed by the University of Chicago School Mathematics Project. *Everyday Mathematics* offers children a broad background in mathematics.

Several features of the program are described below to help familiarize you with the structure and expectations of *Everyday Mathematics.*

A problem-solving approach based on everyday situations By making connections between their own knowledge and their experiences, both in school and outside of school, children learn basic math skills in meaningful contexts so that the mathematics becomes real.

Frequent practice of basic skills Instead of practice presented in a single, tedious drill format, children practice basic skills in more engaging ways. In addition to completing daily review exercises covering a variety of topics, children work with patterns on a number grid, and solve addition and subtraction fact families in different formats. Children will also play games that are specifically designed to develop basic skills.

An instructional approach that revisits concepts regularly To enhance the development of basic skills and concepts, children regularly revisit concepts and repeatedly practice skills encountered earlier. The lessons are designed to build on previously learned concepts and skills throughout the year instead of treating them as isolated bits of knowledge.

A curriculum that explores mathematical content beyond basic arithmetic Mathematics standards around the world indicate that basic arithmetic skills are only the beginning of the mathematical knowledge children will need as they develop critical thinking skills. In addition to basic arithmetic, *Everyday Mathematics* develops concepts and skills in the following topics—number and numeration; operations and computation; data and chance; geometry; measurement and reference frames; and patterns, functions, and algebra.

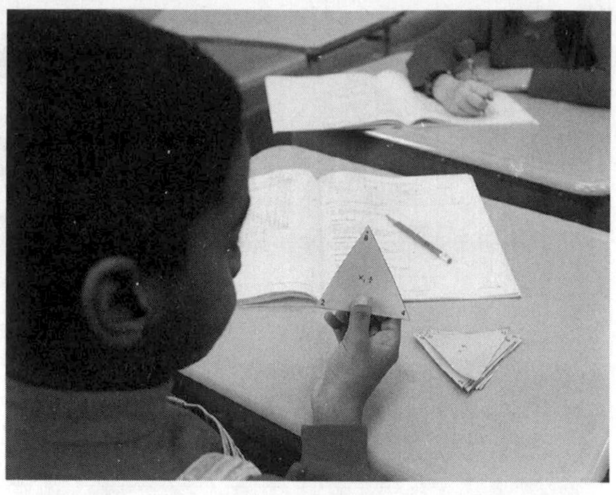

Copyright © Wright Group/McGraw-Hill

Third Grade Everyday Mathematics emphasizes the following content:

Number and Numeration Counting patterns; place value; reading and writing whole numbers through 1,000,000; fractions, decimals, and integers

Operations and Computation Multiplication and division facts extended to multidigit problems; working with properties; operations with fractions and money

Data and Chance Collecting, organizing, and displaying data using tables, charts, and graphs; using basic probability terms

Geometry Exploring 2- and 3-dimensional shapes and other geometric concepts

Measurement Recording equivalent units of length; recognizing appropriate units of measure; finding the areas of rectangles by counting squares

Reference Frames Using multiplication arrays, coordinate grids, thermometers, clocks, calendars; and map scales to estimate distances

Patterns, Functions, and Algebra Finding patterns on the number grid; solving Frames-and-Arrows puzzles having two rules; completing variations of "What's My Rule?" activities; exploring the relationship between multiplication and division; using parentheses in writing number models; naming missing parts of number models

Everyday Mathematics will provide you with ample opportunities to monitor your child's progress and to participate in your child's mathematics experiences.

Throughout the year, you will receive Family Letters to keep you informed of the mathematical content your child will be studying in each unit. Each letter will include a vocabulary list, suggested Do-Anytime Activities for you and your child, and an answer guide to selected Home Link (homework) activities.

You will enjoy seeing your child's confidence and comprehension soar as he or she connects mathematics to everyday life. We look forward to an exciting year!

Routines, Review, and Assessment

The first purpose of Unit 1 is to establish routines that children will use throughout the school year. The second purpose is to review and extend mathematical concepts that were developed in previous grades.

In Unit 1, children will look for examples of numbers for the Numbers All Around Museum. Examples of numbers might include identification numbers, measures, money, telephone numbers, addresses, and codes. Children will also look at number patterns in a problem-solving setting by using number-grid puzzles and Frames-and-Arrows diagrams. (*See examples on the next page.*)

Throughout Unit 1, children will use numbers within the context of real-life situations. After reviewing place-value concepts, children will work with money and pretend to purchase items from a vending machine and a store. The emphasis on applying numbers to the real world is also reflected in the yearlong Length-of-Day Project, a weekly routine that involves collecting, recording, and graphing sunrise/sunset data.

Copyright © Wright Group/McGraw-Hill

Unit 1: Family Letter *cont.*

Vocabulary

Important terms in Unit 1:

digits Any of the symbols 0, 1, 2, 3, 4, 5, 6, 7, 8, and 9 in the base 10 numeration system.

estimate An answer close to, or approximating, an exact answer.

tool kits In *Everyday Mathematics,* a bag or box containing a calculator, measuring tools, and manipulatives often used by students of the program.

number grid In *Everyday Mathematics,* a table in which consecutive numbers are arranged, usually in 10 columns per row. A move from one number to the next within a row is a change of 1; a move from one number to the next within a column is a change of 10.

									0
1	2	3	4	5	6	7	8	9	10
11	12	13	14	15	16	17	18	19	20
21	22	23	24	25	26	27	28	29	30

number-grid puzzle In *Everyday Mathematics,* a piece of the number grid in which some, but not all, of the numbers are missing. Children use number-grid puzzles to practice place-value concepts.

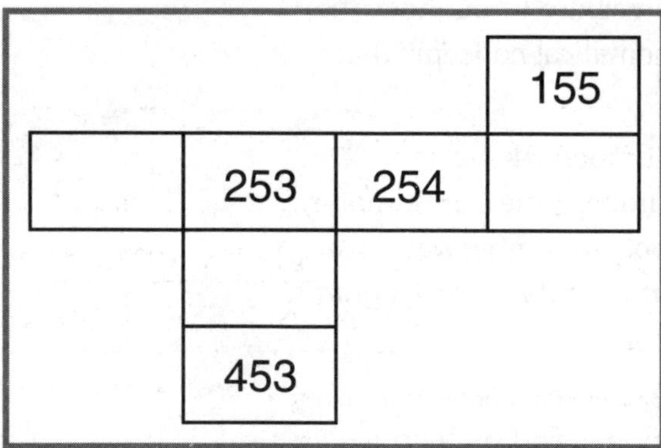

range The difference between the *maximum* and the *minimum* in a set of data. Used as a measure of the spread of data.

mode The value or values that occur most often in a set of data.

name-collection box In *Everyday Mathematics,* a diagram that is used for collecting equivalent names for a number.

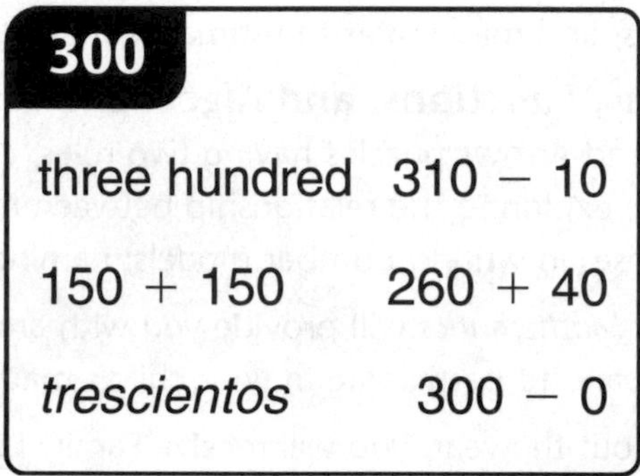

Frames-and-Arrows In *Everyday Mathematics,* diagrams consisting of frames connected by arrows used to represent number sequences. Each frame contains a number and each arrow represents a rule that determines which number goes in the next frame. There may be more than one rule, represented by different colored arrows.

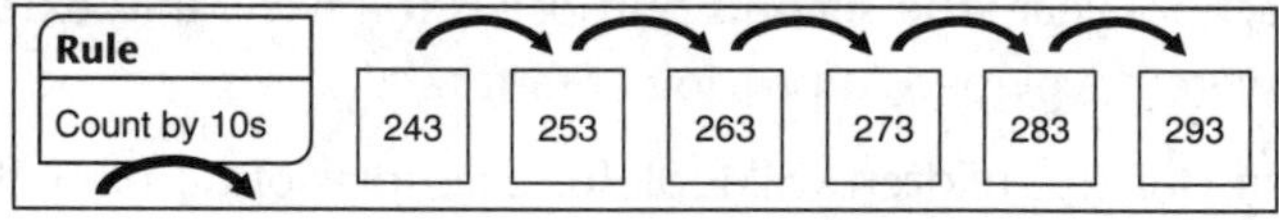

Copyright © Wright Group/McGraw-Hill

As You Help Your Child with Homework

As your child brings home assignments, you may want to go over the instructions together, clarifying them as necessary. The answers listed below will guide you through this unit's Home Links.

Home Link 1•1

1. Answers vary **2.** 7; 7; 7; 7

Home Link 1•2

1. 21; 41 **2.** 164; 166; 184; 186
3. Sample answers: 97; 98; 99; 100; 108; 119; 127; 128; 129; 130
4. 1,372; 1,383; 1,392; 1,393; 1,394

Home Link 1•3

Sample answers:

1. ②, 4~~6~~7 **2.** 2,567 **3.** 2,367 **4.** 899; 908; 910
5. 1,044; 1,055; 1,065 **6.** 9 **7.** 4 **8.** 9 **9.** 5

Home Link 1•4

1. Answers vary. **2.** 8:00 **3.** 3:30 **4.** 6:15
5. 11:45 **6.** 7:10 **7.** 5:40 **8.** Answers vary.

Home Link 1•5

1.

Time Spent Watching TV	
Hours	**Children**
0	/
1	//
2	//
3	////
4	/
5	/

2. 0 **3.** 5 **4.** 5 **5.** 3 **6.** 3

Home Link 1•6

1. **18** Sample answers:
9 + 9
2 × 9
6 + 6 + 6
~~////~~ ~~////~~ ~~////~~ ///
dieciocho 4 × 5 − 2
36 ÷ 2
number of days in two weeks + 4 days

2. **12** ~~////~~ ~~//~~
one dozen
7 + 5
number of months in 1 year
15 − 3
10 + 2
~~18 − 4~~
~~9 − 3~~

3. Answers vary.

Home Link 1•7

Sample answers:
1. sure to happen **2.** sure not to happen
3. may happen, but not sure
4. may happen, but not sure **5.** 7 **6.** 3
7. 4 **8.** 7

Home Link 1•8

1.

131	132	133	134	135	136	137	138	139	140
141	142	143	144	145	146	147	148	149	150
151	152	153	154	155	156	157	158	159	160
161	162	163	164	165	166	167	168	169	170
171	172	173	174	175	176	177	178	179	180

2. 154; 23 **3.** 148; 29 **4.** 22
5. Sample answer: I counted 2 tens from 180 and then 2 ones. **6.** 6 **7.** 7 **8.** 13 **9.** 13

Home Link 1•9

Answers vary. **3.** 3 **4.** 3 **5.** 5 **6.** 3

Home Link 1•10

5. 6; 6; 5; 10 **6.** 6; 5; 2; 8

Home Link 1•11

1. 4 **2.** 11 **3.** 4 **4.** 11

Home Link 1•12

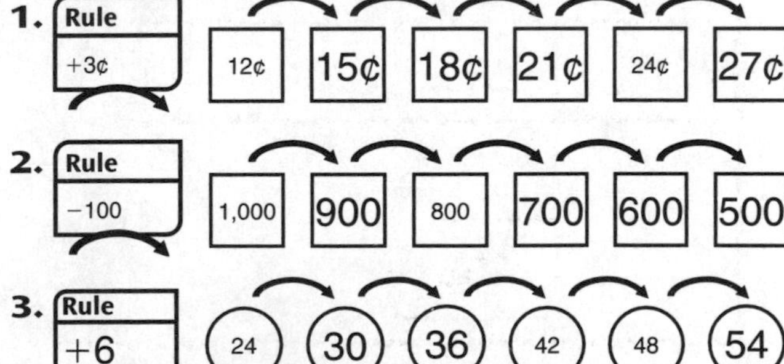

4. 1.46 **5.** 0.87 **6.** 12.06
7. Sample answers: 3Ⓠ1Ⓓ4Ⓟ; 2Ⓠ3Ⓓ1Ⓝ4Ⓟ

Home Link 1•13

4. 4 **5.** 4 **6.** 7 **7.** 7

Copyright © Wright Group/McGraw-Hill

Name Date Time

Numbers All Around Museum

Family Note In the *Third Grade Everyday Mathematics* program, children *do* mathematics.

We expect that children will want to share their enthusiasm for the mathematics activities they do in school with members of their families. Your child will bring home assignments and activities to do as homework throughout the year. These assignments, called Home Links, will be identified by the symbol at the top of the page. The assignments will not take very much time to complete, but most of them involve interaction with an adult or an older child.

There are good reasons for including Home Links in the third-grade program:

- The assignments encourage children to take initiative and responsibility for completing them. As you respond with encouragement and assistance, you help your child build independence and self-confidence.
- Home Links reinforce newly learned skills and concepts. They provide thinking and practice time at each child's own pace.
- These assignments are often designed to relate what is done in school to children's lives outside school. This helps tie mathematics to the real world, which is very important in the *Everyday Mathematics* program.
- The Home Links assignments will give you a better idea of the mathematics your child is learning in school.

Generally, you can help by listening and responding to your child's requests and comments about mathematics. You can help by linking numbers to real life, pointing out ways in which you use numbers (time, TV channels, page numbers, telephone numbers, bus routes, and so on). Extending the notion that "children who are read to, read," *Everyday Mathematics* supports the belief that children who have someone do math with them will learn mathematics. Playful counting and thinking games are very helpful in promoting such learning.

The Family Note will explain what the children are learning in class. Use it to help you understand where the assignment fits into your child's learning.

Copyright © Wright Group/McGraw-Hill

Name Date Time

HOME LINK 1•1

Numbers All Around Museum *continued*

Family Note Numbers on advertisements show quantities and prices (3 cans of soup for $1.00); food containers show weight or capacity (a $15\frac{1}{2}$-oz can of black beans or 1-quart carton of milk); and telephone books show addresses and phone numbers. By helping your child find examples of numbers in everyday life, you will reinforce the idea that numbers are all around us and are used for many reasons. Help your child recognize numbers by filling in the table.

Please return this Home Link to school within the next few days.

1. Find as many different kinds of numbers as you can. Record the numbers in the table below. Be sure to include the unit if there is one.

Number	Unit (if there is one)	Where you found the number
14	oz	cereal box

Find objects or pictures with numbers on them to bring to school. Check with an adult at home first. Do not bring anything valuable.

Practice

2. Solve.

$\begin{array}{r} 5 \\ +2 \\ \hline \square \end{array}$ $\begin{array}{r} \square \\ -2 \\ \hline 5 \end{array}$ $\begin{array}{r} \square \\ -5 \\ \hline 2 \end{array}$ $\begin{array}{r} 2 \\ +5 \\ \hline \square \end{array}$

Copyright © Wright Group/McGraw-Hill

Name Date Time

LESSON 1·1 Number Sequences

Write your own number sequences.

1.

Unit

______; ______; ______; ______; ______; ______; ______;...

2.

______; ______; ______; ______; ______; ______; ______;...

3.

______; ______; ______; ______; ______; ______; ______;...

4.

______; ______; ______; ______; ______; ______; ______;...

5.

______; ______; ______; ______; ______; ______; ______;...

Copyright © Wright Group/McGraw-Hill

Name Date Time

HOME LINK 1·2

Number-Grid Puzzles

Family Note Today your child reviewed patterns on a number grid and completed number grid puzzles. On this Home Link, your child may use either the number grid or its patterns to complete the number grid puzzles. Ask your child to explain how he or she filled in the puzzles.

SRB 7–9

–9	–8	–7	–6	–5	–4	–3	–2	–1	0
1	2	3	4	5	6	7	8	9	10
11	12	13	14	15	16	17	18	19	20
21	22	23	24	25	26	27	28	29	30
31	32	33	34	35	36	37	38	39	40
41	42	43	44	45	46	47	48	49	50
51	52	53	54	55	56	57	58	59	60
61	62	63	64	65	66	67	68	69	70
71	72	73	74	75	76	77	78	79	80
81	82	83	84	85	86	87	88	89	90
91	92	93	94	95	96	97	98	99	100

When you move right, the numbers increase by 1.

When you move left, the numbers decrease by 1.

When you move down, the numbers increase by 10.

When you move up, the numbers decrease by 10.

Fill in the missing numbers. Explain the patterns to someone at home.

1.

	22
31	

2.

	175	

Try This

3. Make up your own.

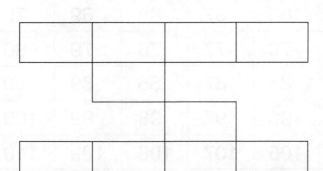

4.

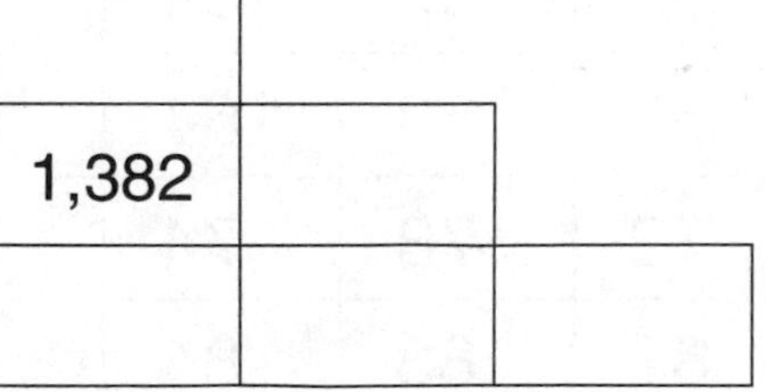

Copyright © Wright Group/McGraw-Hill

Name Date Time

LESSON 1·2

Number Grid

−9	−8	−7	−6	−5	−4	−3	−2	−1	0
1	2	3	4	5	6	7	8	9	10
11	12	13	14	15	16	17	18	19	20
21	22	23	24	25	26	27	28	29	30
31	32	33	34	35	36	37	38	39	40
41	42	43	44	45	46	47	48	49	50
51	52	53	54	55	56	57	58	59	60
61	62	63	64	65	66	67	68	69	70
71	72	73	74	75	76	77	78	79	80
81	82	83	84	85	86	87	88	89	90
91	92	93	94	95	96	97	98	99	100
101	102	103	104	105	106	107	108	109	110

Copyright © Wright Group/McGraw-Hill

−9	−8	−7	−6	−5	−4	−3	−2	−1	0
1	2	3	4	5	6	7	8	9	10
11	12	13	14	15	16	17	18	19	20
21	22	23	24	25	26	27	28	29	30
31	32	33	34	35	36	37	38	39	40
41	42	43	44	45	46	47	48	49	50
51	52	53	54	55	56	57	58	59	60
61	62	63	64	65	66	67	68	69	70
71	72	73	74	75	76	77	78	79	80
81	82	83	84	85	86	87	88	89	90
91	92	93	94	95	96	97	98	99	100
101	102	103	104	105	106	107	108	109	110

Copyright © Wright Group/McGraw-Hill

Name Date Time

Place-Value Practice

Family Note In the last lesson, children learned how to use a number grid and how to solve number-grid puzzles. The **Try This** problems below give children more practice with what they have learned. For information about number grids and number-grid puzzles, see pages 7–9 in the *Student Reference Book.*

Please return this Home Link to school tomorrow. Also bring a clean sock tomorrow to use as an eraser with your slate.

1. Have someone at home tell you a four-digit number to write down.

a. Write the the number. ________

b. Circle the digit in the thousands place.

c. Put an X through the digit in the tens place.

d. Underline the digit in the ones place.

2. Write the number that is 100 more than your number in Problem 1. ________

3. Write the number that is 100 less than your number in Problem 1. ________

Try This

Use the filled-in grid on page 7 of your *Student Reference Book* to help.

4.

898		

5.

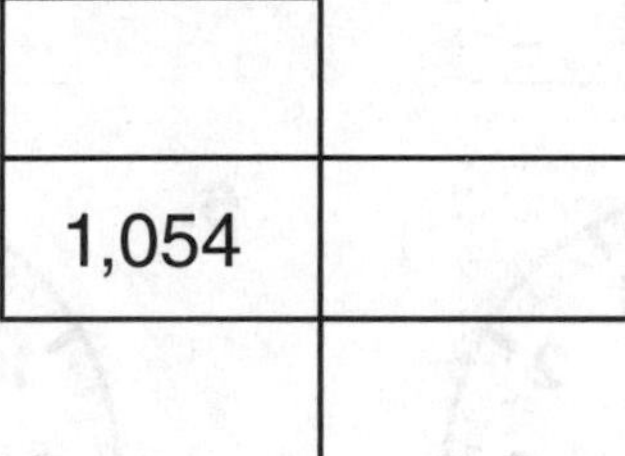

Practice

Solve.

6. $4 + 5 =$ ______

7. ______ $= 9 - 5$

8. ______ $= 5 + 4$

9. $9 - 4 =$ ______

Copyright © Wright Group/McGraw-Hill

Name Date Time

Telling Time

Family Note Today we discussed some of the tools used in mathematics. We reviewed how to read a ruler to the nearest inch and nearest centimeter and how to read a clock face to tell time to the nearest half-hour, nearest quarter-hour, and nearest 5 minutes. Help your child read and write each time.

Please return this Home Link to school tomorrow.

1. Draw the hour hand and the minute hand to show the time right now. Write the time.

_____ : _____

Write the time shown.

2.

_____ : _____

3.

_____ : _____

4.

_____ : _____

5.

_____ : _____

6.

_____ : _____

7.

_____ : _____

8. Show someone at home how you solved the hardest problem on this page.

Copyright © Wright Group/McGraw-Hill

Name Date Time

Five-Minute Marks

1. Color the hour hand red.
2. Color the minute hand green.

12
11
1
10
2
9
3
8
4
7
5
6

hour hand

minute hand

a brad

Copyright © Wright Group/McGraw-Hill

Name Date Time

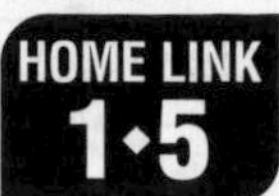

How Much TV Did They Watch?

Family Note You can find information about tally charts on pages 76–78 in the *Student Reference Book*. You can find information about the minimum, maximum, range, mode, and median of a set of data on pages 79 and 81.

Please return this Home Link to school tomorrow.

SRB 76–78 79 81

Paul asked some of his classmates how many hours they watched television over the weekend. His classmates reported the following number of hours:

1 hour 3 hours 1 hour 5 hours 0 hours 2 hours

4 hours 3 hours 2 hours 3 hours 3 hours

1. Make a tally chart for the data.

Time Spent Watching TV	
Hours	**Number of Children**
0	
1	
2	
3	
4	
5	

2. What was the least (minimum) number of hours watched? _____ hours

3. What was the greatest (maximum) number of hours watched? _____ hours

4. What is the range for the data? _____ hours (Remember that *range* is the difference between the greatest number and the least number.)

5. What is the mode for the data? _____ hours (Remember that the *mode* is the number that occurs most often.)

6. What is the median for the data? _____ hours (Remember that the *median* is the number in the middle.)

Copyright © Wright Group/McGraw-Hill

Name Date Time

HOME LINK 1·6

Name-Collection Boxes

Family Note You can find an explanation of name-collection boxes on pages 14 and 15 in the *Student Reference Book.*

Please return this Home Link to school tomorrow.

SRB 14 15

1. Write at least 10 names for the number 18 in the name-collection box. Then explain to someone at home how the box works. Have that person add another name for 18.

18

2. Three of the names do not belong in this box. Cross them out. Then write the name of the box on the tag.

~~||||~~ ~~||||~~ one dozen
7 + 5
number of months in 1 year
15 − 3   10 + 2
18 − 4   9 − 3

3. Make up a problem like Problem 2. Choose a name for the box but do not write it on the tag. Write 4 names for the number and 2 names that are not names for the number.

To check if the problem makes sense, ask someone at home to tell you which 2 names do not belong in the box. Have that person write the name of the box on the tag.

Copyright © Wright Group/McGraw-Hill

Name Date Time

LESSON 1·6 Domino Sort

1. Sort the dominoes by the total number of dots.
2. When you finish sorting the dominoes, write a number model for each domino under its equivalent number.

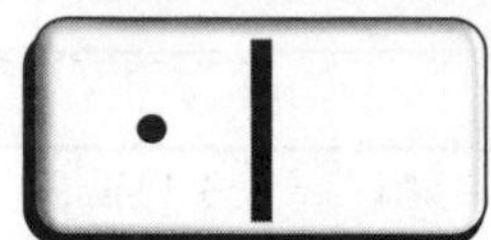

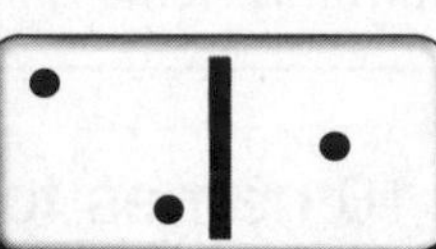

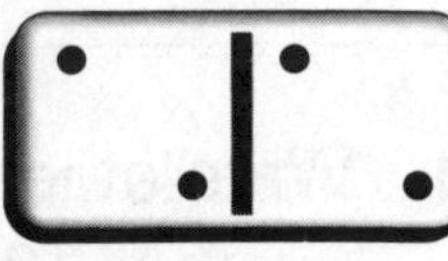

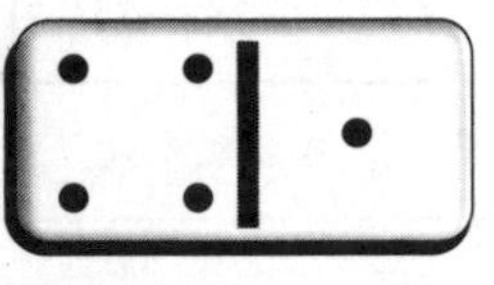

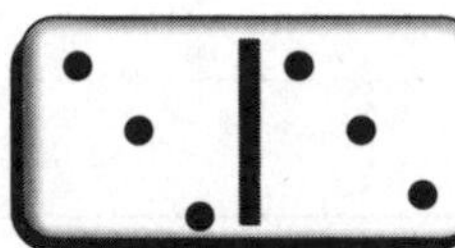

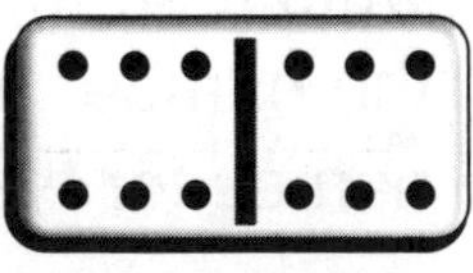

Copyright © Wright Group/McGraw-Hill

Name Date Time

LESSON 1·7 Math Message

1. What is one thing that you are *sure will happen* this week?

2. What is one thing that you are *sure will not happen* this week?

3. What is one thing that *may* or *may not happen* this week? (You are not sure.)

Copyright © Wright Group/McGraw-Hill

Name Date Time

Math Message

1. What is one thing that you are *sure will happen* this week?

2. What is one thing that you are *sure will not happen* this week?

3. What is one thing that *may* or *may not happen* this week? (You are not sure.)

Copyright © Wright Group/McGraw-Hill

Name Date Time

HOME LINK 1·7 Likely and Unlikely Events

Family Note During the next two weeks, please help your child find and cut out items in newspapers and magazines that discuss events that might or might not happen. Have your child bring these items to school to share with the class.

Please return this Home Link to school tomorrow.

SRB 92

For the next two weeks, look for items in newspapers and magazines that tell about events that **might** or **might not** happen. Get permission to cut them out and bring them to school. You might look for items like the following:

- a weather forecast (What are the chances that it will rain tomorrow?)
- the sports page (Which team is favored to win the baseball game?)
- a news story (What are the chances that people will explore distant planets in the next 20 years?)

Tell whether each event below is sure to happen, sure not to happen, or may happen, but not sure. Circle the answer.

1. You will grow taller next year.
sure to happen sure not to happen may happen, but not sure

2. You will live to be 200 years old.
sure to happen sure not to happen may happen, but not sure

3. You will watch TV next Saturday.
sure to happen sure not to happen may happen, but not sure

4. You will travel to the moon.
sure to happen sure not to happen may happen, but not sure

Practice

Unit

Solve.

5. 3 + 4 = _____

6. _____ = 7 − 4

7. _____ = 7 − 3

8. 4 + 3 = _____

Copyright © Wright Group/McGraw-Hill

Name Date Time

How Likely?

Circle the box that shows how likely.

1. How likely is it that the wild turkey weighed 500 pounds?

very unlikely	unlikely	likely	very likely

2. How likely is it that Hugh is about 8 years old?

very unlikely	unlikely	likely	very likely

3. How likely is it that Hugh had mosquitoes for company?

very unlikely	unlikely	likely	very likely

4. How likely is it that Hugh caught a million fish?

very unlikely	unlikely	likely	very likely

5. How likely is it that pirate treasure was hidden among the cypress trees?

very unlikely	unlikely	likely	very likely

6. Write your own.

____

____

very unlikely	unlikely	likely	very likely

Copyright © Wright Group/McGraw-Hill

Name Date Time

Finding Differences

Family Note It is not expected that your child knows how to use a traditional method of subtraction to solve these problems. Formal methods will be covered in the next unit. You can find an explanation of how to find differences on a number grid on page 8 in the *Student Reference Book.*

Please return this Home Link to school tomorrow.

SRB 8

1. Fill in the numbers on the number grid below.

	132								
									150
			154						
						177			

Use the number grid above to help you answer the following questions.

2. Which is more, 154 or 131? ________ How much more? ________

3. Which is less, 177 or 148? ________ How much less? ________

4. The difference between 180 and 158 is ________.

Try This

5. Explain how you found your answer in Problem 4.

____

Practice

Solve.

Unit

6. 13 = 7 + ______

7. 13 = 6 + ______

8. 6 = ______ − 7

9. 7 = ______ − 6

Copyright © Wright Group/McGraw-Hill

Name Date Time

LESSON 1·8

Number Grid

−9	−8	−7	−6	−5	−4	−3	−2	−1	0
1	2	3	4	5	6	7	8	9	10
11	12	13	14	15	16	17	18	19	20
21	22	23	24	25	26	27	28	29	30
31	32	33	34	35	36	37	38	39	40
41	42	43	44	45	46	47	48	49	50
51	52	53	54	55	56	57	58	59	60
61	62	63	64	65	66	67	68	69	70
71	72	73	74	75	76	77	78	79	80
81	82	83	84	85	86	87	88	89	90
91	92	93	94	95	96	97	98	99	100
101	102	103	104	105	106	107	108	109	110

Copyright © Wright Group/McGraw-Hill

Name _______________ Date _______________ Time _______________

LESSON 1·8

Skip Counting on the Number Grid

1. Start at 0 and count by 2s on the number grid. Mark an X through each number in your count.

2. Start at 0 again and count by 5s on the number grid. Draw a circle around each number in your count.

									0
1	2	3	4	5	6	7	8	9	10
11	12	13	14	15	16	17	18	19	20
21	22	23	24	25	26	27	28	29	30
31	32	33	34	35	36	37	38	39	40
41	42	43	44	45	46	47	48	49	50
51	52	53	54	55	56	57	58	59	60
61	62	63	64	65	66	67	68	69	70
71	72	73	74	75	76	77	78	79	80
81	82	83	84	85	86	87	88	89	90
91	92	93	94	95	96	97	98	99	100
101	102	103	104	105	106	107	108	109	110
111	112	113	114	115	116	117	118	119	120
121	122	123	124	125	126	127	128	129	130
131	132	133	134	135	136	137	138	139	140
141	142	143	144	145	146	147	148	149	150

3. List the numbers that are marked with an X and a circle.

_______, _______, _______, _______, _______, _______, _______, _______, _______,

_______, _______, _______, _______, _______, _______, _______

Copyright © Wright Group/McGraw-Hill

Name Date Time

Large and Small Numbers

Family Note We have been reviewing place-value concepts in this lesson. For more information about place value, see pages 18 and 19 in the *Student Reference Book.*

Please return this Home Link to school tomorrow.

You will need a die or a deck of cards numbered from 0–9, or slips of paper numbered 0–9.

1. Roll a die 4 times (or draw 4 cards).

a. Record the digit for each roll (or each card) in a blank.

____ ____ ____ ____

b. Make the largest 4-digit number you can using these digits.

____, ____ ____ ____

c. Make the smallest 4-digit number you can using these digits. The number may not begin with a zero.

____, ____ ____ ____

2. Roll a die 5 times (or draw 5 cards).

a. Record the digit for each roll (or each card) in a blank.

____ ____ ____ ____ ____

b. Make the largest 5-digit number you can using these digits.

____ ____, ____ ____ ____

c. Make the smallest 5-digit number you can using these digits. The number may not begin with a zero.

____ ____, ____ ____ ____

Practice

Solve.

3. 8 = ____ + 5

4. 8 = 5 + ____

5. ____ = 8 − 3

6. ____ = 8 − 5

Copyright © Wright Group/McGraw-Hill

Name Date Time

Ad Hunt

Family Note The children have been working on dollars-and-cents notation (for example, $4.95). Help your child locate ads that clearly show prices.

Please return this Home Link to school tomorrow.

1. Cut out four small advertisements from newspapers or magazines. Each ad must show the price of an item.
2. Put the ads in order from the least expensive item to the most expensive item.
3. Tape or glue your four ads in order on this page.
4. Bring extra ads to school to add to the Numbers All Around Museum.

Practice

Unit

5. Solve.

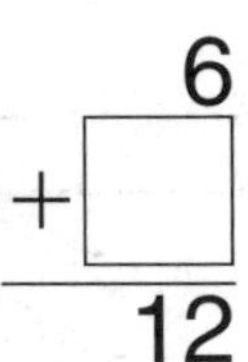

$6 + \square = 12$ $12 - \square = 6$ $\square + 5 = 10$ $\square - 5 = 5$

6. $13 - 7 =$ ____ ____ $+ 9 = 14$ $11 = 9 +$ ____ $12 - 4 =$ ____

Copyright © Wright Group/McGraw-Hill

Name Date Time

Sharing Money

Six friends found five $1–bills. They turned them in to the lost-and-found at school. The school clerk told them that if no one claimed the money in a week, they could keep it. One week passed, and the six friends had to decide how to share the $5. Draw a picture to show how the children might have split the money. Use Ⓟ, Ⓝ, Ⓓ and Ⓠ.

Think:

① What are you trying to figure out?

② What are the clues?

Copyright © Wright Group/McGraw-Hill

Name Date Time

Sharing Money

Six friends found five $1–bills. They turned them in to the lost-and-found at school. The school clerk told them that if no one claimed the money in a week, they could keep it. One week passed, and the six friends had to decide how to share the $5. Draw a picture to show how the children might have split the money. Use Ⓟ, Ⓝ, Ⓓ and Ⓠ.

Copyright © Wright Group/McGraw-Hill

Name Date Time

Shopping in the Newspaper

Family Note In this activity, your child will be looking for at least five different items to buy with $100. If any money is left over, your child can find something else to buy. If your child buys something in quantity (for example, 4 CDs), list each item and price on a separate line.

Please return this Home Link to school tomorrow.

SRB 191 193 194

1. Pretend that you have $100 to spend. Have someone at home help you find ads for at least five different items that you can buy. List the items and their prices below. DO NOT CALCULATE your total. Instead, estimate the total. You do not need to spend exactly $100.

Item	Actual Price	Estimated Price
CD	$15.75	$16

2. Explain to someone at home how you estimated the total price of your items.

Practice

Solve.

Unit

3. 11 − ☐ = 7

4. 4 + 7 = ☐

5. 7 + ☐ = 11

6. ☐ − 7 = 4

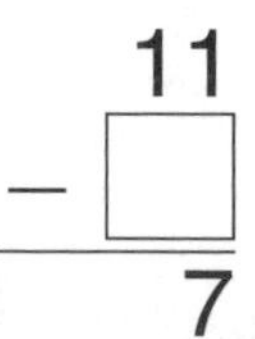

Copyright © Wright Group/McGraw-Hill

Name Date Time

Frames and Arrows

1.

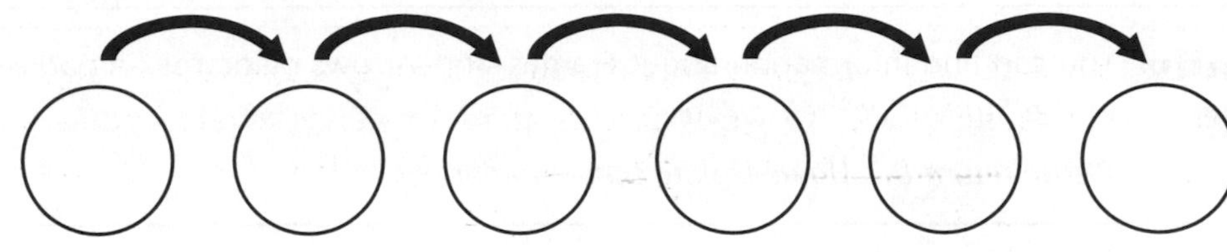

2.

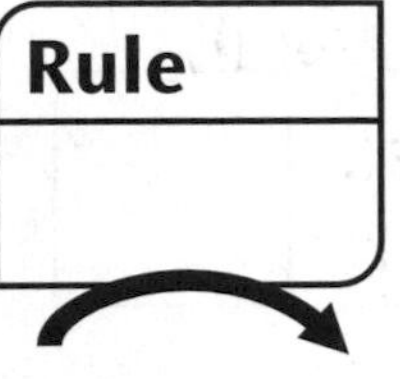

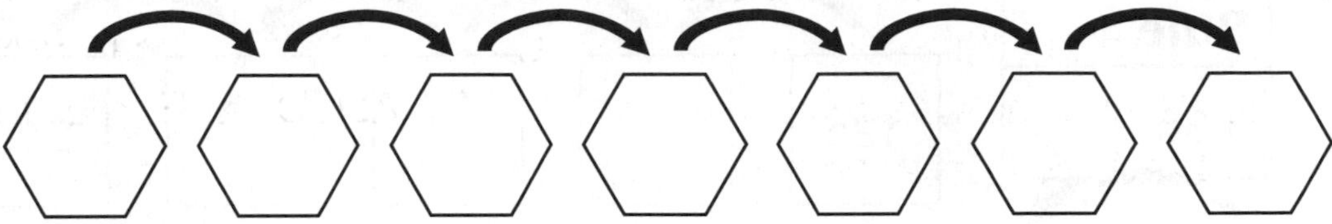

3.

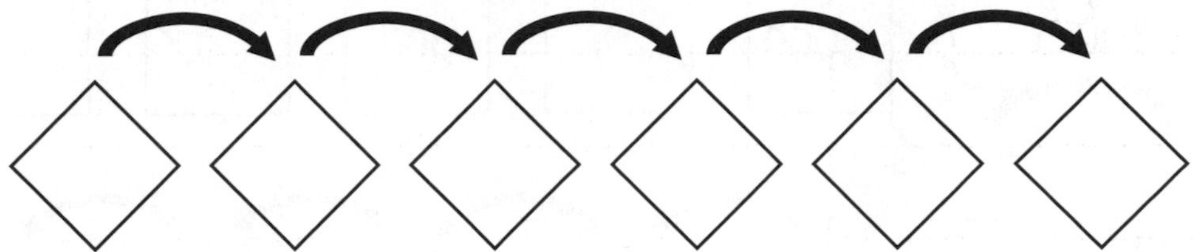

4.

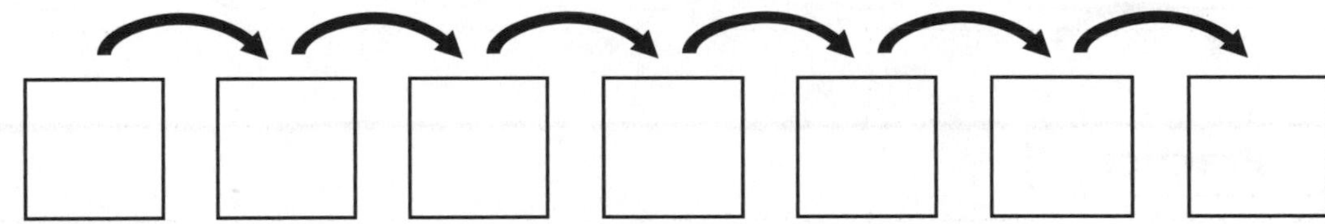

Copyright © Wright Group/McGraw-Hill

Name Date Time

HOME LINK 1•12

Frames-and-Arrows

Family Note You can find information about Frames–and–Arrows diagrams on pages 200 and 201 in the *Student Reference Book*.

Please return this Home Link to school tomorrow.

Show someone at home how to complete these Frames-and-Arrows diagrams.

1. Rule: +3¢

12¢ → ☐ → ☐ → ☐ → 24¢ → ☐

2.

1,000 → ☐ → 800 → ☐ → ☐ → ☐

3.

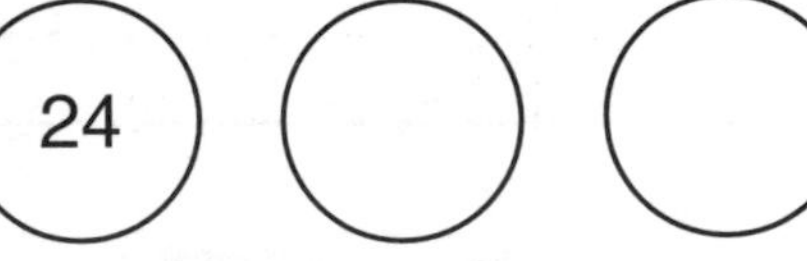

24 → ◯ → ◯ → 42 → 48 → ◯

Practice

Write each amount in dollars-and-cents notation.

4. [$1] Ⓠ Ⓓ Ⓝ Ⓝ Ⓟ = $________

5. Ⓓ Ⓓ Ⓠ Ⓝ Ⓟ Ⓓ Ⓠ Ⓟ = $________

6. [$10] [$1] [$1] Ⓝ Ⓟ = $________

7. Draw coins to show $0.89 in at least two different ways.

____

____

Copyright © Wright Group/McGraw-Hill

Name Date Time

Count on the Number Line

1. Start at 0. Count up by 3s. Circle the numbers you say. Do you add or subtract when you count up by 3s?

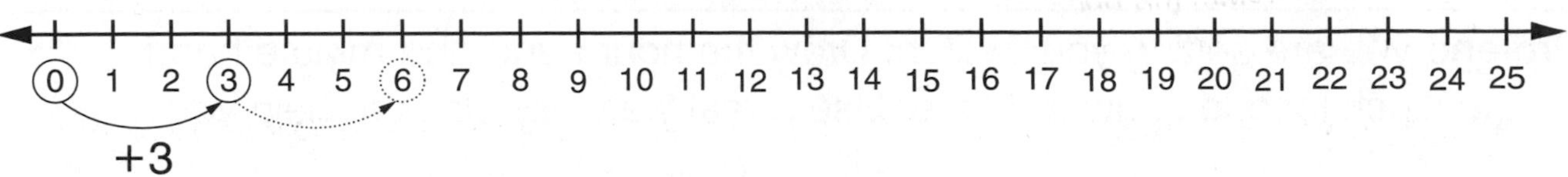

2. Start at 50. Count up by 5s. Circle the numbers you say. Do you add or subtract when you count up by 5s?

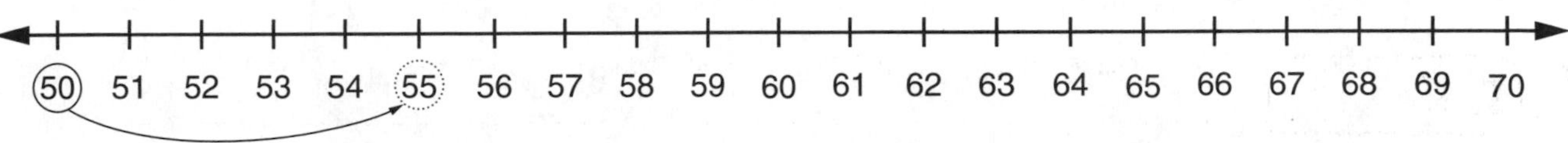

3. Start at 20. Count back by 4s. Circle the numbers you say. Do you add or subtract when you count back by 4s?

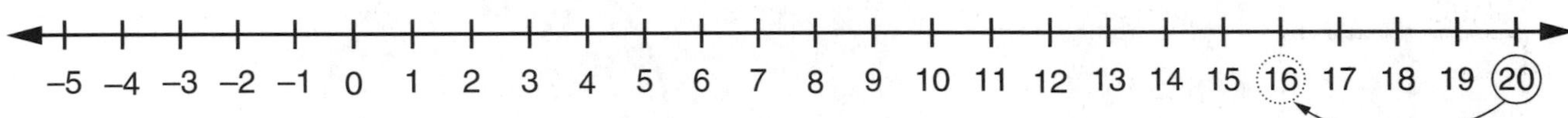

Copyright © Wright Group/McGraw-Hill

Name Date Time

HOME LINK 1•13

Time Practice

Family Note Your child has been learning about elapsed time in this lesson.

Please return this Home Link to school tomorrow.

Pretend you are setting your watch. Draw the hour hand and minute hand on the clock face to show the time. Use a real watch or clock to help you.

1. a. Show a quarter to 6.

b. Show the time 2 hours and 15 minutes later.

2. a. Show half-past 8.

b. Show the time 4 hours and 20 minutes earlier.

3. a. Show 25 minutes past 11.

b. Show the time 3 hours and 40 minutes later.

Copyright © Wright Group/McGraw-Hill

Practice

Solve.

4. 4 + ____ = 8 **5.** ____ = 8 − 4 **6.** 14 = ____ + 7 **7.** 14 − ____ = 7

Name Date Time

My Schedule of Activities

Decide if your schedule is for school days, for Saturdays, or for Sundays.

____

My Schedule			
Activity	Time		Time Spent
	From	To	

Copyright © Wright Group/McGraw-Hill

Name Date Time

HOME LINK 1•14

Unit 2: Family Letter

Adding and Subtracting Whole Numbers

Unit 2 will focus on addition and subtraction of whole numbers, emphasizing problem-solving strategies and computational skills. In *Second Grade Everyday Mathematics,* children used shortcuts, fact families, Fact Triangles, and games to help them learn basic addition and subtraction facts. Such devices will continue to be used in third grade. Knowledge of the basic facts and their extensions is important. Knowing that 6 + 8 = 14, for example, makes it easy to solve such problems as 56 + 8 = ? and 60 + 80 = ? Later, knowing that 5 × 6 = 30 will make it easy to solve 5 × 60 = ?, 50 × 60 = ?, and so on.

In Unit 2, children will learn new methods for solving addition and subtraction problems. *Everyday Mathematics* encourages children to choose from any of these methods or to invent their own computation methods. When children create—and share—their own ways of doing operations instead of simply learning one method, they begin to realize that any problem can be solved in more than one way. They are more willing and able to take risks, think logically, and reason analytically.

Blair Chewning, a teacher in Richmond, Virginia, gave her Everyday Mathematics *students this problem to solve. Here are just a few of the strategies her students used.*

Jill needs to earn $45.00 for a class trip. She earns $2 per day on Mondays, Tuesdays, and Wednesdays. She earns $3 each day on Thursdays, Fridays, and Saturdays. She does not work on Sundays. How many weeks will it take her to earn $45?

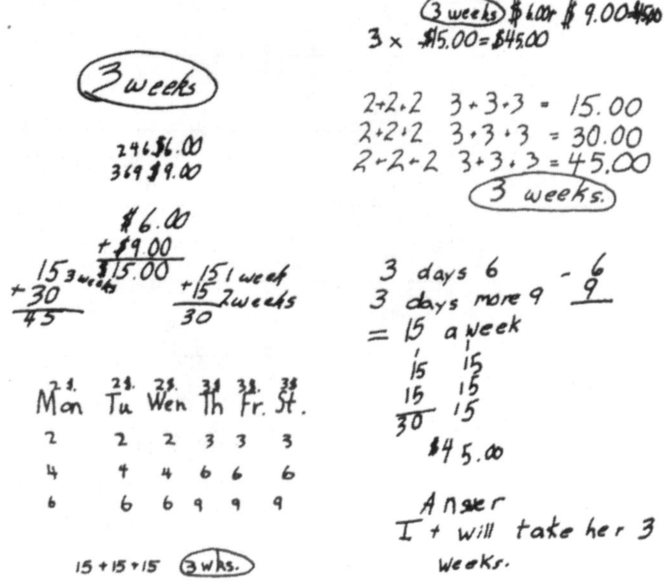

Finally, Unit 2 introduces another yearlong project—the National High/Low Temperatures Project. Children will calculate, record, and graph differences in temperatures from cities around the United States.

Copyright © Wright Group/McGraw-Hill

Unit 2: Family Letter *cont.*

Vocabulary

ballpark estimate A rough estimate. A ballpark estimate can be used when you don't need an exact answer or to check if an answer makes sense.

fact family A collection of 4 related addition and subtraction facts, or multiplication and division facts, relating 3 numbers.

$3 + 8 = 11$
$8 + 3 = 11$
$11 - 3 = 8$
$11 - 8 = 3$

function machine In *Everyday Mathematics,* an imaginary machine that processes numbers and pairs them with output numbers according to a set rule. A number (input) is put into the machine and is transformed into a second number (output) through the application of the rule.

in
Rule
+5
out

"What's My Rule?" problems A problem in which number pairs are related to each other according to the same rule. Sometimes the rule and one number in each pair are given, and the other number is to be found. Sometimes the pairs are given and the rule is to be found.

in	out
3	8
5	10
8	13
10	15
16	21

number family Same as a fact family.

number model A number sentence that shows how the parts of a number story are related. For example, $5 + 8 = 13$ models the number story: *5 children skating. 8 children playing ball. How many children in all?*

parts-and-total diagram A diagram used to represent problems in which two or more quantities are combined to form a total quantity. Sometimes the parts are known and the total is unknown. Other times the total and one or more parts are known, but one part is unknown.

For example, the parts-and-total diagram here represents this number story: *Leo baked 24 cookies. Nina baked 26 cookies. How many cookies in all?*

Total	
50	
Part 24	Part 26

change diagram A diagram used to represent addition or subtraction problems in which a given quantity is increased or decreased. The diagram includes the starting quantity, the ending quantity, and the amount of the change.

For example, the change diagram here represents this subtraction problem: *Rita had $28 in her wallet. She spent $12 at the store. How much money is in Rita's wallet now?*

Start	Change	End
28	−12	16

comparison diagram A diagram used to represent problems in which two quantities are given and then compared to find how much more or less one quantity is than the other.

For example, the comparison diagram here represents this problem: *34 children ride the bus to school. 12 children walk to school. How many more children ride the bus?*

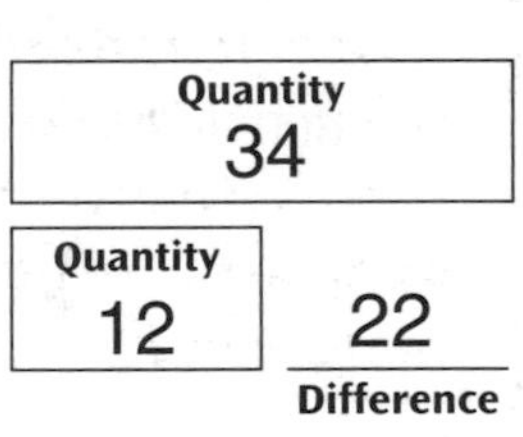

unit box In *Everyday Mathematics,* a box displaying the unit for numbers in the problems at hand.

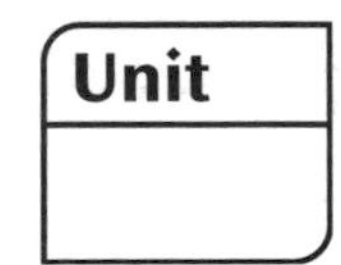

Unit box

Copyright © Wright Group/McGraw-Hill

Math Tools

Your child will be using **Fact Triangles** to practice and review addition and subtraction facts. Fact Triangles are a new and improved version of flash cards; the addition and subtraction facts shown are made from the same three numbers, and this helps your child understand the relationships among those facts.

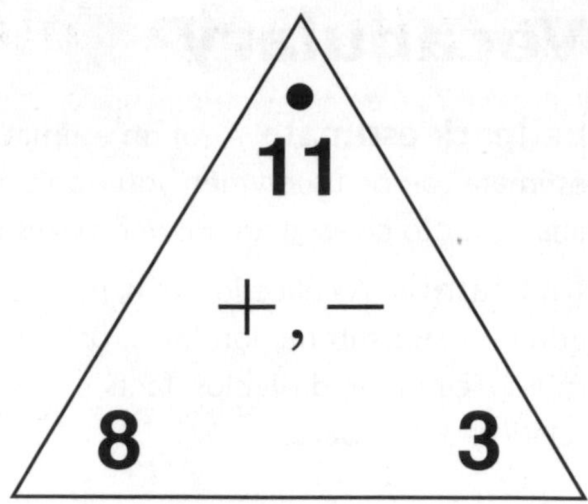

Do-Anytime Activities

To work with your child on the concepts taught in this unit and in the previous unit, try these interesting and rewarding activities:

1. Review addition and subtraction facts. Make +,− Fact Triangles for facts that your child needs to practice.

2. Practice addition and subtraction fact extensions. *For example:*

6 + 7 = 13	13 − 7 = 6
60 + 70 = 130	23 − 7 = 16
600 + 700 = 1,300	83 − 7 = 76

3. When your child adds or subtracts multidigit numbers, talk about the strategy that works best. Try not to impose the strategy that works best for you! Here are some problems to try:

   267 + 743 = ________

   794 − 554 = ________

   ________ = 851 + 697

   840 − 694 = ________

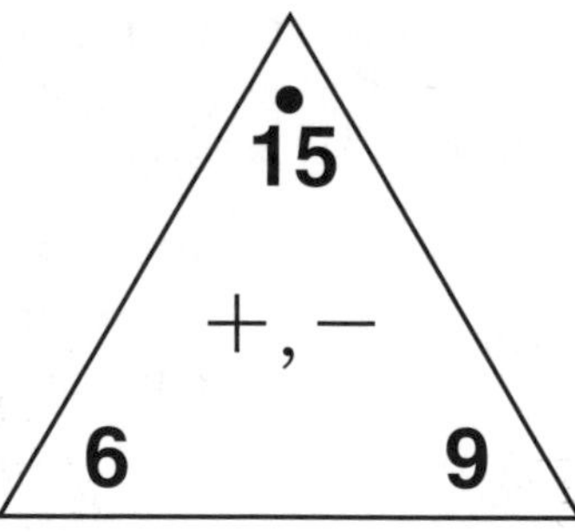

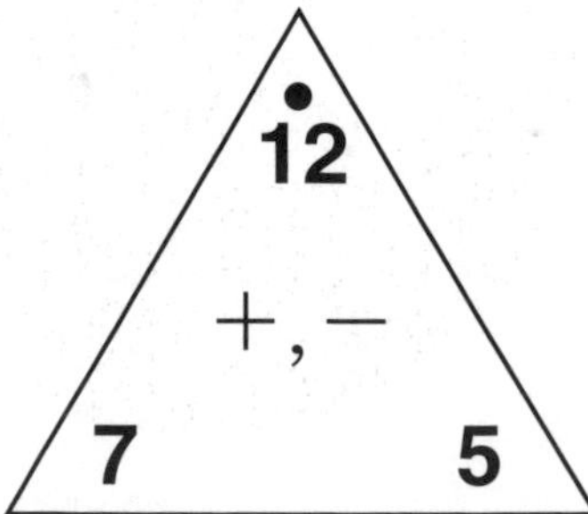

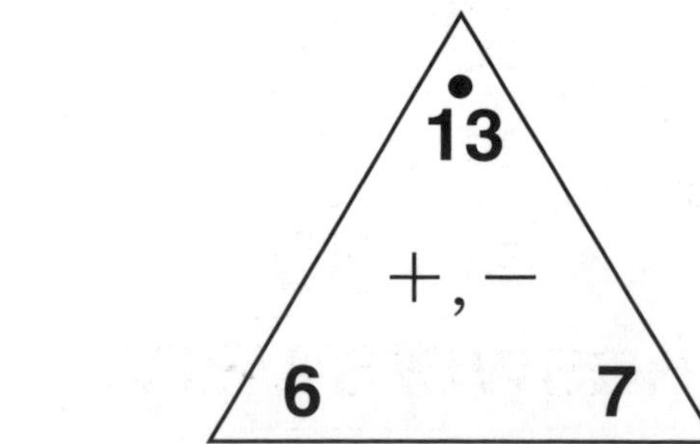

Copyright © Wright Group/McGraw-Hill

HOME LINK 1•14 **Unit 2: Family Letter** *cont.*

As You Help Your Child with Homework

As your child brings home assignments, you may want to go over the instructions together, clarifying them as necessary. The answers listed below will guide you through this unit's Home Links.

Home Link 2•1

1. 9 + 6 = 15; 6 + 9 = 15; 15 − 9 = 6; 15 − 6 = 9

2. 25 + 50 = 75; 50 + 25 = 75; 75 − 25 = 50; 75 − 50 = 25 **3.** Answers vary.

4. 10 **5.** 12 **6.** 4 **7.** 10

Home Link 2•2

1. 16; 26; 76; 106 **2.** 12; 22; 62; 282

3. 8; 28; 58; 98 **4.** 5; 15; 115; 475

5. 13; 130; 1,300; 13,000

Home Link 2•3

1.

in	out
14	7
7	0
12	5
15	8
10	3
21	14

2.

in	out
7	16
9	18
37	46
77	86
49	58

Answers vary.

3.

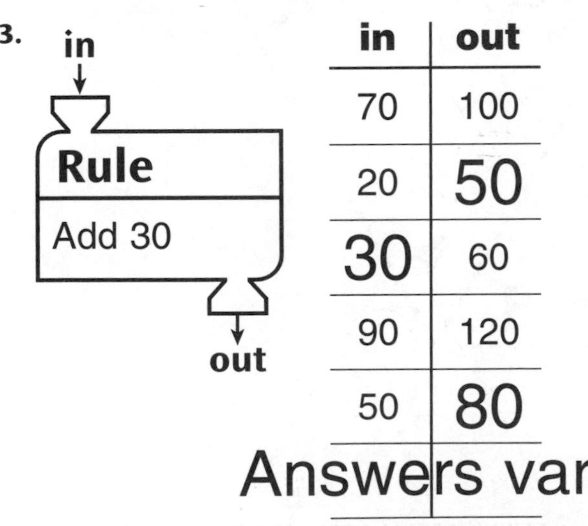

in	out
70	100
20	50
30	60
90	120
50	80

Answers vary.

Home Link 2•4

1. 55 minutes; 25 + 30 = 55

2. 700 cans; 300 + 400 = 700

Home Link 2•5

1. $9; 25 − 16 = 9 or 16 + 9 = 25 **2.** $49; 35 + 14 = 49

Home Link 2•6

1. $29; 42 − 13 = 29 or 13 + 29 = 42 **2.** 9 days; 28 − 19 = 9 or 19 + 9 = 28

3. 15 children; 40 − 25 = 15

Home Link 2•7

1. 337 **2.** 339 **3.** 562

4. 574 **5.** 627 **6.** 1,214

Home Link 2•8

1. 194 **2.** 202 **3.** 122

4. 206 **5.** 439 **6.** 487

Home Link 2•9

1. 38 **2.** 213 **3.** 40

4. 70 **5.** 915 **6.** 55; 18 + 15 + 22 = 55

7. 19; 17 + 22 + 19 = 58

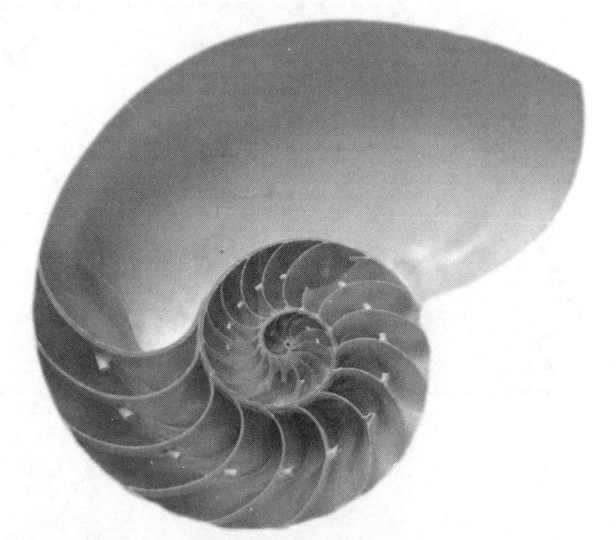

Copyright © Wright Group/McGraw-Hill

Name Date Time

LESSON 2·1

+, − Fact Triangles

4, 2, 3 +, −
5, 2, 3 +, −
6, 2, 3 +, −
6, 4, 3 +, −
7, 3, 4 +, −
7, 2, 5 +, −
8, 3, 5 +, −
8, 4, 4 +, −
8, 6, 2 +, −
9, 4, 5 +, −
9, 6, 3 +, −
9, 2, 7 +, −
10, 5, 5 +, −
10, 4, 6 +, −
10, 7, 3 +, −
10, 2, 8 +, −
11, 3, 8 +, −
11, 7, 4 +, −

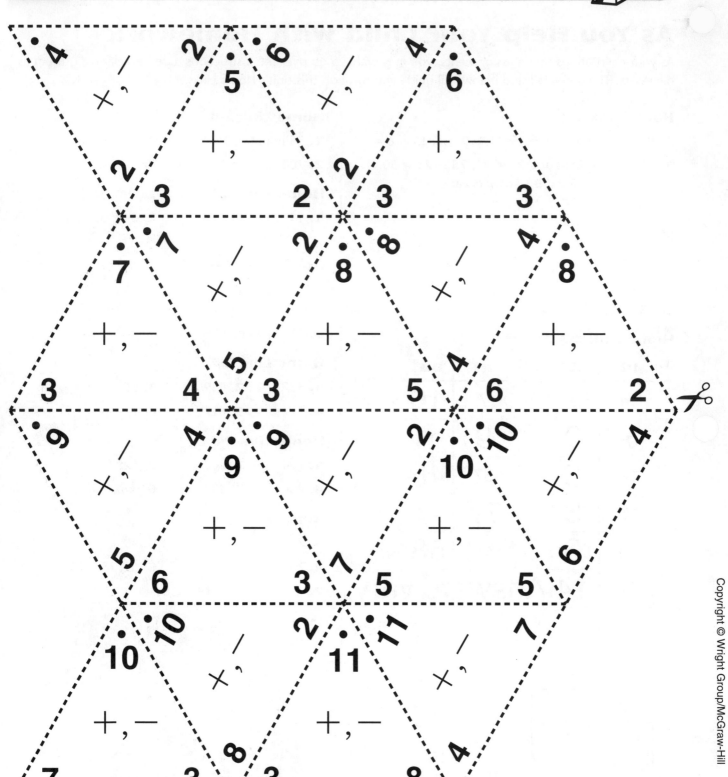

Copyright © Wright Group/McGraw-Hill

Name Date Time

LESSON 2•1

+, − Fact Triangles

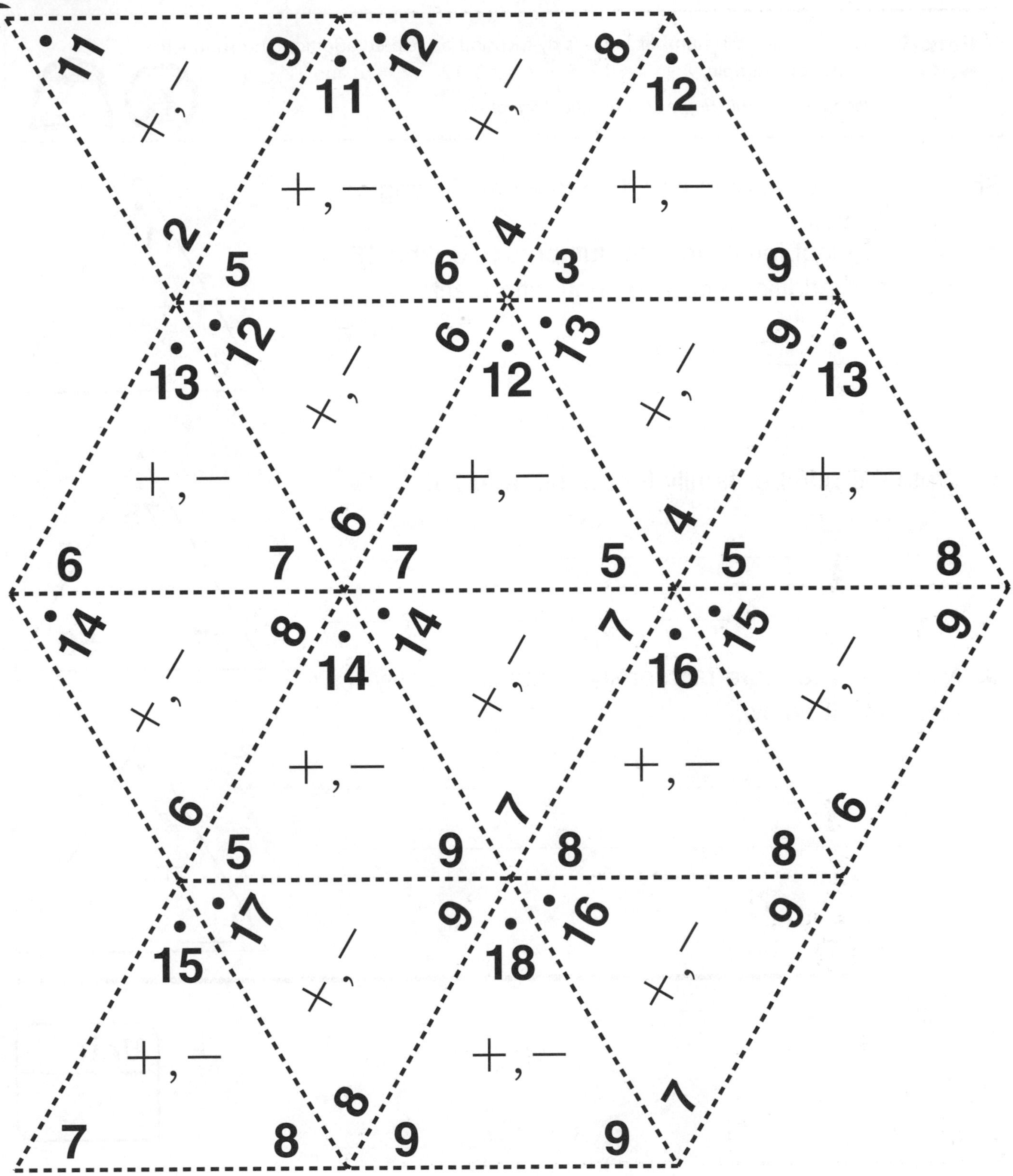

•11 +, − 9 2

•11 +, − 5 6

•12 +, − 8 4

•12 +, − 3 9

•13 +, − 6 7

•12 +, − 6 6

•12 +, − 7 5

•13 +, − 9 4

•13 +, − 5 8

•14 +, − 8 6

•14 +, − 5 9

•14 +, − 7 7

•16 +, − 8 8

•15 +, − 9 6

•15 +, − 7 8

•17 +, − 9 8

•18 +, − 9 9

•16 +, − 9 7

Copyright © Wright Group/McGraw-Hill

Name Date Time

Fact Families and Number Families

Family Note Work on fact and number families by focusing on related addition and subtraction facts. For example, 7 + 5 = 12, 5 + 7 = 12, 12 − 7 = 5, and 12 − 5 = 7.

Please return this Home Link to school tomorrow.

Show someone at home how to use a Fact Triangle.

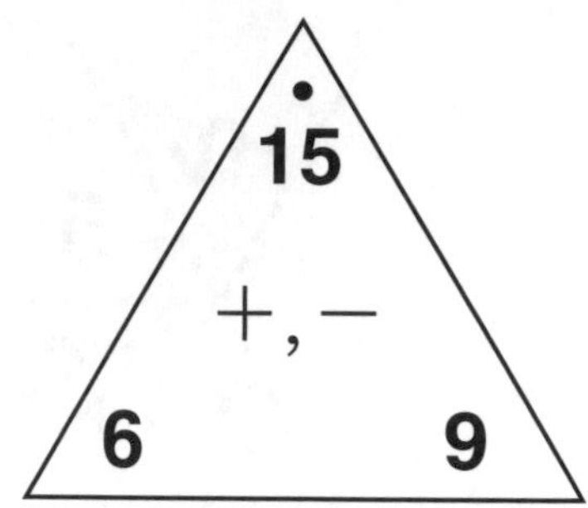

1. Write the fact family for the numbers 9, 6, and 15. Write two addition and two subtraction facts.

______ ______

______ ______

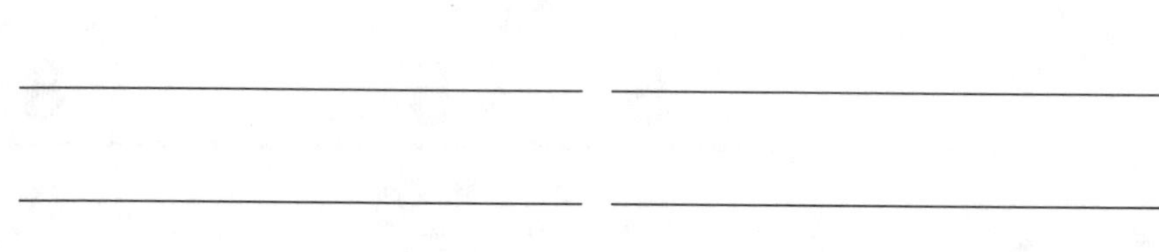

2. Write the number family for 25, 50, and 75.

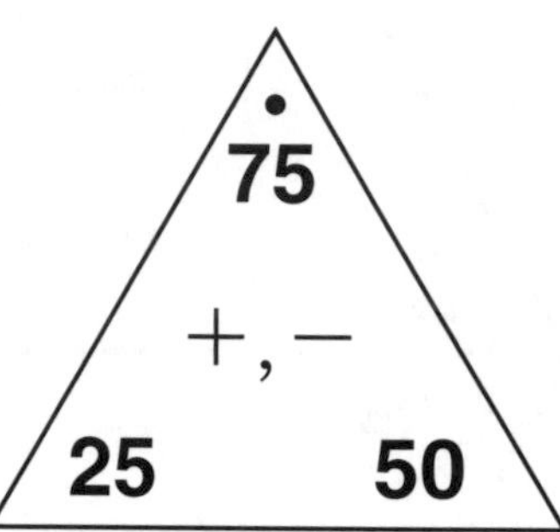

______ ______

______ ______

3. Make up one more fact family or number family and write it below.

______ ______

______ ______

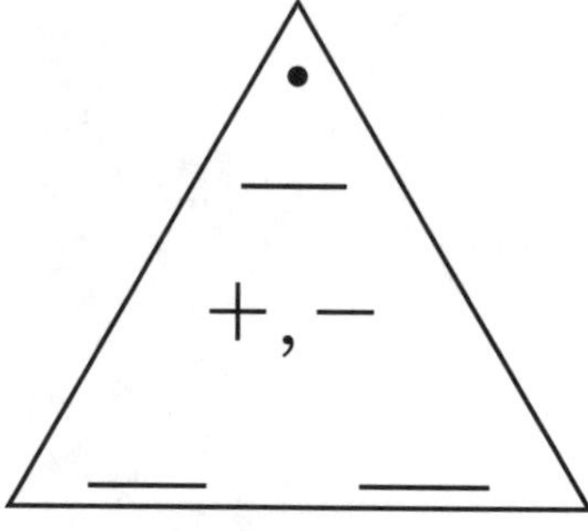

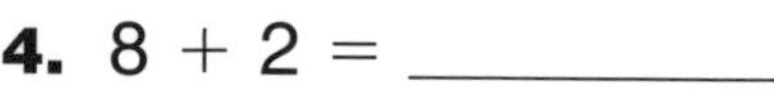

Practice

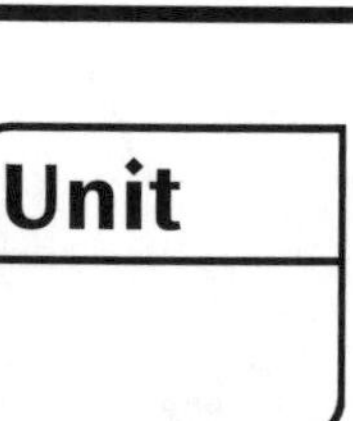

Solve.

4. 8 + 2 = ______

5. 5 + 7 = ______

6. ______ = 0 + 4

7. ______ = 1 + 9

Copyright © Wright Group/McGraw-Hill

Name Date Time

Fact Extensions with Multiples of 10

Turn	Numbers on Cards	Multiples of 10
1st turn	3 6 3 + 6 = 9	30 60 30 + 60 = 90
2nd turn	____ ____ ____ + ____ = ____	____0 ____0 ____ + ____ = ____
3rd turn	____ ____ ____ + ____ = ____	____0 ____0 ____ + ____ = ____
4th turn	____ ____ ____ + ____ = ____	____0 ____0 ____ + ____ = ____
5th turn	____ ____ ____ + ____ = ____	____0 ____0 ____ + ____ = ____
6th turn	____ ____ ____ + ____ = ____	____0 ____0 ____ + ____ = ____
7th turn	____ ____ ____ + ____ = ____	____0 ____0 ____ + ____ = ____

Copyright © Wright Group/McGraw-Hill

Name Date Time

Fact Extensions

Family Note Knowing basic facts, such as 6 + 7 = 13, makes it easy to solve similar problems with larger numbers, such as 60 + 70 = 130. Help your child think of more fact extensions to complete this Home Link.

Please return this Home Link to school tomorrow.

Write the answer for each problem.

1. I know: $\begin{array}{r} 9 \\ +\ 7 \\ \hline \end{array}$ This helps me know: $\begin{array}{r} 19 \\ +\ 7 \\ \hline \end{array}$ $\begin{array}{r} 69 \\ +\ 7 \\ \hline \end{array}$ $\begin{array}{r} 99 \\ +\ 7 \\ \hline \end{array}$

2. I know: $\begin{array}{r} 8 \\ +\ 4 \\ \hline \end{array}$ This helps me know: $\begin{array}{r} 18 \\ +\ 4 \\ \hline \end{array}$ $\begin{array}{r} 58 \\ +\ 4 \\ \hline \end{array}$ $\begin{array}{r} 278 \\ +\ 4 \\ \hline \end{array}$

3. I know: $\begin{array}{r} 15 \\ -\ 7 \\ \hline \end{array}$ This helps me know: $\begin{array}{r} 35 \\ -\ 7 \\ \hline \end{array}$ $\begin{array}{r} 65 \\ -\ 7 \\ \hline \end{array}$ $\begin{array}{r} 105 \\ -\ 7 \\ \hline \end{array}$

4. I know: $\begin{array}{r} 13 \\ -\ 8 \\ \hline \end{array}$ This helps me know: $\begin{array}{r} 23 \\ -\ 8 \\ \hline \end{array}$ $\begin{array}{r} 123 \\ -\ 8 \\ \hline \end{array}$ $\begin{array}{r} 483 \\ -\ 8 \\ \hline \end{array}$

5. I know: $\begin{array}{r} 6 \\ +\ 7 \\ \hline \end{array}$ This helps me know: $\begin{array}{r} 60 \\ +\ 70 \\ \hline \end{array}$ $\begin{array}{r} 600 \\ +\ 700 \\ \hline \end{array}$ $\begin{array}{r} 6{,}000 \\ +\ 7{,}000 \\ \hline \end{array}$

Make up another set of fact extensions.

6. I know:  This helps me know: 

Copyright © Wright Group/McGraw-Hill

Name Date Time

“What’s My Rule?”

1.

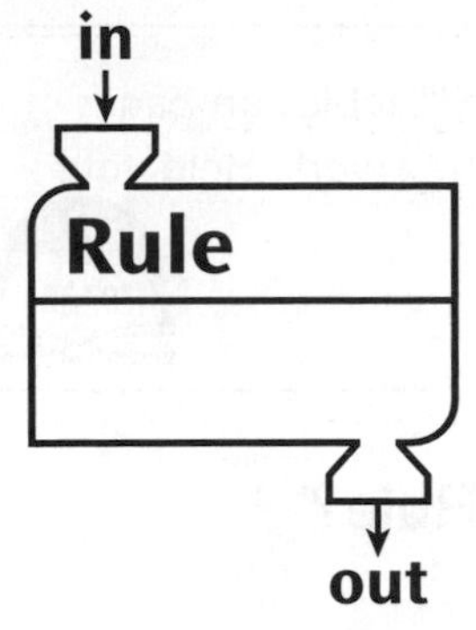

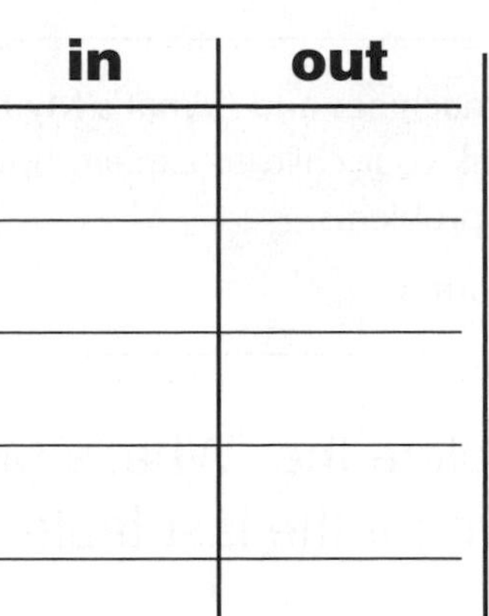

in	out

2.

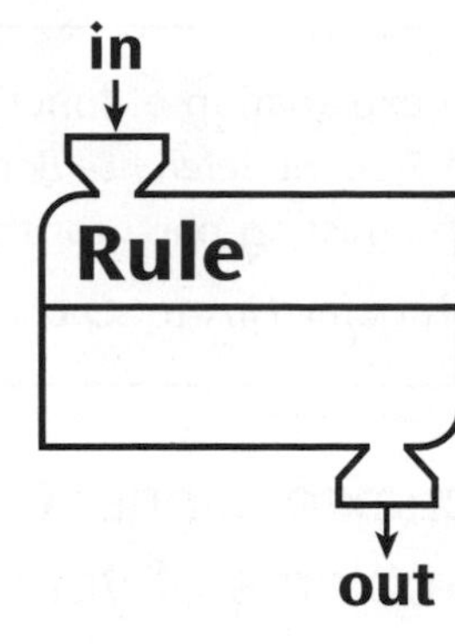

in	out

3. in

Rule

out

in	out

4.

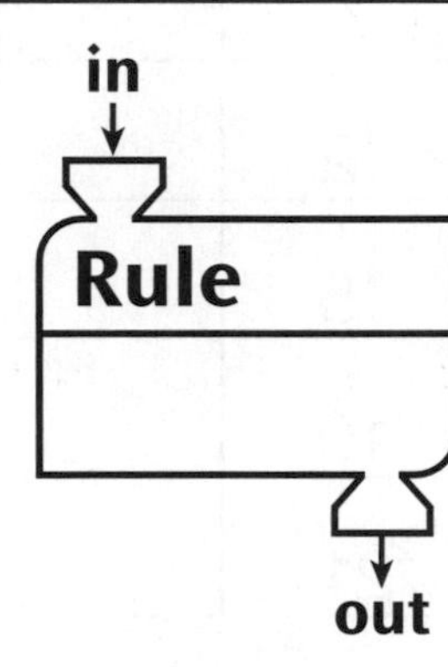

in	out

5. in

Rule

out

in	out

6.

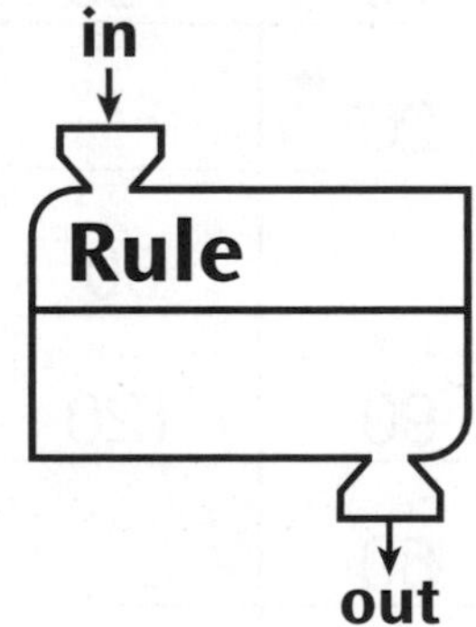

in	out

Copyright © Wright Group/McGraw-Hill

Name Date Time

"What's My Rule?"

Family Note You can find an explanation of function machines and "What's My Rule?" tables on pages 202–204 in the *Student Reference Book.* Ask your child to explain how they work. Help your child fill in all the missing parts for these problems.

Please return this Home Link to school tomorrow.

SRB 202 204

Practice facts and fact extensions. Complete the "What's My Rule?" problems. Make up problems of your own for the last table.

1. in

Rule

Subtract 7

out

in	out
14	
7	
12	
15	
10	
21	

2. in

Rule

Add 9

out

in	out
7	
	18
37	
	86
49	

3.

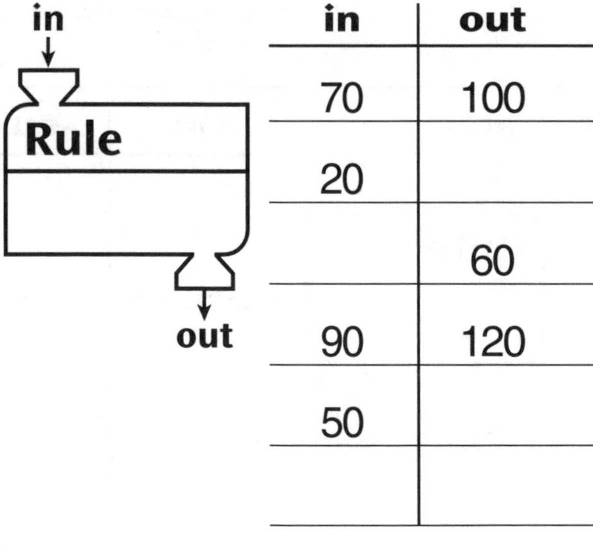

in	out
70	100
20	
	60
90	120
50	

4.

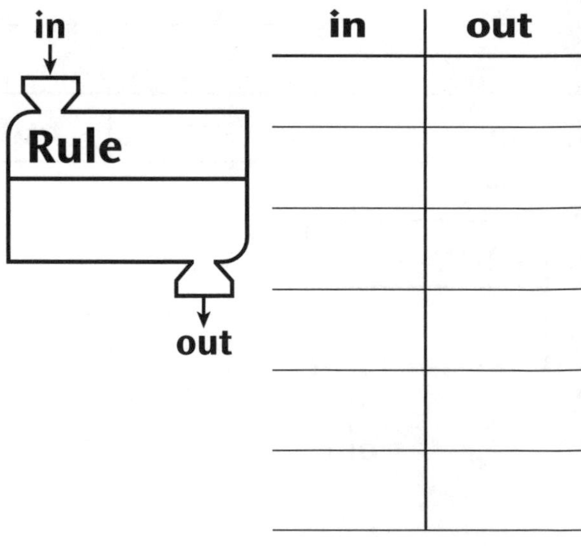

in	out

Copyright © Wright Group/McGraw-Hill

Name Date Time

Parts-and-Total Number Stories

Family Note Today your child learned about a diagram that helps organize the information in a number story. We call it a *parts-and-total diagram.* For more information, see pages 256 and 257 in the *Student Reference Book.*

Please return this Home Link to school tomorrow.

SRB 256 257

For each problem, write *?* for the number you want to find. Write the numbers you know in the diagram. Then write the answer and a number model. Finally, write how you know that each answer makes sense.

1. Marisa read her book for 25 minutes on Monday and 30 minutes on Tuesday. How many minutes in all did she read?

Total	
Part	**Part**

Answer the question: ______________ (unit)

Number model: ______________

Check: How do you know your answer makes sense?

____

____

2. The second graders collected 300 cans to recycle. The third graders collected 400 cans. What was the total number of cans they collected?

Total	
Part	**Part**

Answer the question: ______________ (unit)

Number model: ______________

Check: How do you know your answer makes sense?

____

____

Copyright © Wright Group/McGraw-Hill

Name Date Time

Parts-and-Total Diagrams

Total	
Part	Part

Total	
Part	Part

Total	
Part	Part

Total	
Part	Part

Total		
Part	Part	Part

Total		
Part	Part	Part

Total			
Part	Part	Part	Part

Total			
Part	Part	Part	Part

Copyright © Wright Group/McGraw-Hill

Name Date Time

Change Diagrams

Change
Start  End

Change
Start  End

Change
Start  End

Change
Start  End

Change
Start  End

Change
Start  End

Change
Start  End

Change
Start  End

Change
Start  End

Change
Start  End

Copyright © Wright Group/McGraw-Hill

Name ________________ Date ________________ Time ________________

Change Number Stories

Family Note Today your child learned about another diagram that helps organize the information in a number story. It is called a *change diagram.* For more information, see pages 254 and 255 in the *Student Reference Book.*

Please return this Home Link to school tomorrow.

SRB 254 255

For each number story, write ? in the diagram for the number you want to find. Write the numbers you know in the change diagram. Then, write the answer and a number model. Finally, write how you know that each answer makes sense.

1. Marcus had $25 in his wallet. He spent $16 at the store. How much money was in Marcus's wallet then?

Start	Change →	End
	______	

Answer the question: ________________ (unit)

Number model: ________________________________

Check: How do you know your answer makes sense?

____

____

2. Jasmine had $35. She earned $14 helping her neighbors. How much money did she have then?

Start	Change	End
	 ______	

Answer the question: ________________ (unit)

Number model: ________________

Check: How do you know your answer makes sense?

____

____

Copyright © Wright Group/McGraw-Hill

Name ________ Date ________ Time ________

LESSON 2·5

Changing the Calculator Display

Solve the calculator problems. Use a number grid to help. Check your answers on a calculator. Write a number model to show what you did.

Example:

How can you change 24 to 35? ____________________

Number model: ____________________

1. How can you change 18 to 38? ____________________

Number model: ____________________

2. How can you change 30 to 80? ____________________

Number model: ____________________

3. How can you change 21 to 63? ____________________

Number model: ____________________

4. How can you change 97 to 45? ____________________

Number model: ____________________

5. How can you change 100 to 62? ____________________

Number model: ____________________

Copyright © Wright Group/McGraw-Hill

Name Date Time

LESSON 2•6

National High/Low Temperatures

Date	Highest Temperature (maximum)		Lowest Temperature (minimum)		Difference (range)
	Place	Temperature	Place	Temperature	
		°F		°F	°F
		°F		°F	°F
		°F		°F	°F
		°F		°F	°F
		°F		°F	°F
		°F		°F	°F
		°F		°F	°F
		°F		°F	°F
		°F		°F	°F
		°F		°F	°F
		°F		°F	°F
		°F		°F	°F
		°F		°F	°F
		°F		°F	°F
		°F		°F	°F
		°F		°F	°F
		°F		°F	°F
		°F		°F	°F
		°F		°F	°F
		°F		°F	°F

Copyright © Wright Group/McGraw-Hill

Name Date Time

Comparison Diagrams

Quantity

Quantity

Difference

Quantity

Quantity

Difference

Quantity

Quantity

Difference

Quantity

Quantity

Difference

Quantity

Quantity

Difference

Quantity

Quantity

Difference

Quantity

Quantity

Difference

Quantity

Quantity

Difference

Copyright © Wright Group/McGraw-Hill

Name Date Time

LESSON 2·6

Comparing Numbers

1. Compare 19 and 8.
Draw an orange line from 0 to 19 above the number line.
Draw a blue line from 0 to 8 below the number line.

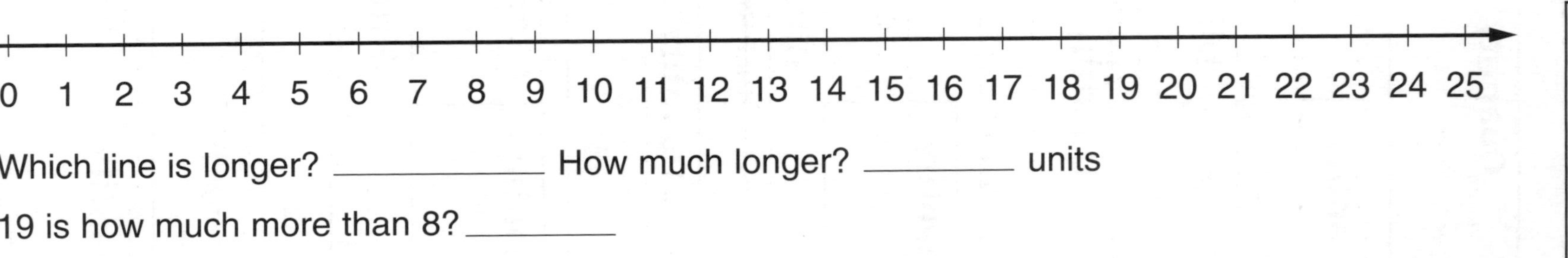

Which line is longer? ________ How much longer? ______ units

19 is how much more than 8? ______

2. Compare 20 and 2.
Draw an orange line from 0 to 20 above the number line.
Draw a blue line from 0 to 2 below the number line.

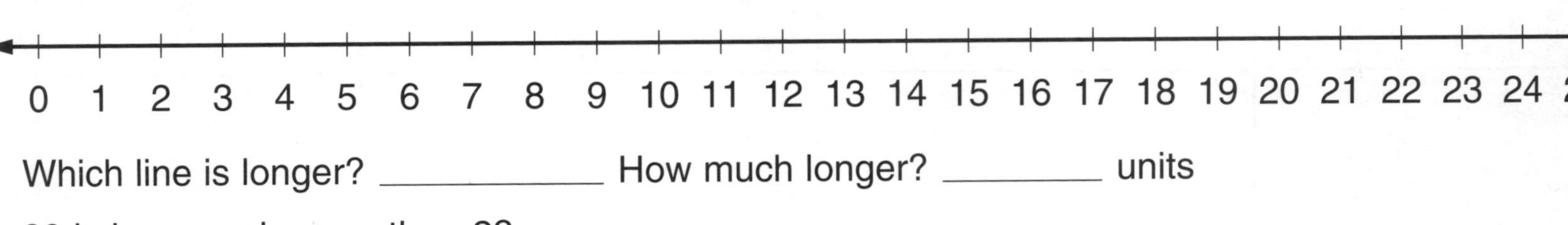

Which line is longer? ________ How much longer? ______ units

20 is how much more than 2? ______

3. Compare 24 and 15.
Draw an orange line from 0 to 24 above the number line.
Draw a blue line from 0 to 15 below the number line.

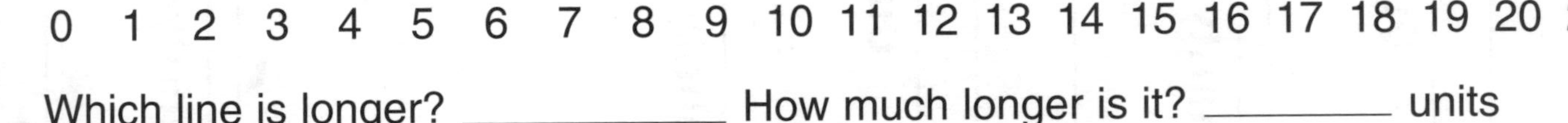

Which line is longer? ________ How much longer is it? ______ units

24 is how much more than 15? ______

Copyright © Wright Group/McGraw-Hill

Name ____________________ Date ____________ Time ____________

Comparison Number Stories

Family Note Today your child learned about a comparison diagram. It helps organize information in a number story. To read more, see page 258 in the *Student Reference Book.*

Please return this Home Link to school tomorrow.

Write ? in the diagram for the number you want to find. Write the numbers you know in the diagram. Then write the answer and a number model. Tell someone at home how you know that your answers make sense.

1. Jenna has $42. Her brother has $13. How much more money does Jenna have?

Answer the question: ____________ (unit)

Number model:

____

Quantity

Quantity

______ **Difference**

2. There are 28 days until Pat's birthday and 19 days until Ramon's birthday. How many more days does Pat have to wait than Ramon?

Answer the question: ____________ (unit)

Number model:

____

Quantity

Quantity

______ **Difference**

3. There are 25 children in the soccer club and 40 children in the science club. How many fewer children are in the soccer club?

Answer the question: ____________ (unit)

Number model:

____

Quantity

Quantity

______ **Difference**

Copyright © Wright Group/McGraw-Hill

Name Date Time

HOME LINK 2•7

The Partial-Sums Addition Method

Family Note Today your child learned about adding two 3-digit numbers using a procedure called the *partial-sums method.* Your child may choose to use this method or may prefer a different procedure. For more information, see pages 57 and 58 in the *Student Reference Book.*

Please return this Home Link to school tomorrow.

Solve each addition problem. You may want to use the partial-sums method. Use a ballpark estimate to check that your answer makes sense. Write a number model to show your estimate.

1. Ballpark estimate: ______	**2.** Ballpark estimate: ______	**3.** Ballpark estimate: ______
100s 10s 1s 2 4 5 + 9 2	124 + 215	245 + 317
4. Ballpark estimate: ______	**5.** Ballpark estimate: ______	**6.** Ballpark estimate: ______
366 + 208	459 + 168	769 + 445

Copyright © Wright Group/McGraw-Hill

Name Date Time

LESSON 2•7

Addition: The Partial-Sums Method

Example:

100s	10s	1s
3	2	9
+ 4	1	8
7	0	0
	3	0
+	1	7
7	4	7

Ballpark estimate:

300 + 400 = 700

1. Ballpark estimate:

100s | 10s | 1s

2. Ballpark estimate:

100s | 10s | 1s

3. Ballpark estimate:

100s | 10s | 1s

4. Ballpark estimate:

100s | 10s | 1s

Copyright © Wright Group/McGraw-Hill

Name Date Time

HOME LINK 2·8

Subtraction Methods

Family Note Over the past 2 days, your child practiced subtracting two 3-digit numbers using the counting-up method and the trade-first method. For more information, see pages 60, 61, and 63 in the *Student Reference Book.*

Please return this Home Link to school tomorrow.

Fill in the unit. Solve the problems. You may use any method you wish. Use a ballpark estimate to check that your answer makes sense. Write a number model for your estimate. On the back of this Home Link, explain how you solved one of the problems.

Unit

1. Ballpark estimate: ______ 468 −274	**2.** Ballpark estimate: ______ 531 −329	**3.** Ballpark estimate: ______ 331 −209
4. Ballpark estimate: ______ 653 −447	**5.** Ballpark estimate: ______ 925 −486	**6.** Ballpark estimate: ______ 724 −237

Copyright © Wright Group/McGraw-Hill

Name Date Time

LESSON 2•8

The Trade-First Subtraction Method

Example:

100s	10s	1s
1	14	
2	4	7
−1	8	6
	6	1

Ballpark estimate:

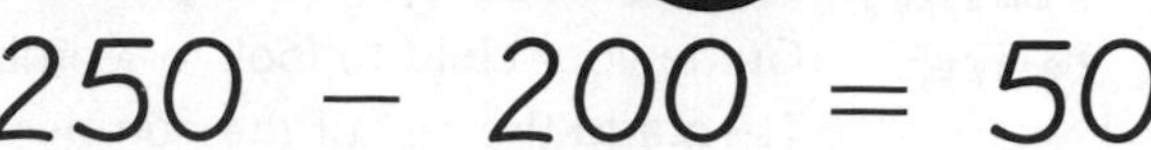

250 − 200 = 50

1. Ballpark estimate:

100s	10s	1s

2. Ballpark estimate:

100s	10s	1s

3. Ballpark estimate:

100s	10s	1s

4. Ballpark estimate:

100s	10s	1s

Copyright © Wright Group/McGraw-Hill

Name Date Time

HOME LINK 2•9

Three or More Addends

Family Note This Home Link provides practice in looking for combinations that make addition easier. Guide your child to look for combinations that add up to 10, 20, 30, 40 and so on. Then add the rest of the numbers.

Please return this Home Link to school tomorrow.

Remember that when you add:

- The numbers can be in any order.
- Some combinations make the addition easier.

Add. Write the numbers in the order you added them. Tell someone at home why you added the numbers in that order.

Example: 5 + 17 + 25 + 3 = 50 I added in this order: 5 + 25 + 17 + 3	**1.** 6 + 18 + 14 = ______ I added in this order: ______
2. 125 + 13 + 75 = ______ I added in this order: ______	**3.** 15 + 6 + 14 + 5 = ______ I added in this order: ______
4. 33 + 22 + 8 + 7 = ______ I added in this order: ______	**5.** 150 + 215 + 300 + 50 + 200 = ______ I added in this order: ______ ______

Copyright © Wright Group/McGraw-Hill

Name Date Time

Three or More Addends *continued*

Solve these number stories.

6. Nico's baby brother has a basket of wooden blocks. 18 blocks are red, 15 are blue, and 22 are yellow. How many red, blue, and yellow blocks are in the basket?

Total		
Part	Part	Part

Answer the question: ______ blocks

Number model: ____________________

7. Marianna has 3 days to read a 58-page book. She read 17 pages on Monday and 22 pages on Tuesday. How many more pages does she need to read to finish the book?

Total		
Part	Part	Part

Answer the question: ______ pages

Number model: ____________________

8. Make up a number story with three or more addends.

____

____

____

____

____

Answer the question: ________________ (unit)

Number model: ____________________

Check: Does my answer make sense?

Copyright © Wright Group/McGraw-Hill

Name Date Time

Addition and Subtraction Puzzles

Study the examples. Can you figure out what must be done to solve this type of puzzle?

Example 1:

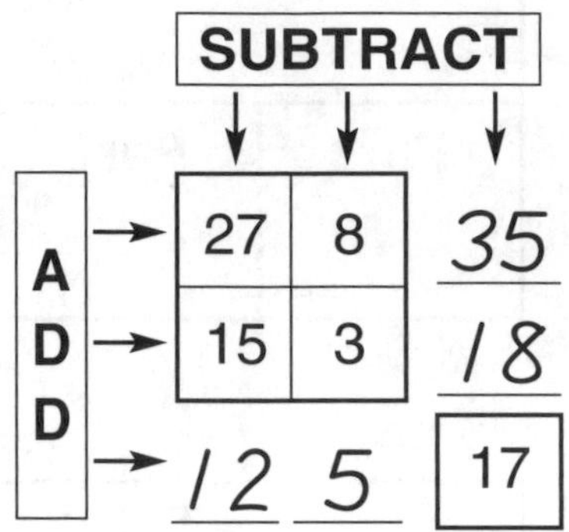

Example 2:

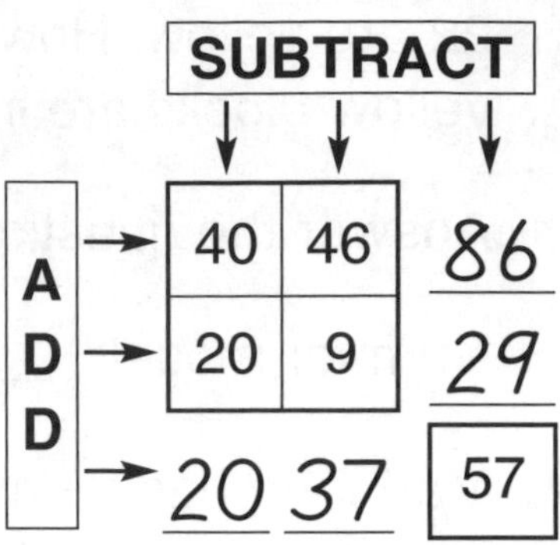

Solve these addition and subtraction puzzles.

1.

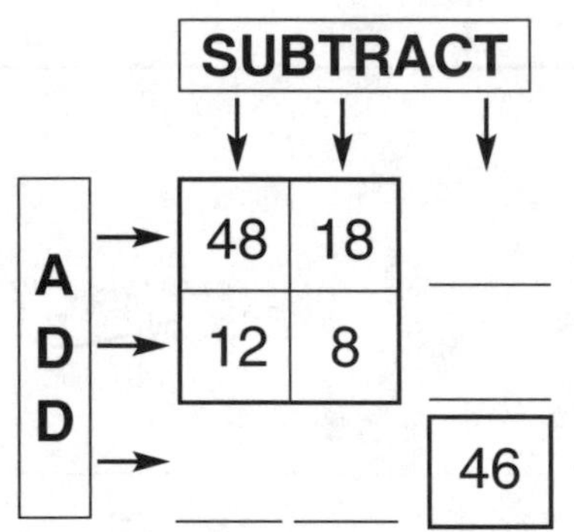

2.

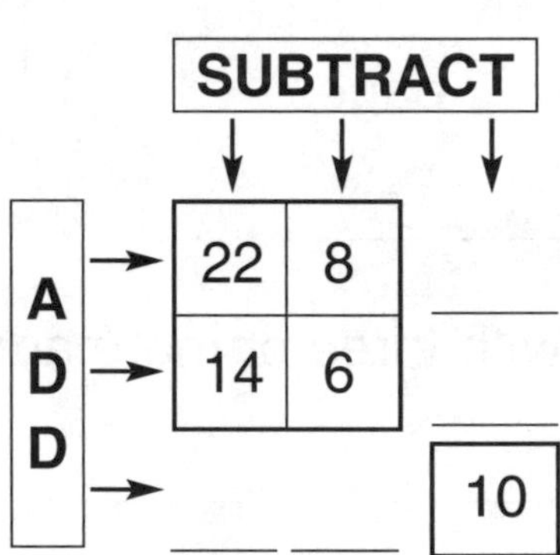

3.

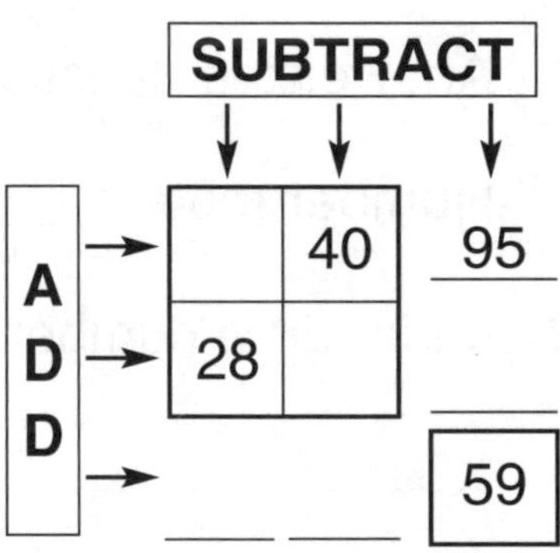

Make up addition and subtraction puzzles of your own.

4.

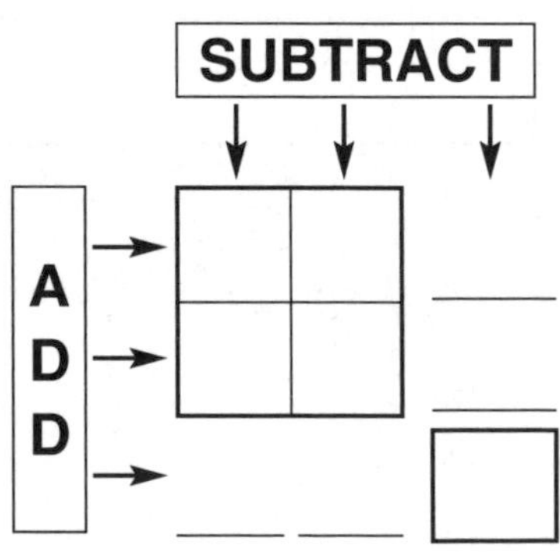

5.

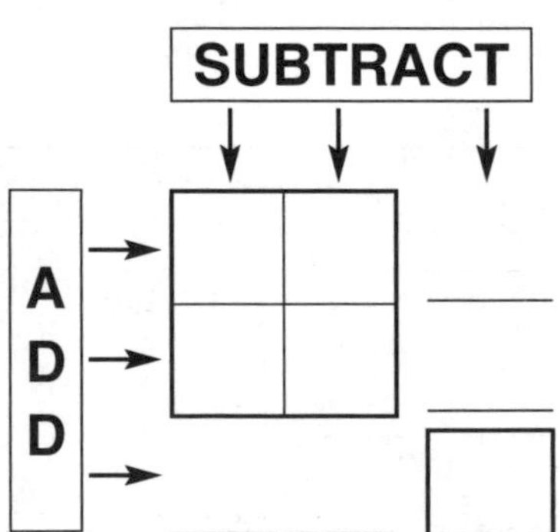

6.

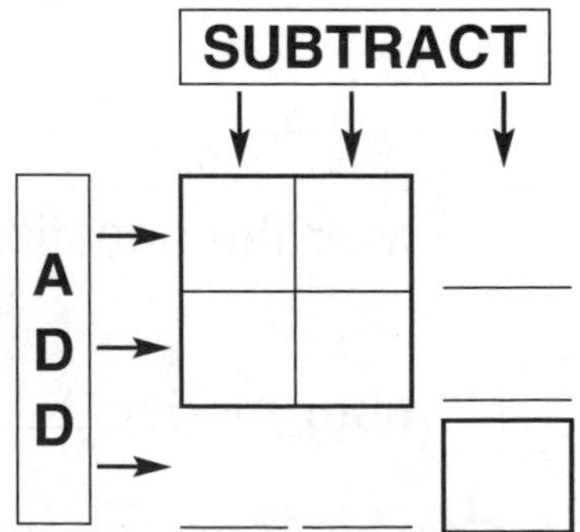

Copyright © Wright Group/McGraw-Hill

Name Date Time

Addition and Subtraction Puzzles

LESSON 2·9

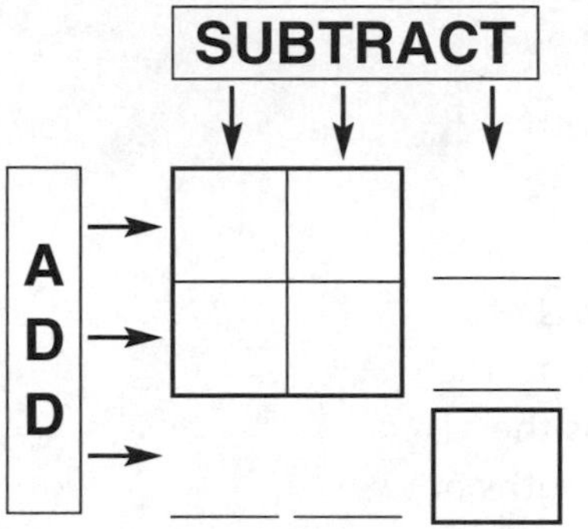
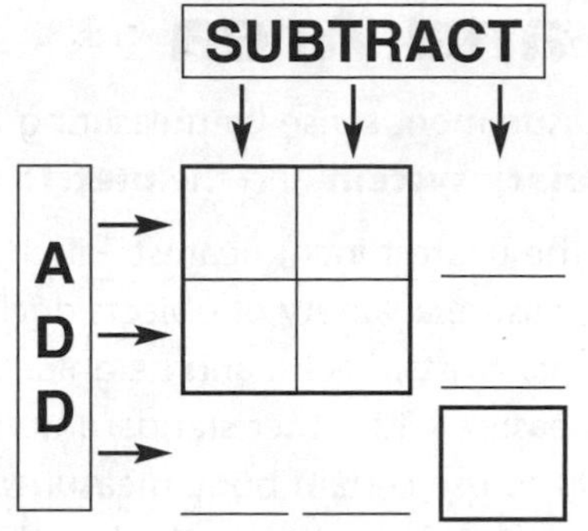
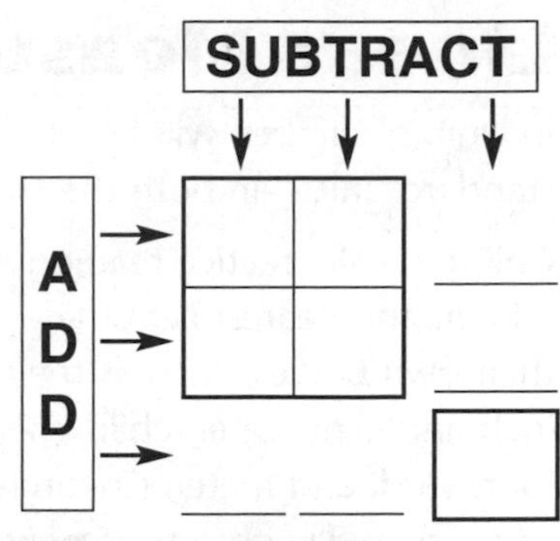
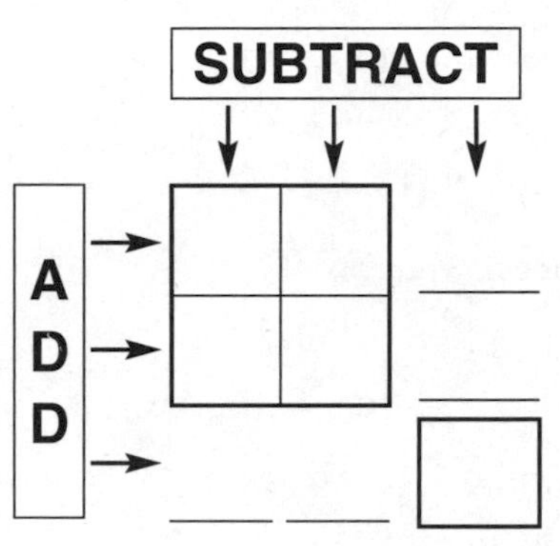
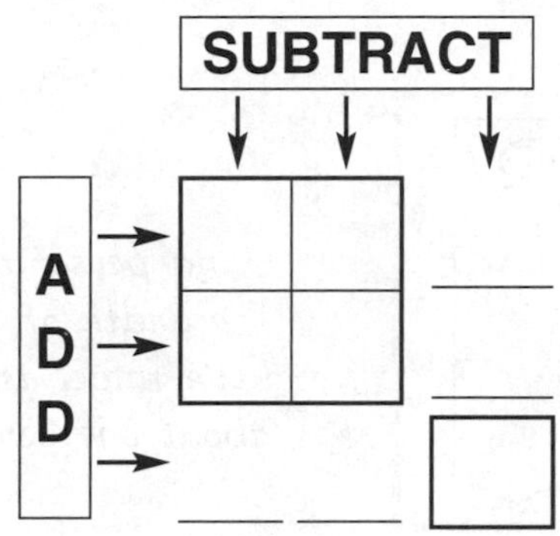
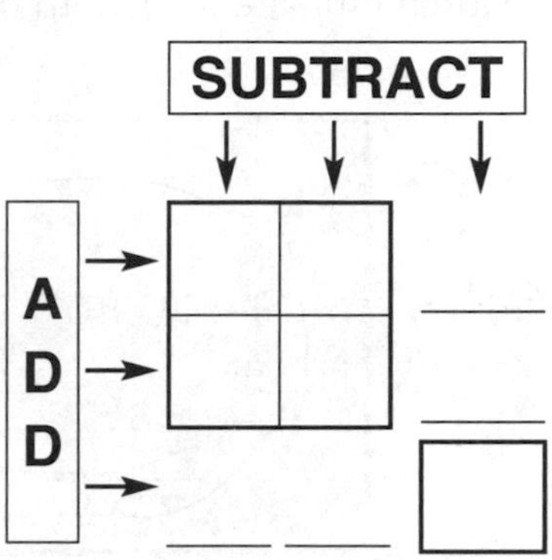
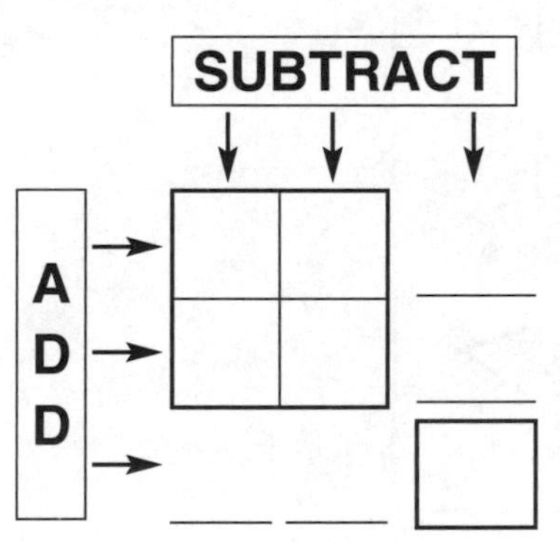
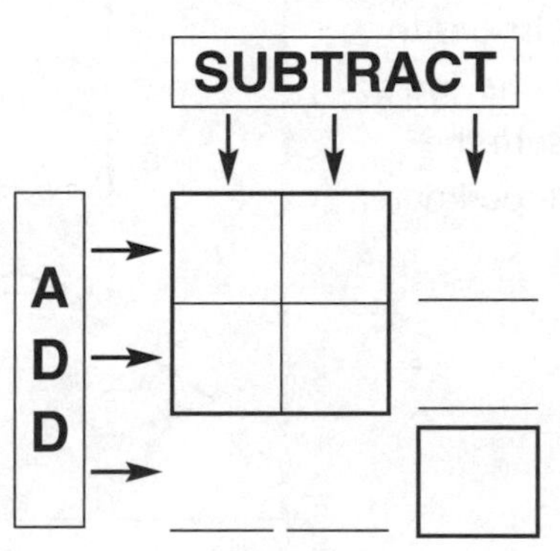
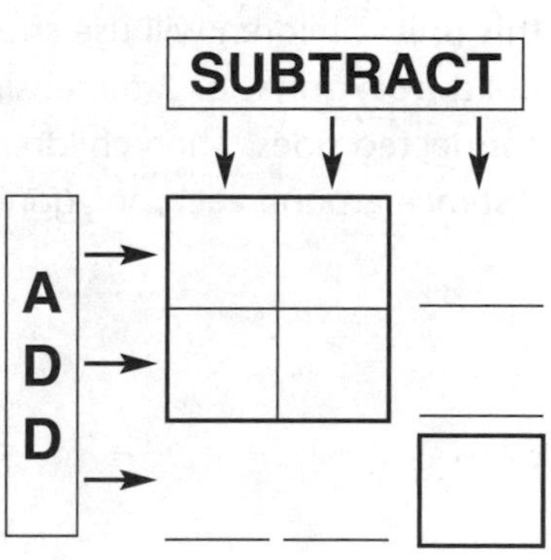
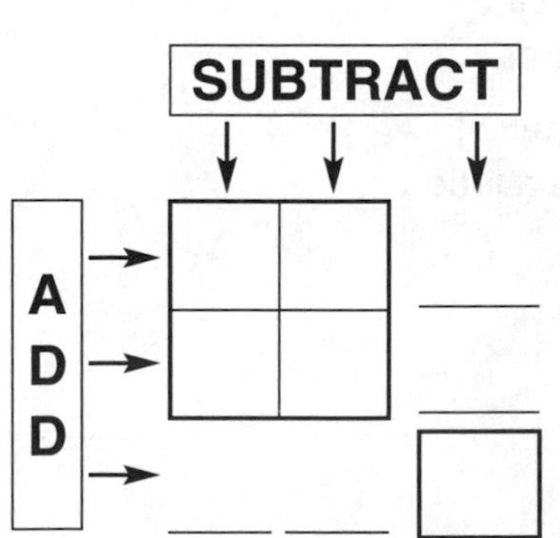
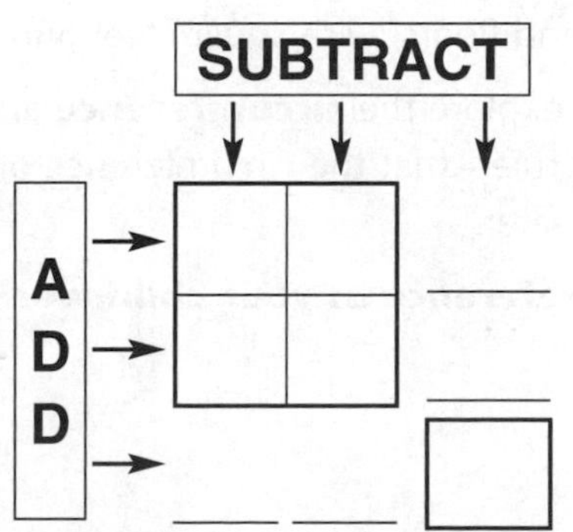
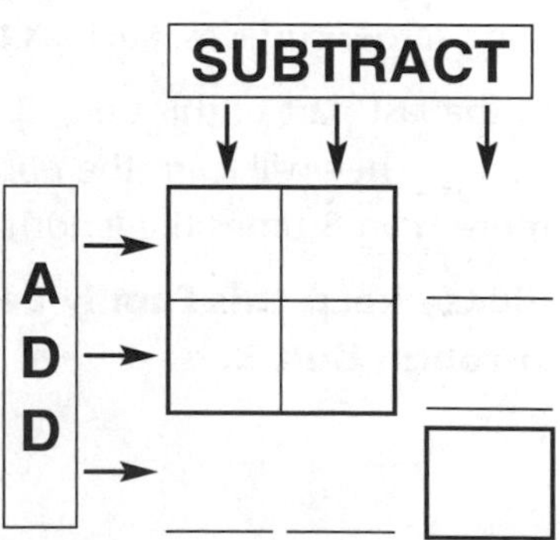

Copyright © Wright Group/McGraw-Hill

Name Date Time

HOME LINK 2•10

Unit 3: Family Letter

Linear Measures and Area

In Unit 3, children will develop their measurement sense by measuring lengths with standard units—in both the **U.S. customary system** and the **metric system.**

Children will practice reading a ruler to the nearest inch, nearest $\frac{1}{2}$ inch, nearest $\frac{1}{4}$ inch, and nearest centimeter as they measure a variety of objects, including parts of their own bodies, such as their hand spans, wrists, necks, and heights. In addition to the inch and centimeter, children will also measure with other standard units, such as the foot, yard, and meter. Children will begin to use certain body measures or the lengths of some everyday objects as **personal references** to estimate the lengths of other objects or distances. For example, a sheet of notebook paper that is about 1 foot long can help children estimate the length of a room in feet.

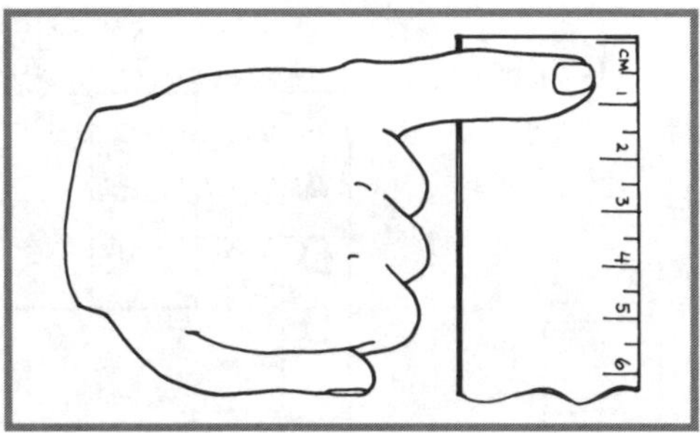

Using personal references: The width of my little finger is about one centimeter.

The concept of **perimeter** is also investigated in this unit. Children will use straws and twist-ties to build **polygons,** or 2-dimensional figures having connected sides. Then children will measure the distance around each polygon to find the perimeter.

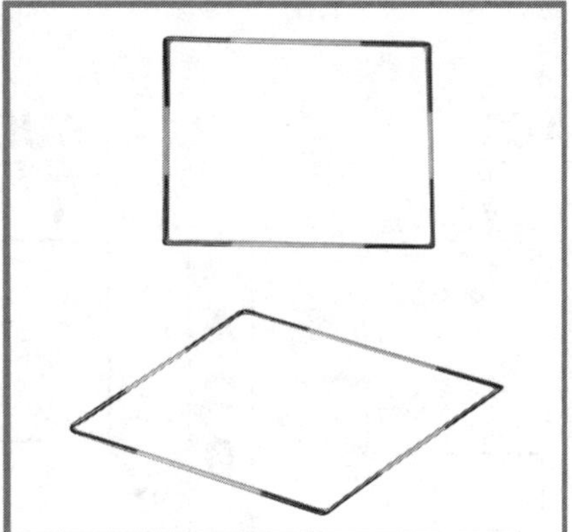

Children will also discover the meaning of **area** by tiling small rectangles with blocks and counting how many blocks cover the rectangles. Children see how to calculate area by tiling larger surfaces, such as tabletops and floors, with square feet and square yards.

In the last part of this unit, children will explore the **circumference** and **diameter** of circles. They will learn the *about 3 times* rule—that the circumference of a circle is a little more than 3 times the length of its diameter.

Please keep this Family Letter for reference as your child works through Unit 3.

Copyright © Wright Group/McGraw-Hill

Vocabulary

Important terms in Unit 3:

unit An agreed-upon unit of measure, for example foot, pound, gallon, meter, kilogram, liter.

length The distance between two points.

U.S. customary system The measurement system used in the United States. For example, inches, feet, yards, and miles are used to measure length.

metric system of measurement A measurement system based on the base-ten numeration system. It is used in most countries around the world. For example, millimeters, centimeters, meters, and kilometers are used to measure length.

benchmark A well-known count or measure that can be used to check whether other counts, measures, or estimates make sense. For example, a benchmark for land area is that a football field is about one acre. A benchmark for length is that the width of a man's thumb is about one inch. Benchmarks are also called *personal-measurement references.*

perimeter The distance around the boundary of a 2-dimensional shape. The perimeter of a circle is called its *circumference.* A formula for the perimeter P of a rectangle with length l and width w is $P = 2 \times (l + w)$.

circumference The perimeter of a circle.

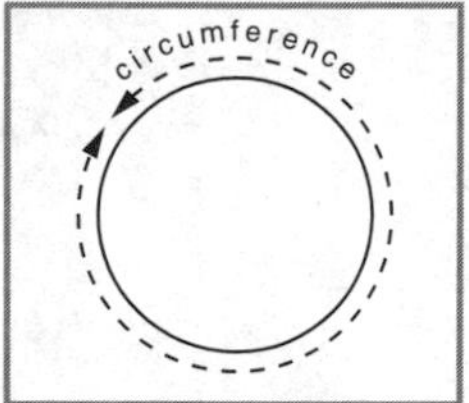

diameter A line segment that passes through the center of a circle or sphere. The length of such a segment.

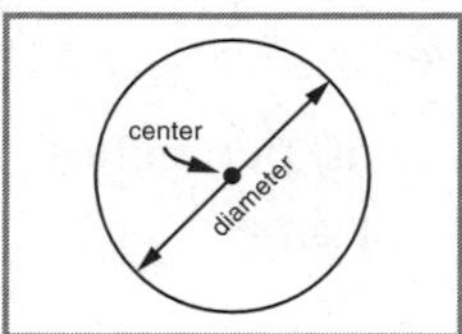

polygon A 2-dimensional figure formed by 3 or more line segments (sides) that meet only at their endpoints (vertices) to make a closed path. The line segments of a polygon may not cross.

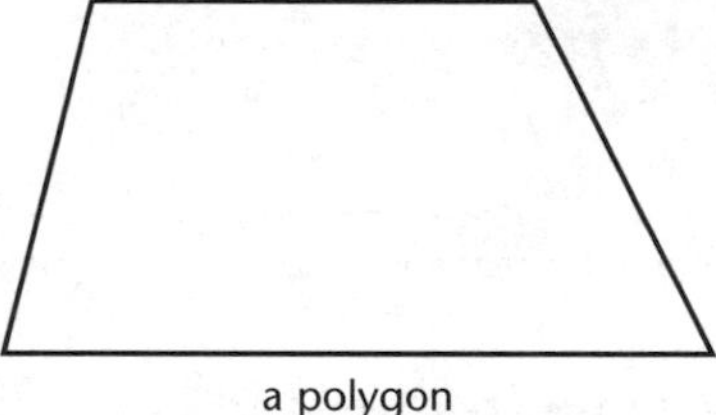

a polygon

tiling The covering of a surface with shapes so that there are no gaps or overlaps.

area The amount of surface inside a 2-dimensional figure. Area is measured in square units, such as square inches or square centimeters.

square unit A unit used to measure area; a square that measures 1 inch, 1 centimeter, 1 yard, or 1 other standard measure of length on each side.

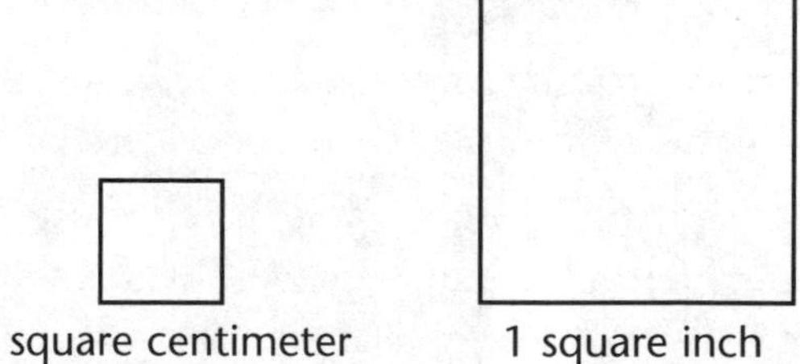

Copyright © Wright Group/McGraw-Hill

Do-Anytime Activities

To work with your child on the concepts taught in this unit and in previous units, try these interesting and rewarding activities:

1. Encourage your child to find some personal references for making several measurements of length at home.
2. Practice using the personal references by *estimating* some lengths, and then practice using a ruler by *measuring* the actual lengths.
3. Practice finding perimeters of objects and circumferences of circular objects around your home.

Copyright © Wright Group/McGraw-Hill

HOME LINK 2•10 **Unit 3: Family Letter** *cont.*

As You Help Your Child with Homework

As your child brings home assignments, you may want to go over the instructions together, clarifying them as necessary. The answers listed below will guide you through this unit's Home Links.

Home Link 3•4

2. perimeter of polygon A = 20 cm
perimeter of polygon B = 20 cm

3. a. 12 ft **3. b.** 60 in.

Home Link 3•5

1. 6 **2.** 2 **3.** 4 **4.** 3

5. 3 **6.** 95 **7.** 62

Home Link 3•7

1. Area = 24 square units
Sample answer:

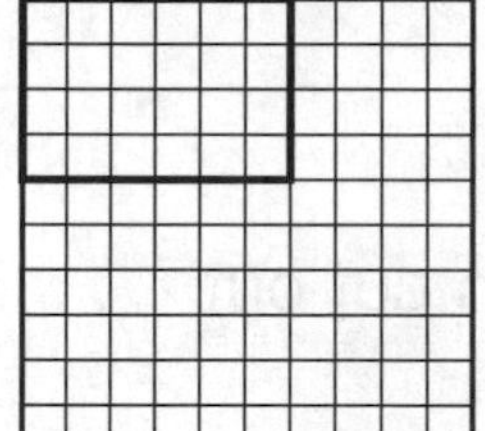

2. Area = 27 square units
Sample answer:

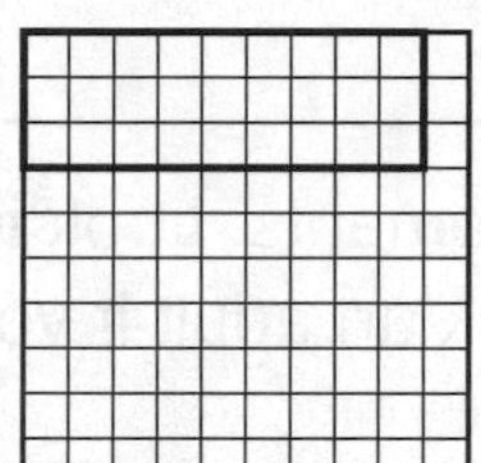

3. This is a 2-by-6 rectangle. Area = 12 square units

4. This is a 5-by-4 rectangle. Area = 20 square units

5. 307 **6.** 119

Home Link 3•8

1. 80 tiles **2.** $160

3.

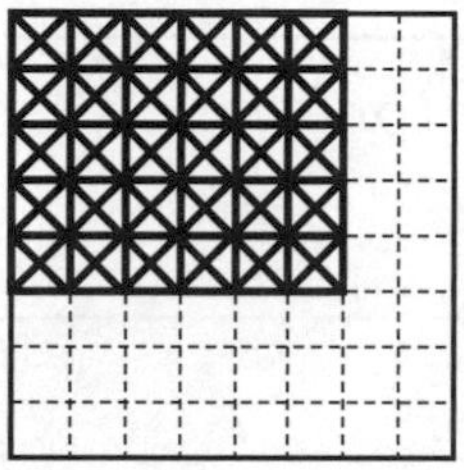

4. 30 plants

5. 489

6. 673

7. 307

Building Skills through Games

In Unit 3, your child will practice addition skills by playing the following games. For detailed instructions, see the *Student Reference Book.*

Addition Top-It

Each player turns over two cards and calls out their sum. The player with the higher sum then takes all the cards from that round.

Subtraction Top-It

Each player turns over two cards and calls out their difference. The player with the larger difference then takes all the cards from that round.

Copyright © Wright Group/McGraw-Hill

Name Date Time

HOME LINK 3•1

Measurements at Home

Family Note Help your child find labels, pictures, and descriptions that contain measurements. If possible, collect them in an envelope or folder so that your child can bring them to school tomorrow, along with this Home Link.

Please return this Home Link to school tomorrow.

1. Find items with measurements on them. Look at boxes and cans. List the items and their measurements.

Item	Measurement
milk carton	*1 quart*

2. Find pictures and ads that show measurements. Look in newspapers, magazines, or catalogs. Ask an adult if you can cut out some examples and bring them to school.

Practice

Write these problems on the back of this page. Write a number model for your ballpark estimate. Use any method you wish to solve each problem. Show your work.

3. 259 + 432 = ______________________

4. 542 − 387 = ______________________

Copyright © Wright Group/McGraw-Hill

Name Date Time

LESSON 3•2 Measuring Line Segments

Measure the line segments with the rulers.

1. Use Ruler A to measure to the nearest inch (in.).

____

____

____

2. Use Ruler B to measure to the nearest $\frac{1}{2}$ inch (in.).

____

____

____

3. Use Ruler C to measure to the nearest $\frac{1}{4}$ inch (in.).

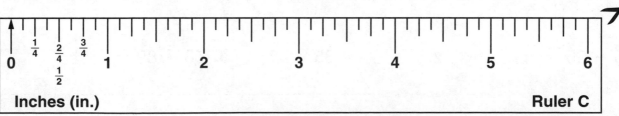

____

____

____

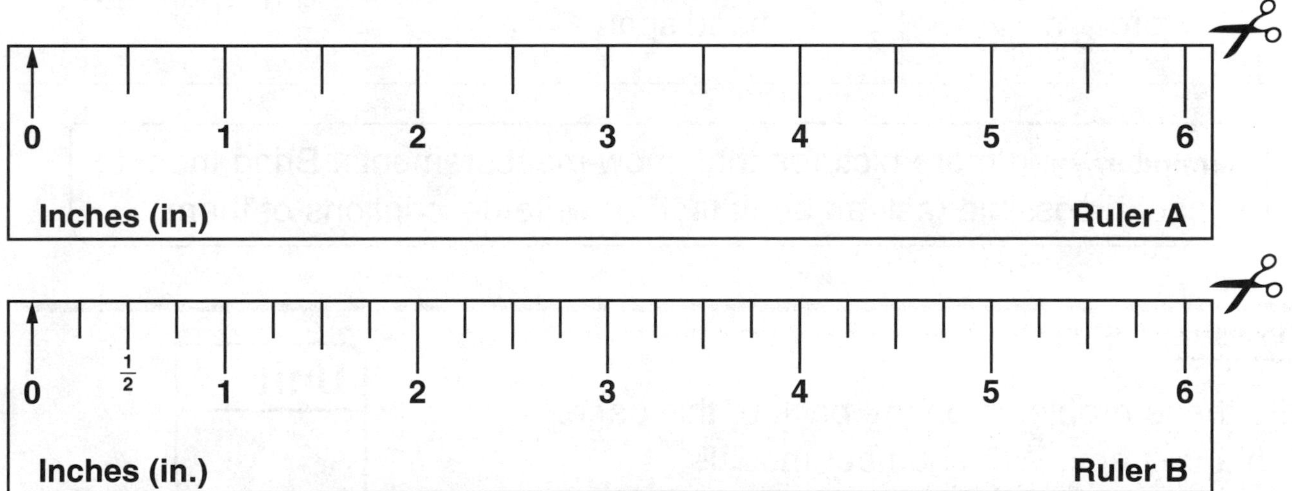

Ruler B: 0, $\frac{1}{2}$, 1, 2, 3, 4, 5, 6 — Inches (in.)

Ruler C: 0, $\frac{1}{4}$, $\frac{2}{4}$, $\frac{1}{2}$, $\frac{3}{4}$, 1, 2, 3, 4, 5, 6 — Inches (in.)

Name Date Time

Body Measures

Family Note Help your child measure an adult at home. Use a tape measure if you have one, or use a piece of string. Mark lengths on the string with a pen, and then measure the string with a ruler.

Please return this Home Link to school tomorrow.

Measure an adult at home to the nearest $\frac{1}{2}$ inch. Fill in the information below:

Name of adult: ____________________

Height: about ______ inches

Length of shoe: about ______ inches

Around neck: about ______ inches

Around wrist: about ______ inches

Distance from waist to floor:

about ______ inches

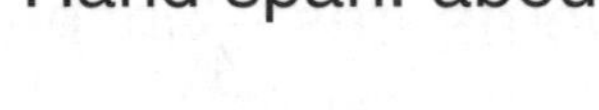

Forearm: about ______ inches	Hand span: about ______ inches	Arm span: about ______ inches
forearm	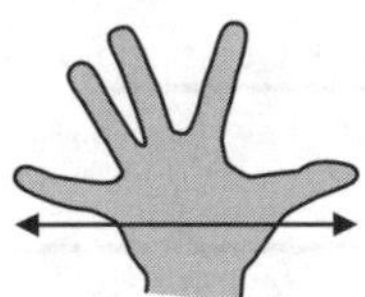 hand span	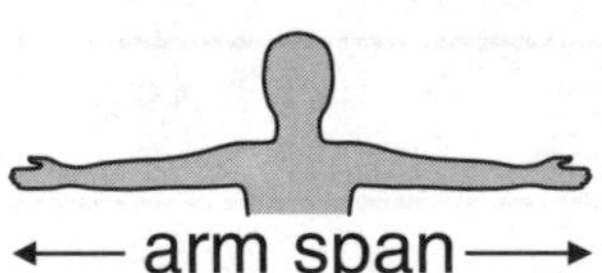 arm span

Reminder: Find more pictures that show measurements. Bring them to school if possible (ask an adult first) or write descriptions of them.

Practice

Write these problems on the back of this page. Fill in a unit box. Write number models for your ballpark estimates. Show your work.

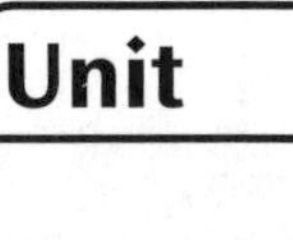

1. 83 − 25 = ______ **2.** ______ = 35 + 47 **3.** 58 + 89 = ______

Copyright © Wright Group/McGraw-Hill

Name Date Time

Measuring Height

Family Note Measuring the height of the ceiling is easiest with such tools as a yardstick, a carpenter's ruler, or a metal tape measure. Another way is to attach a string to the handle of a broom and raise it to the ceiling. Have the string extend from the ceiling to the floor, cut the string to that length, and then measure the string with a ruler.

Please return this Home Link to school tomorrow.

Work with someone at home.

1. Measure the height of the ceiling in your room.

The ceiling in my room is about ________ feet high.

2. Measure the height of a table.

The table is between ________ and ________ feet high.

3. About how many tables could you stack in your room, one on top of the other?

about ________ tables

4. Draw a picture on the back of this page to show how the tables might look stacked in your room.

Practice

Write these problems on the back of this page. Draw and fill in a unit box. Write a number model for your ballpark estimate. Use any method you wish to solve each problem. Show your work.

5. ________ = 63 + 28

6. 149 − 76 = ________

Copyright © Wright Group/McGraw-Hill

Name Date Time

Perimeter

Family Note The perimeter of a geometric figure is the distance around the figure. If the figure is a polygon, like those on this page, the perimeter can be found by adding the lengths of the sides. If you want to review this topic in detail with your child, use the *Student Reference Book*, pages 150 and 151.

Please return this Home Link to school tomorrow.

SRB 150 151

1. Estimate: Which has the larger perimeter, polygon A or polygon B? ______

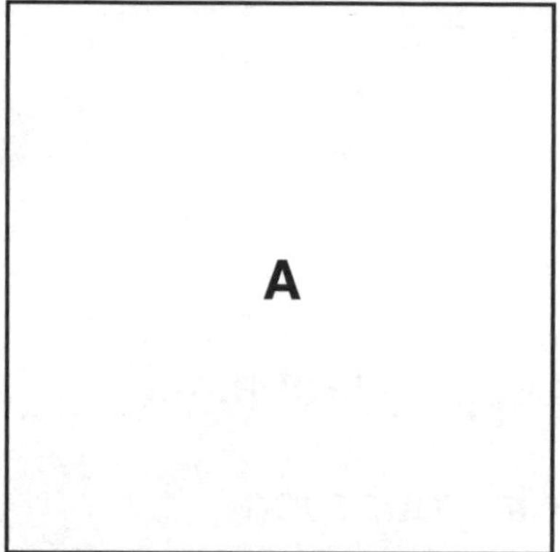

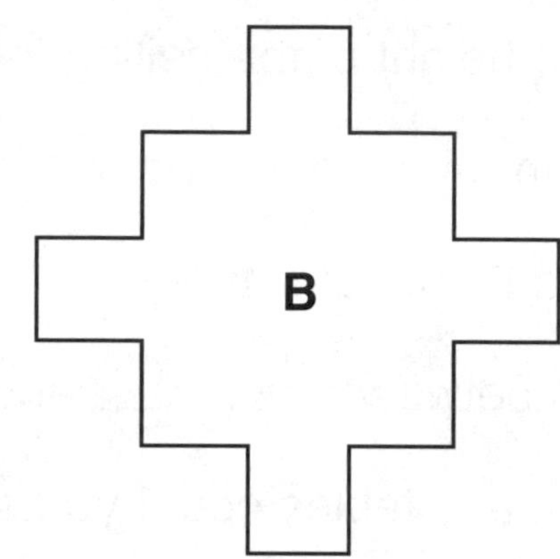

2. Check your estimate by measuring the perimeter of each polygon in centimeters. If you don't have a centimeter ruler, cut out the one at the bottom of the page.

perimeter of polygon A = ______ cm   perimeter of polygon B = ______ cm

3. What is the perimeter of each figure below?

a.

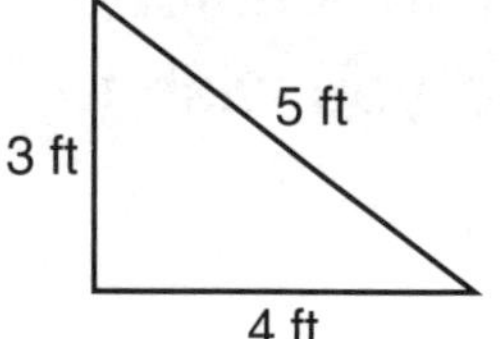

perimeter = ______ ft

b. each side 10 inches

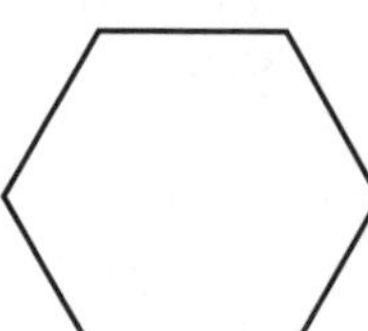

perimeter = ______ in.

Copyright © Wright Group/McGraw-Hill

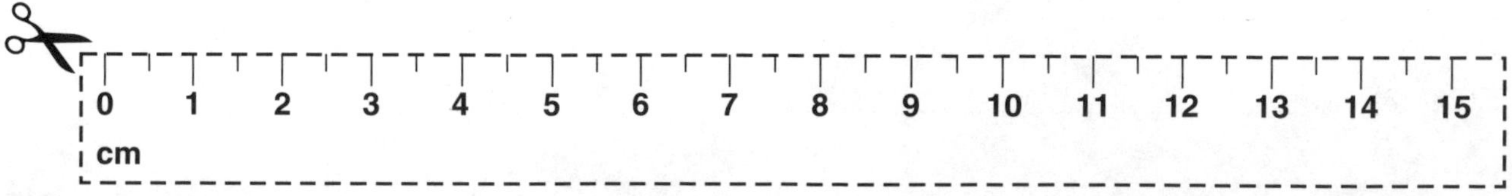

Name Date Time

Describing Data

Family Note You can find information about minimum, maximum, range, median, and mode for a set of data on pages 79–82 in the *Student Reference Book*.

Please return this Home Link to school tomorrow.

SRB 79–82

Children in the Science Club collected pill bugs. The tally chart shows how many they collected. Use the data from the tally chart to complete a line plot.

Number of Pill Bugs	Number of Collectors
0	
1	
2	///
3	~~////~~
4	
5	//
6	//

Number of Children

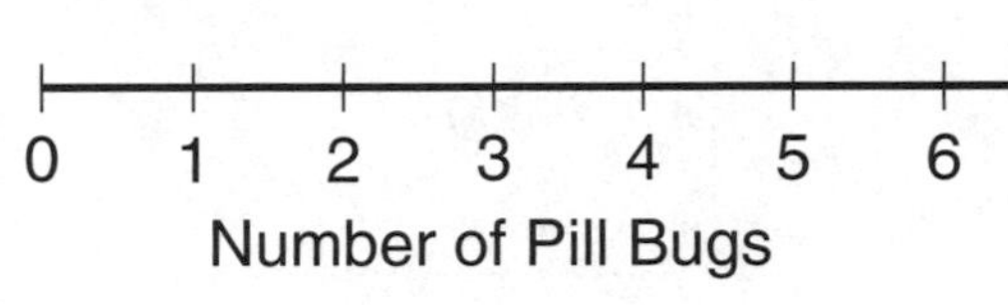

Use the data to answer the questions.

1. What is the maximum (greatest) number of pill bugs found? _____ pillbugs
2. What is the minimum (least) number of pill bugs found? _____ pillbugs
3. What is the range for the data? _____ pill bugs
4. What is the median for the data? _____ pill bugs
5. What is the mode for the data? _____ pill bugs

Practice

Make ballpark estimates. Solve on the back of this paper. Show your work.

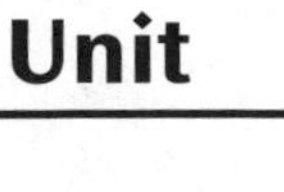

6. 67 + 28 = ____________________
7. 33 + 29 = ____________________

Copyright © Wright Group/McGraw-Hill

Name Date Time

Group Tally Chart

Block: ____________________

Result	Tallies	Total
on an edge		
not on an edge		
Total number of tosses		

Copyright © Wright Group/McGraw-Hill

Name Date Time

Group Tally Chart

Block: ____________________

Result	Tallies	Total
on an edge		
not on an edge		
Total number of tosses		

Copyright © Wright Group/McGraw-Hill

Name Date Time

Room Perimeters

Family Note A personal measurement reference is something you know the measure of—for example, your height or ounces in a water bottle. Personal references can help you estimate measures that you don't know. A person's pace can be defined as the length of a step, measured from heel to heel or from toe to toe. It will be helpful for you to read about Personal Measurement References on pages 141, 142, 148, and 149 in the *Student Reference Book* with your child.

SRB 141 142 148 149

Please return this Home Link to school tomorrow.

Your pace is the length of one of your steps.

1. Find the perimeter, in paces, of your bedroom.
Walk along each side and count the number of paces.

The perimeter of my bedroom is about ________ paces.

2. Which room in your home has the largest perimeter? Use your estimating skills to help you decide.

The ____________________________ has the largest perimeter.

Its perimeter is about _______ paces.

3. Draw this room on another sheet of paper.
Plan to share your drawing with the class.

Practice

Write these problems on the back of this page. Fill in a unit box. Write a number model for your ballpark estimate. Use any method you wish to solve each problem. Show your work.

4. 38 + 9 = ________________________________

5. 143 − 37 = ________________________________

6. ________________________________ = 576 − 67

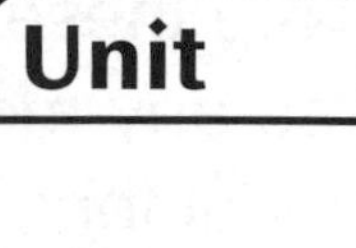

Copyright © Wright Group/McGraw-Hill

Name Date Time

Areas of Rectangles

Family Note Today we discussed the concept of area. Area is a measure of the amount of surface inside a 2-dimensional shape. One way to find area is by counting same-size units inside a shape. For more information, see pages 154–156 in the *Student Reference Book*. In the next lesson, we will look at ways to calculate area.

Please return this Home Link to school tomorrow.

SRB 154–156

Show someone at home how to find the area of each rectangle. Make a dot in each square as you count the squares inside the rectangle.

1. Draw a 4-by-6 rectangle on the grid.

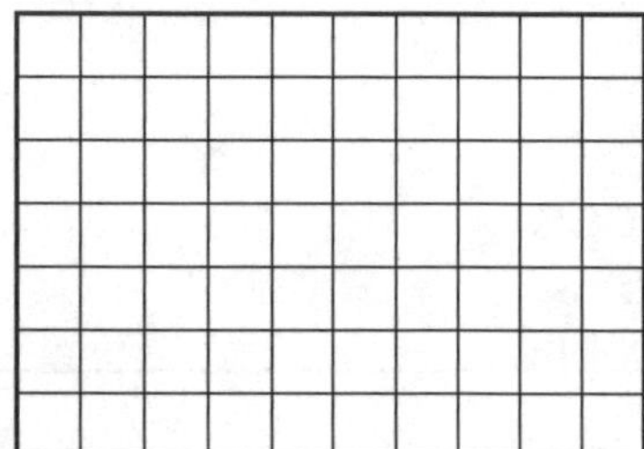

2. Draw a 3-by-9 rectangle.

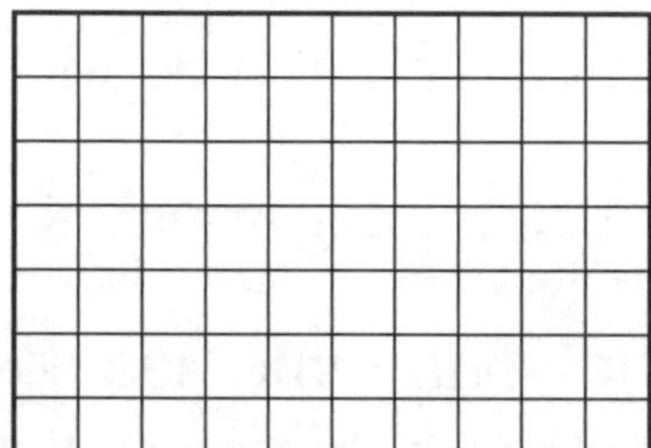

Fill in the blanks.

3.

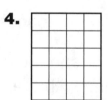

This is a _____-by-_____ rectangle.

Area = _____ square units

4.

This is a _____-by-_____ rectangle.

Area = _____ square units

Practice

Write these problems on the back of this page. Fill in a unit box. Use any method you wish to solve each problem. Write a number model for your ballpark estimate. Show your work.

5. $\begin{array}{r} 571 \\ -\ 264 \\ \hline \end{array}$

6. $\begin{array}{r} 805 \\ -\ 686 \\ \hline \end{array}$

Copyright © Wright Group/McGraw-Hill

Name Date Time

Exploring Area

1. Rectangle A is drawn on centimeter grid paper. Find its area.

Area = _____ square centimeters

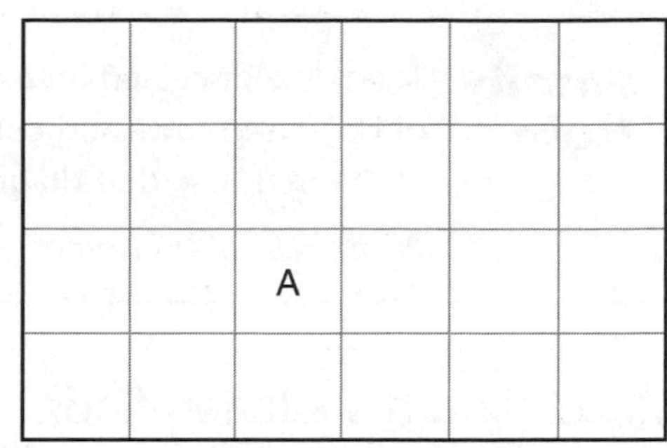

2. Rectangle B has the same area as Rectangle A. Cut out Rectangle B. Then cut it into 5 pieces, any way you want.

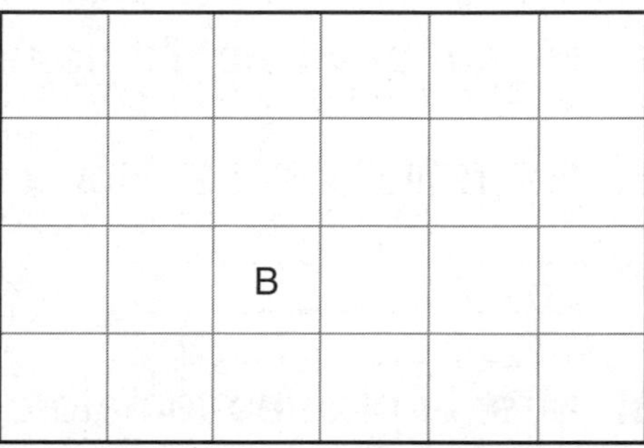

Rearrange the pieces into a new shape that is not a rectangle. Then tape the pieces together in the space below. What is the area of the new shape?

Area of new shape = _____ square centimeters

3. Explain how you found the area of your new shape.

____

____

____

Copyright © Wright Group/McGraw-Hill

Name Date Time

Area

Family Note Today we discussed area as an array, or diagram. An array is a rectangular arrangement of objects in rows and columns. Help your child draw an array of the tomato plants in Problem 3. Use that diagram to find the total number of plants.

Please return this Home Link to school tomorrow.

SRB 64 65

Mr. Li tiled his kitchen floor.
This is what the tiled floor looks like.

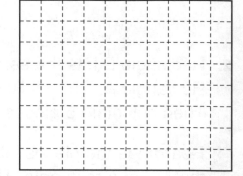

1. How many tiles did he use? _____ tiles

2. Each tile cost $2. How much did all the tiles cost? $__________

3. Mrs. Li planted tomato plants. She planted 5 rows with 6 plants in each row. Draw a diagram of her tomato plants.
Hint: You can show each plant with a large dot or an X.

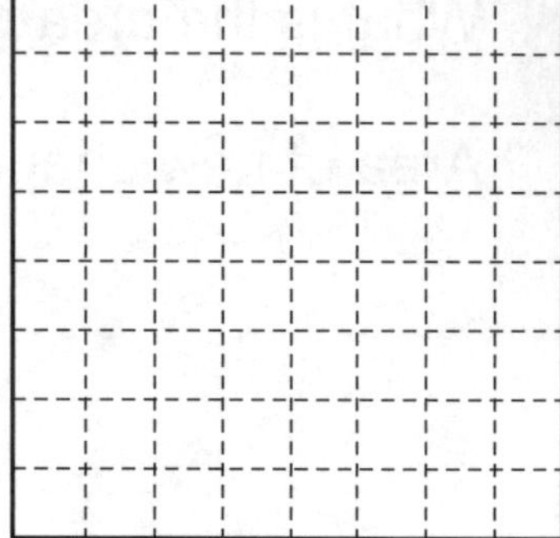

4. How many tomato plants are there in all?

_____ plants

Practice

Write these problems on the back of this page. Fill in a unit box. Write a number model for your ballpark estimate. Use any method you wish to solve each problem. Show your work.

Unit

5. 548 − 59 = _____

6. _____ = 616 + 57

7. _____ = 571 − 264

Copyright © Wright Group/McGraw-Hill

Name Date Time

LESSON 3•8

A Shopping Trip

1. List the items you are buying in the space below. You must buy at least four items.

   If you buy the same item 2 times, list it 2 times.

Item	Sale Price

2. Estimate how many dollar bills you will need to pay for your items. ______

3. Give the clerk the dollar bills.

4. The clerk calculates the total cost. You owe $______.

5. The clerk calculates the change you should be getting. $______

6. Record your change. Use Ⓟ, Ⓝ, Ⓓ, Ⓠ. ______

Try This

Use the Stationery Store Poster in your *Student Reference Book,* page 214.

7. Linda wants to buy a box of pens and a box of pencils. How much will she save by buying them on sale?

	Regular price	Sale price	Difference	
pens	$___.___	$___.___	Regular total	$___.___
pencils	$___.___	$___.___	Sale total	$___.___
Total cost	$___.___	$___.___	**Amount saved**	$___.___

Copyright © Wright Group/McGraw-Hill

Name Date Time

Finding and Comparing Areas

1. Cut out the square.
2. Use square pattern blocks to find the area of the square.
3. Cut the square into 2 equal triangles.
4. Find the area of each triangle.

Names: ____________________

1. Area of square: _____ sq. in.
2. Area of first triangle: about _____ sq. in.
3. Area of second triangle: about _____ sq. in.
4. How do the areas of the two triangles compare?

   ____

5. How does the area of one triangle compare to the area of the original square?

   ____

Copyright © Wright Group/McGraw-Hill

Name Date Time

LESSON 3·9

Centimeter Sheet

0 1 2 3 4 5 6 7 8 9 10 11 12 13 14 15 16

1 2 3 4 5 6 7 8 9 10 11 12 13 14 15 16 17 18 19 20 21

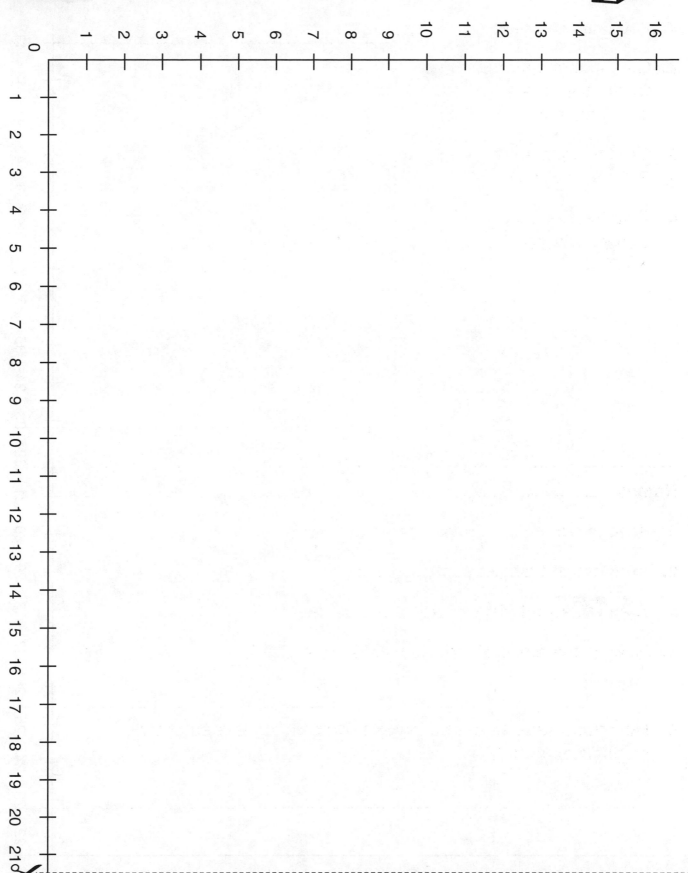

Copyright © Wright Group/McGraw-Hill

Name Date Time

LESSON 3•9 Centimeter Sheet *continued*

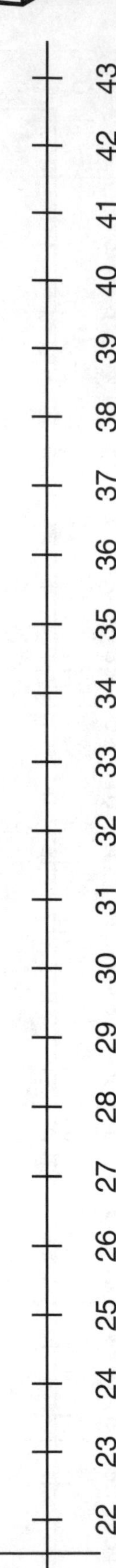

Copyright © Wright Group/McGraw-Hill

Do not cut. Paste along solid line.

Name Date Time

HOME LINK 3•9

Circumference and Diameter

Family Note Today in school your child learned the definitions of *circumference* and *diameter.* Ask your child to explain them to you. Help your child find and measure circular objects, such as cups, plates, clocks, cans, and so on. The *about 3 times* circle rule says that the circumference of any circle, no matter what size, is about 3 times its diameter. It will be helpful for you to review pages 152 and 153 in the *Student Reference Book* with your child.

SRB 152 153

Please return this Home Link to school tomorrow.

Measure the diameters and circumferences of circular objects at home. Use a tape measure if you have one, or use a piece of string. Mark lengths on the string with your finger or a pen, and then measure the string. Record your measures in the chart below.

Does the *about 3 times* circle rule seem to work? Share the *about 3 times* rule with someone at home.

Diameter = 9 cm

Circumference = about 27 cm

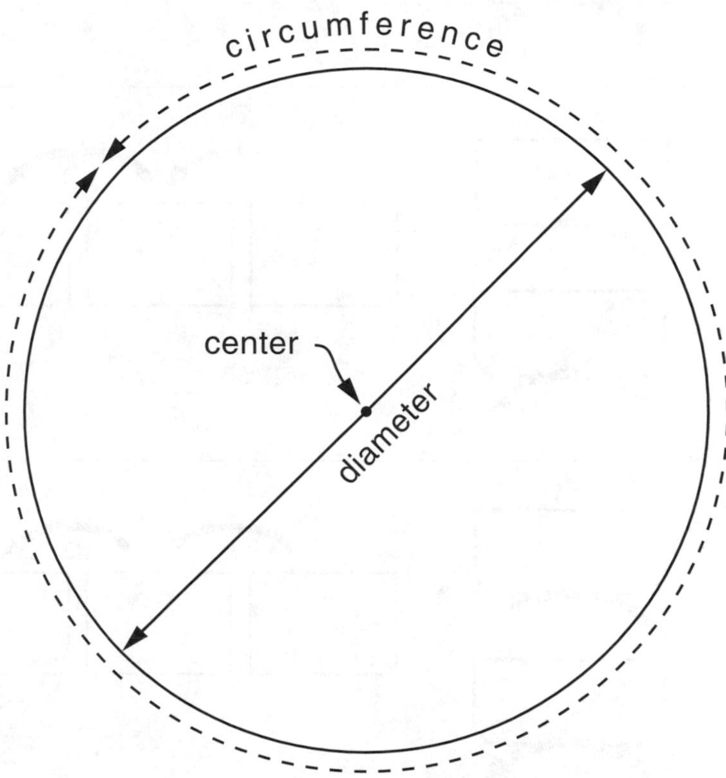

Object	Diameter	Circumference

Copyright © Wright Group/McGraw-Hill

Name Date Time

LESSON 3·9

Two-Rule Frames and Arrows

Solve the Frames-and-Arrows problems.

1.

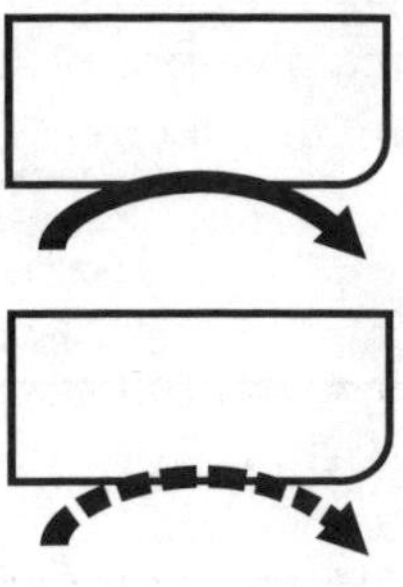

2.

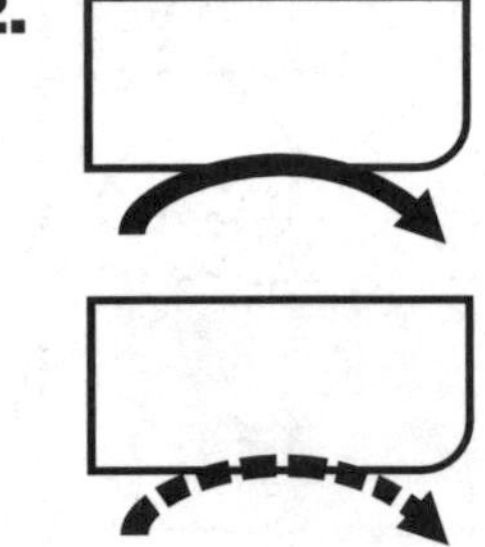

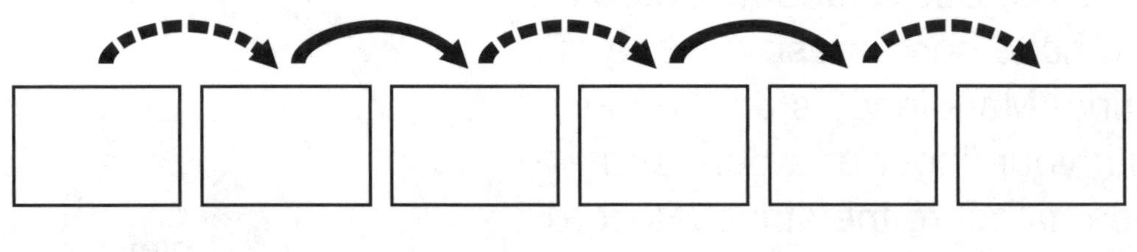

3.

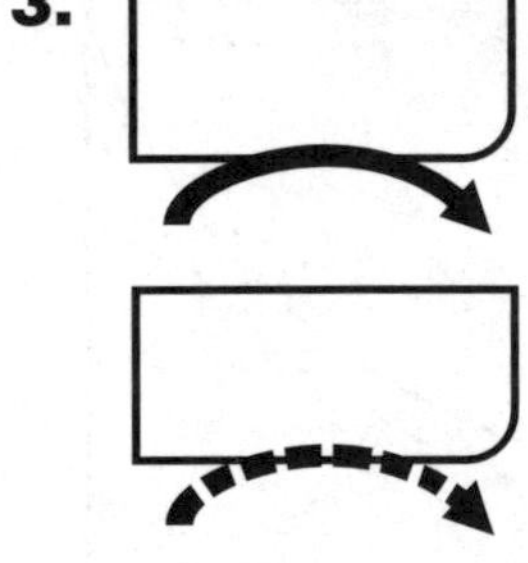

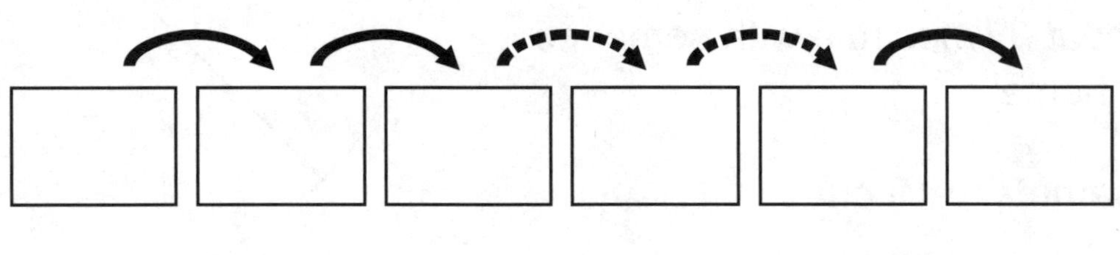

4.

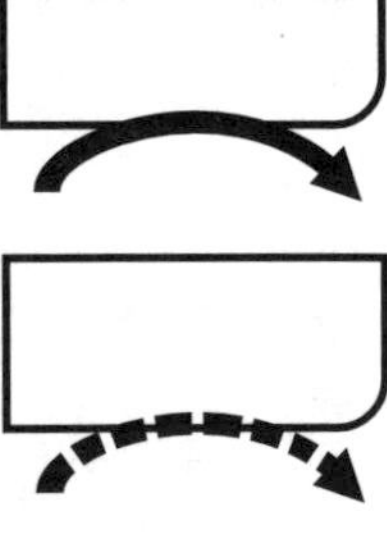

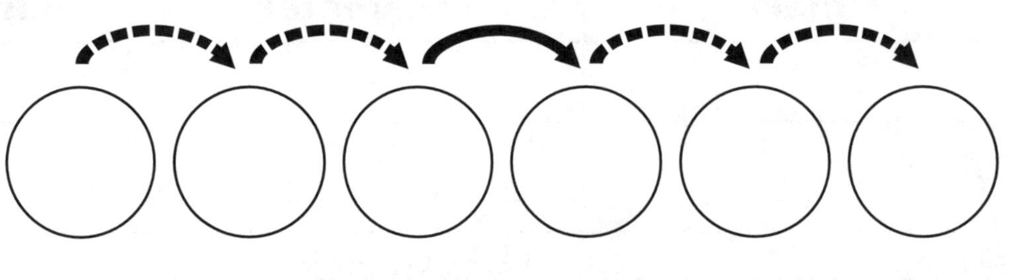

Copyright © Wright Group/McGraw-Hill

Name Date Time

HOME LINK 3•10

Unit 4: Family Letter

Multiplication and Division

Unit 4 focuses on the most common uses of multiplication and division—problems that involve equal sharing and equal grouping. In *Second Grade Everyday Mathematics,* children were exposed to multiplication and division number stories and multiplication and division facts. To solve multiplication and division number stories, children will refer to familiar strategies introduced in second grade:

- **Acting out problems using concrete objects, such as counters** (below)

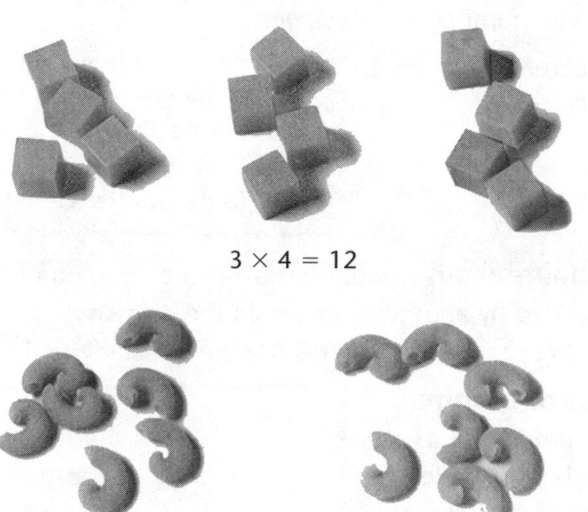

$3 \times 4 = 12$

$2 \times 7 = 14$

- **Representing problems with pictures and arrays** (below)

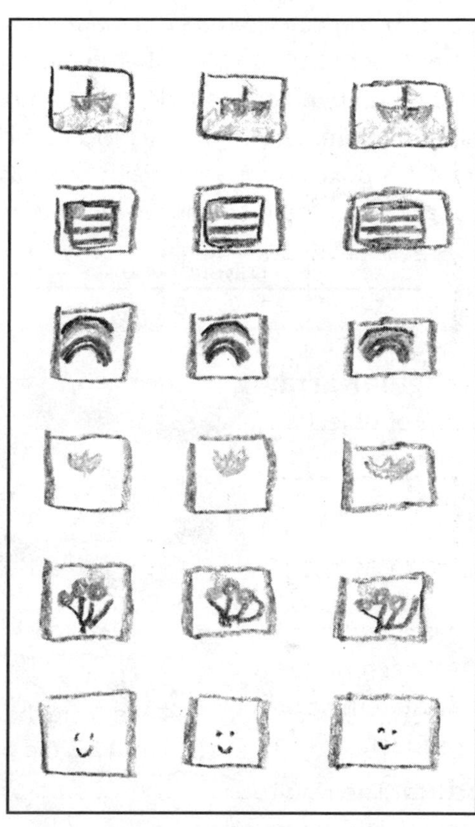

A sheet of stamps has 6 rows. Each row has 3 stamps. How many stamps are on a sheet?

$6 \times 3 = 18$

- **Using diagrams to sort out quantities** (below)

children	pennies per child	pennies in all
4	?	28

- **Using number models to represent solution strategies** (below)

Problem:	**Solution strategies:**
Each child has 2 apples. There are 16 apples. How many children have apples?	*$2 \times ? = 16$, or I know that $16 \div 2 = 8$. If there are 16 apples and each child has 2, then there must be 8 children.*

Copyright © Wright Group/McGraw-Hill

Unit 4: Family Letter *cont.*

Vocabulary

Important terms in Unit 4:

multiples of a number The product of the number and a counting number. For example, multiples of 2 are 2, 4, 6, and 8....

multiplication/division diagram In *Everyday Mathematics*, a diagram used to represent problems in which the total number of objects in several equal groups is being considered. The diagram has three parts: number of groups, number in each group, and total number. For example, the multiplication/division diagram here represents this number story: There are 3 boxes of crayons. Each box has 8 crayons. There are 24 crayons in all.

boxes	crayons per box	crayons
3	**8**	**24**

rectangular array A group of objects placed in rows and columns.

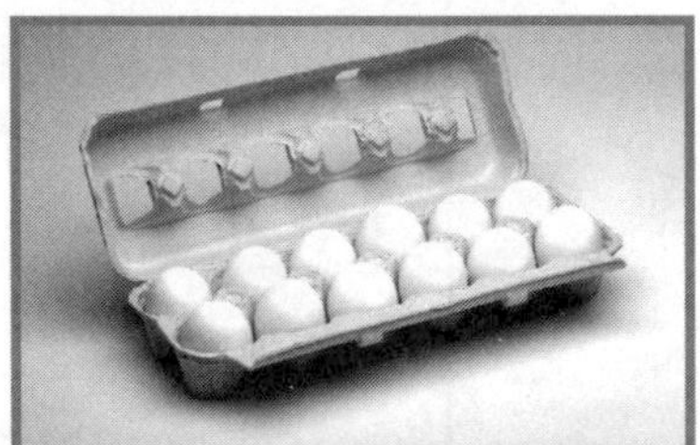

A 2-by-6 array of eggs

factor Each of the two or more numbers in a product.

In **4 × 3 = 12,**
4 and **3** are the **factors,**
and **12** is the **product.**

product The result of multiplying two numbers.

equal groups Sets with the same number of elements, such as tables with 4 legs, rows with 6 chairs, boxes of 100 paper clips, and so on.

dividend The number in division that is being divided.

divisor In division, the number that divides another number, the *dividend.*

quotient The result of division.

In **28 ÷ 4 = 7,**
28 is the **dividend,**
4 is the **divisor,** and
7 is the **quotient.**

remainder An amount left over when one number is divided by another number. In the division number model 16 ÷ 3 → 5 R1, the remainder is 1.

square number The product of a number multiplied by itself; any number that can be represented by a square array of dots or objects. A square array has the same number of rows as columns.

• • •
• • •
• • •

3 × 3 = 9
The number 9 is a **square number.**

Building Skills through Games

In Unit 4, your child will practice division and multiplication by playing the following games. For detailed instructions, see the *Student Reference Book.*

Division Arrays

Players make arrays with counters. They use number cards to determine the number of counters and a toss of a die to establish the number of rows.

Beat the Calculator

A Calculator (a player who uses a calculator) and a Brain (a player who solves the problem without a calculator) compete to see who will be first to solve multiplication problems.

Copyright © Wright Group/McGraw-Hill

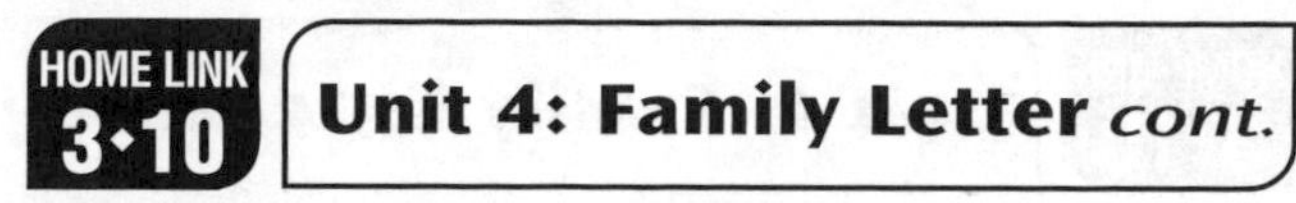

Do-Anytime Activities

To work with your child on concepts taught in this unit and in previous units, try these interesting and rewarding activities:

1. Together with your child, sort objects into equal groups. Discuss what you could do with any leftover objects.

2. Review multiplication-fact shortcuts:

- **turn-around facts** The order of the factors does not change the product. Thus, if you know $3 \times 4 = 12$, you also know $4 \times 3 = 12$.
- **multiplication by 1** The product of 1 and another number is always equal to the other number. For example, $1 \times 9 = 9$; $1 \times 7 = 7$.
- **multiplication by 0** The product of 0 and another number is always 0. For example, $4 \times 0 = 0$; $0 \times 2 = 0$.
- **square numbers** Arrays for numbers multiplied by themselves are always squares. For example, 2×2 and 4×4 are square numbers.

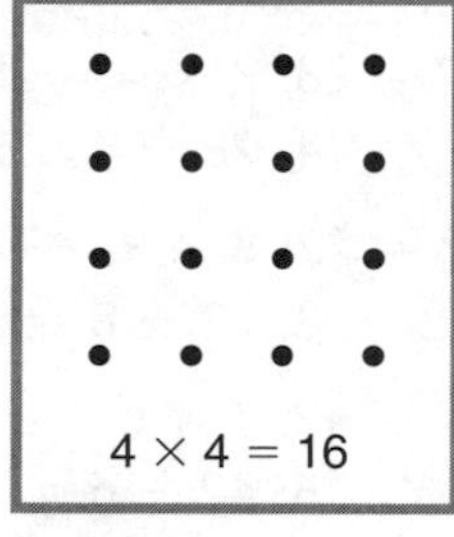

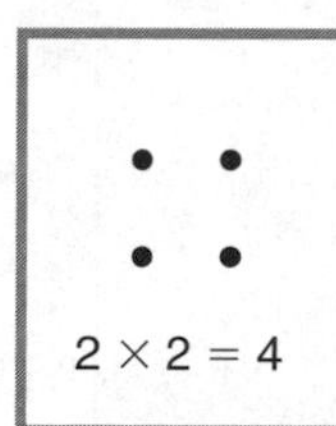

3. Use the ×, ÷ Fact Triangles (a set will be sent home later) to practice the basic facts. Act as a partner by covering one number on the card and then asking your child to create a multiplication or division number model using the other two numbers.

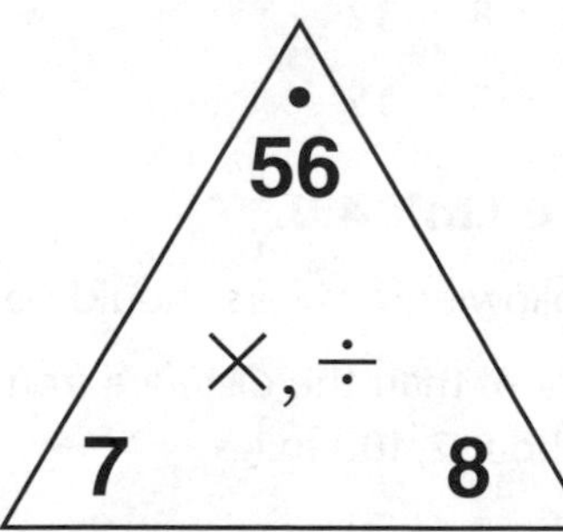

$7 \times 8 = 56$
$8 \times 7 = 56$
$56 \div 8 = 7$
$56 \div 7 = 8$

4. Write any number–for example, 34,056. Then ask questions like the following: How many are in the thousands place? *(4)* What is the value of the digit 5? *(50)*

5. Ask questions like the following:
Is $467 + 518$ more or less than 1,000? *(less)* Is $754 - 268$ more or less than 500? *(less)*

Copyright © Wright Group/McGraw-Hill

As You Help Your Child with Homework

As your child brings home assignments, you might want to go over the instructions together, have your child explain the activities, and clarify them as necessary. The answers listed below will guide you through this unit's Home Links.

Home Link 4·1

1. 30 apples

Home Link 4·2

1. 24 counters **2.** 24 counters

3. 24 counters **4.** 358

5. 204 **6.** 428

Home Link 4·3

1. 5 counters per person; 0 counters remaining

2. 2 counters per person; 5 counters remaining

3. 4 weeks in January; 3 days remaining

4. 4 teams; 2 children remaining

5. 2 pencils; 4 pencils left over

6. 11 jelly beans; 0 jelly beans left over

7. 577 **8.** 31 **9.** 801

Home Link 4·4

1. 6 marbles; 0 marbles left over

2. 2 cookies; 1 cookie left over

3. 4 complete rows; 6 stamps left over

Home Link 4·5

1. 10; 10 **2.** 15; 15 **3.** 20; 20 **4.** 9; 9

5. 90; 90 **6.** 365; 365 **7.** 0; 0 **8.** 0; 0

9. 0; 0 **10.** 20 **11.** 20 **12.** 18

13. 14 **14.** 15 **15.** 50

Home Link 4·6

1. 10; 10; 10; 10 **2.** 12; 12; 12; 12

3. $2 \times 7 = 14$; $7 \times 2 = 14$;
$14 \div 2 = 7$; $14 \div 7 = 2$

4. $2 \times 8 = 16$; $8 \times 2 = 16$;
$16 \div 2 = 8$; $16 \div 8 = 2$

5. $5 \times 4 = 20$; $4 \times 5 = 20$;
$20 \div 5 = 4$; $20 \div 4 = 5$

6. $10 \times 6 = 60$; $6 \times 10 = 60$;
$60 \div 10 = 6$; $60 \div 6 = 10$

Home Link 4·7

1. $5 \times 6 = 30$; $6 \times 5 = 30$;
$30 \div 6 = 5$; $30 \div 5 = 6$

2. $8 \times 3 = 24$; $3 \times 8 = 24$;
$24 \div 3 = 8$; $24 \div 8 = 3$

3. $2 \times 9 = 18$; $9 \times 2 = 18$;
$18 \div 2 = 9$; $18 \div 9 = 2$

4. $4 \times 7 = 28$; $7 \times 4 = 28$;
$28 \div 7 = 4$; $28 \div 4 = 7$

5. $9 \times 8 = 72$; $8 \times 9 = 72$;
$72 \div 9 = 8$; $72 \div 8 = 9$

6. $6 \times 7 = 42$; $7 \times 6 = 42$;
$42 \div 7 = 6$; $42 \div 6 = 7$

Home Link 4·8

1. 7; 5; $7 \times 5 = 35$; 35 square units

2. 6; 7; $6 \times 7 = 42$; 42 square units

3. $4 \times 8 = 32$

4. $9 \times 5 = 45$

Home Link 4·9

The following answers should be circled:

1. more than the distance from Chicago to Dallas; about 2,400 miles

2. about 600 miles; less than the distance from Chicago to Denver

3. more than the distance from New York to Chicago

4. less than the distance from Denver to Atlanta; more than the distance from New York to Portland; about 750 miles

Copyright © Wright Group/McGraw-Hill

Name Date Time

Multiplication Number Stories

Family Note Today your child learned about another tool to use when solving number stories, a multiplication/division diagram. It can help your child organize the information in a number story. With the information organized, your child can decide which operation (×, ÷) will solve the problem. Refer to pages 259 and 260 in the *Student Reference Book* for more information.

Please return this Home Link to school tomorrow.

For the number story:

- Fill in a multiplication/division diagram. Write ? for the number you will find. Then write the numbers you know.
- Use counters or draw pictures to help you find the answer.
- Write the answer and unit. Check whether your answer makes sense.

1. Elsa buys 5 packages of apples for the party. There are 6 apples in each package. How many apples does she have?

packages	apples per package	apples in all

Answer: ______________
(unit)

Does your answer make sense?

____

2. Find equal groups of objects in your home, or around your neighborhood. Record them on the back of this page.

Examples

3 lights on each traffic light, 12 eggs per carton

3. Write a multiplication number story about one of your groups. Use the back of this paper. Solve the number story.

Copyright © Wright Group/McGraw-Hill

Name Date Time

LESSON 4•1

Exploring Equal Groups

Work with a partner.

Materials
- ☐ 1 six-sided die
- ☐ 1 sheet of plain paper
- ☐ 36 counters (for example: pennies, centimeter cubes, or dried beans)
- ☐ 6 quarter-sheets of paper

Pretend that the quarter-sheets of paper are flags.

Pretend that the pennies, cubes, or beans are stars.

1. Roll the die twice.
- ◆ The first roll tells how many flags to use.
- ◆ The second roll tells how many stars to put on each flag.

2. Work together to set up the flags and stars for the numbers you rolled. How many stars are there on all of the flags?

3. Use your sheet of plain paper and draw a picture.
- ◆ Show all flags.
- ◆ Draw dots to show all the stars on each flag.

4. Repeat Steps 1–3.

Copyright © Wright Group/McGraw-Hill

Name Date Time

Arrays

Family Note Your child is learning how to represent multiplication problems using pictures called *arrays.* An array is a group of items arranged in equal rows and equal columns. Help your child use counters, such as pennies or macaroni, to build the array in each problem. Your child should record each solution on the dots next to the problem.

SRB 64 65

Please return this Home Link to school tomorrow.

For the next few weeks, look for pictures of items arranged in equal rows and columns, or **arrays.** Look in newspapers or magazines. Have people in your family help you. Explain that your class is making an Arrays Exhibit.

This is a 5-by-6 array. There are 5 rows. There are 6 dots in each row.

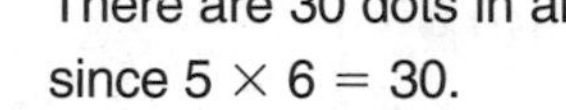

There are 30 dots in all, since $5 \times 6 = 30$.

Make an array with counters. Mark the dots to show the array.

1. 4 rows with 6 counters per row

a **4-by-6 array**

______ counters

2. 3 rows with 8 counters per row

a **3 × 8 array**

______ counters

3. 2 rows with 12 counters per row

a **2 × 12 array**

______ counters

Practice

Write these problems on the back of this page. Solve. Show your work.

4. 331 + 27 = ______

5. ______ = 187 + 17

6. 907 − 479 = ______

Unit

Copyright © Wright Group/McGraw-Hill

Name Date Time

Building Arrays

Materials ☐ cm cubes or other counters

☐ 1 six-sided die

☐ centimeter grid paper (*Math Masters,* p. 416)

1. Roll the die 2 times. The first number tells how many rows to put in the array. The second number tells how many counters to put in each row.

Example

You roll a 1 first and then a 5. You make this figure.

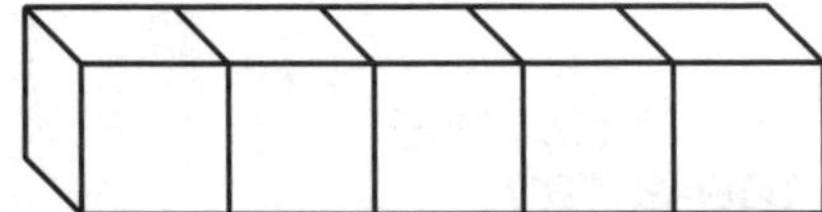

2. Draw the arrays you make on centimeter grid paper.

3. Then, fill in the Array Table below.

	How many rows?	How many cubes in each row?	How many cubes in all?
1			
2			
3			
4			
5			

Copyright © Wright Group/McGraw-Hill

Name Date Time

Square Products

Work in a small group.

Materials
- ☐ centimeter grid paper (*Math Masters,* p. 416)
- ☐ centimeter cubes or pennies (or both)
- ☐ tape

Directions

1. Each person chooses a different number from 2 to 10.
2. Build an array that shows your number multiplied by itself. Use centimeter cubes or pennies.
3. Draw each array on centimeter grid paper. Write each number model under each array.

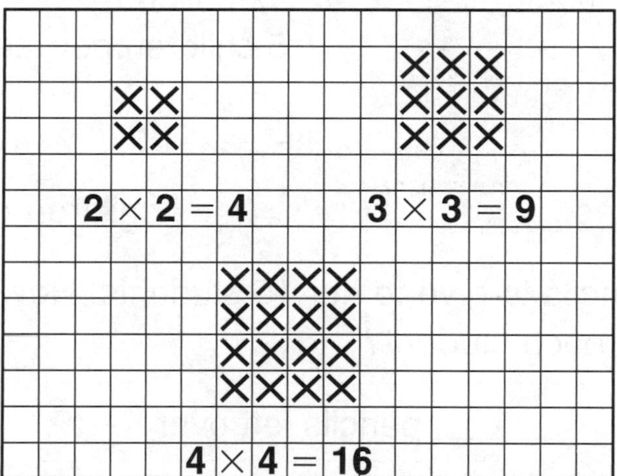

4. Continue to build arrays with other numbers. Draw the arrays on grid paper. You may need to tape pieces of grid paper together for the larger arrays.
5. Look at the arrays you made. Why do you think the products of the number models you wrote are called square products?

___

___

Copyright © Wright Group/McGraw-Hill

Name Date Time

Division with Counters

Family Note Your child is beginning to use division to solve number stories. A first step is to use counters, such as uncooked macaroni or pennies, to represent each problem. This helps your child to understand the meaning of division.

Please return this Home Link to school tomorrow.

Show someone at home how to do division using pennies, uncooked macaroni, or other counters.

1. 25 counters are shared equally by 5 people.

_____ counters per person

_____ counters remaining

2. 25 counters are shared equally by 10 people.

_____ counters per person

_____ counters remaining

3. 31 days in January
7 days per week

_____ weeks in January

_____ days remaining

4. 22 children
5 children per team

_____ teams

_____ children remaining

5. Mrs. Blair has 34 pencils to give to her 15 students. How many pencils can she give each student?

_____ pencils _____ pencils left over

6. Caleb shared 22 jelly beans with his sister. How many jelly beans did each child get?

_____ jelly beans _____ jelly beans left over

Practice

Write these problems on the back of this page. Solve. Show your work.

Unit

7. _____ = 614 − 37 **8.** 23 + 8 = _____

9. 123 + 678 = _____

Copyright © Wright Group/McGraw-Hill

Name Date Time

Equal Groups of Cookies

1. Draw circles to show how many cookies are on each plate at the beginning of the story.

2. How many cookies did Grandma make altogether? ______

3. Tom and Hannah arrive. Now 4 children share the cookies. Draw a picture to show how they share the cookies.

4. Draw a picture to show how 6 children share.

5. At the end, there are 12 children. If each child gets 3 cookies, how many cookies do they have altogether? Draw a picture to show how you found your answer.

Copyright © Wright Group/McGraw-Hill

Name Date Time

Division Number Stories

Family Note Help your child solve the division number stories by using counters such as pennies or uncooked macaroni to model the problems. Refer to pages 73, 74, 259, and 260 in the *Student Reference Book.* Your child is not expected to know division facts at this time.

Please return this Home Link to school tomorrow.

SRB 73 74 259 260

Use counters or draw pictures to show someone at home how you can use division to solve number stories. Fill in the diagrams.

1. Jamal gave 24 marbles to 4 friends. Each friend got the same number of marbles. How many marbles did each friend get?

_____ marbles

friends	**marbles per friend**	**marbles in all**

How many marbles were left over? _____ marble(s)

2. Ellie had 29 cookies to put in 14 lunch bags. She put the same number in each bag. How many cookies did she put in each bag?

_____ cookies

bags	**cookies per bag**	**cookies in all**

How many cookies were left over? _____ cookie(s)

3. A sheet of stamps has 46 stamps. A complete row has 10 stamps. How many complete rows are there?

_____ complete rows

complete rows	**stamps per row**	**stamps in all**

How many stamps were left over? _____ stamp(s)

Copyright © Wright Group/McGraw-Hill

Name ______ Date ______ Time ______

LESSON 4·4

Equal Groups

Copyright © Wright Group/McGraw-Hill

Follow the directions to solve each problem.

1. 15 ÷ 3 = ?

0 1 2 3 4 5 6 7 8 9 10 11 12 13 14 15 16 17 18 19 20 21 22 23 24 25

Start at 0. Show hops of 3. Stop at 15. How many hops? ________ 15 ÷ 3 = ____

2. 16 ÷ 4 = ?

0 1 2 3 4 5 6 7 8 9 10 11 12 13 14 15 16 17 18 19 20 21 22 23 24 25

Start at 0. Show hops of 4. Stop at 16. How many hops? ________ 16 ÷ 4 = ____

3. 18 ÷ 6 = ?

0 1 2 3 4 5 6 7 8 9 10 11 12 13 14 15 16 17 18 19 20 21 22 23 24 25

Start at 0. Show hops of ____. Stop at ____. How many hops? ________ 18 ÷ 6 = ____

4. 20 ÷ 5 = ?

0 1 2 3 4 5 6 7 8 9 10 11 12 13 14 15 16 17 18 19 20 21 22 23 24 25

Start at ____. Show hops of ____. Stop at ____. How many hops? ________ 20 ÷ 5 = ____

Name Date Time

Equal Sharing Mystery Number

1. Find the Mystery Number for three different Start Numbers.
   - In Trial #1, the Start Number and 2nd Number should be less than 10.
   - In Trial #3, the Start Number and 2nd Number should each have three digits. Use your calculator.

Step	What to Do	Trial #1	Trial #2	Trial #3
1	Start Number—write a number greater than 1.			
2	2nd Number—write a number greater than 1.			
3	Multiply the Start Number times your 2nd Number.			
4	Subtract the Start Number from the number in Step 3.			
5	Subtract 1 from the 2nd Number.			
6 **Mystery Number!**	Divide the number in Step 4 by the number in Step 5.			

2. Look for patterns in the table and discuss the patterns with a partner.

3. Predict what the Mystery Number will be if the Start Number is 4.

____

4. Use counters to show what happened when you followed the steps in Trial #1. Draw a picture on the back of this page.

Copyright © Wright Group/McGraw-Hill

Name Date Time

LESSON 4•5

4 × 3 Grid

Copyright © Wright Group/McGraw-Hill

Name Date Time

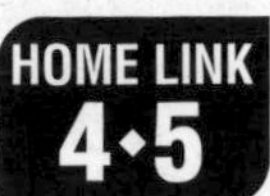

Multiplication-Fact Shortcuts

Family Note Your child is learning the basic multiplication facts. Listen to your child explain multiplication-fact shortcuts as he or she works the problems. Review some 1s, 2s, 5s, and 10s multiplication facts (facts like $1 \times 3 = ?$, $? = 2 \times 4$, $5 \times 5 = ?$, and $10 \times 4 = ?$).

Please return this Home Link to school tomorrow.

Tell someone at home about multiplication-fact shortcuts.

The turn-around rule: $3 \times 4 = 12$ helps me know $4 \times 3 = 12$.

1. $2 \times 5 =$ __________ and $5 \times 2 =$ __________
2. __________ $= 5 \times 3$ and __________ $= 3 \times 5$
3. $10 \times 2 =$ __________ and $2 \times 10 =$ __________

If 1 is multiplied by any number, the product is that number.
The same is true if any number is multiplied by 1.

4. __________ $= 1 \times 9$ and __________ $= 9 \times 1$
5. $1 \times 90 =$ __________ and $90 \times 1 =$ __________
6. $365 \times 1 =$ __________ and $1 \times 365 =$ __________

If 0 is multiplied by any number, the product is 0.
The same is true if any number is multiplied by 0.

7. $0 \times 12 =$ __________ and $12 \times 0 =$ __________
8. $99 \times 0 =$ __________ and $0 \times 99 =$ __________
9. __________ $= 9{,}365 \times 0$ and __________ $= 0 \times 9{,}365$

Think about counting by 2s, 5s, and 10s.

10. $\begin{array}{r} 10 \\ \times\ 2 \\ \hline \end{array}$ **11.** $\begin{array}{r} 5 \\ \times\ 4 \\ \hline \end{array}$ **12.** $\begin{array}{r} 9 \\ \times\ 2 \\ \hline \end{array}$ **13.** $\begin{array}{r} 2 \\ \times\ 7 \\ \hline \end{array}$ **14.** $\begin{array}{r} 5 \\ \times\ 3 \\ \hline \end{array}$ **15.** $\begin{array}{r} 10 \\ \times\ 5 \\ \hline \end{array}$

Copyright © Wright Group/McGraw-Hill

Name Date Time

LESSON 4•5 Building Facts on a Geoboard

For each problem:

Use a rubber band to make each rectangle on a geoboard.

Draw the rectangle onto this record sheet.

Record the number of pins inside the rubber band as the answer to the problem.

Example

$2 \times 4 =$ 8 pins

1. $3 \times 3 =$ _____ pins

2. $4 \times 3 =$ _____ pins

3. $3 \times 2 =$ _____ pins

4. $4 \times 4 =$ _____ pins

Make up problems of your own.

5. _______ × _______ = _______ pins

6. _______ × _______ = _______ pins

Copyright © Wright Group/McGraw-Hill

Name Date Time

Multiplication/Division Facts Table

Multiplication/Division Facts Table										
×, ÷	**1**	**2**	**3**	**4**	**5**	**6**	**7**	**8**	**9**	**10**
1	1	2	3	4	5	6	7	8	9	10
2	2	4	6	8	10	12	14	16	18	20
3	3	6	9	12	15	18	21	24	27	30
4	4	8	12	16	20	24	28	32	36	40
5	5	10	15	20	25	30	35	40	45	50
6	6	12	18	24	30	36	42	48	54	60
7	7	14	21	28	35	42	49	56	63	70
8	8	16	24	32	40	48	56	64	72	80
9	9	18	27	36	45	54	63	72	81	90
10	10	20	30	40	50	60	70	80	90	100

Copyright © Wright Group/McGraw-Hill

Name Date Time

HOME LINK 4·6

×, ÷ Fact Triangles

Family Note

Fact Triangles build mental-math reflexes. They are the *Everyday Mathematics* version of traditional flash cards. Fact Triangles are better tools for memorizing, however, because they emphasize fact families.

A **fact family** is a group of facts made from the same 3 numbers. For 6, 4, and 24, the multiplication and division fact family is $4 \times 6 = 24$, $6 \times 4 = 24$, $24 \div 6 = 4$, $24 \div 4 = 6$.

Use Fact Triangles to practice basic facts with your child. Cut out the triangles from the two attached sheets.

To practice multiplication:

Cover the number under the large dot—the product.

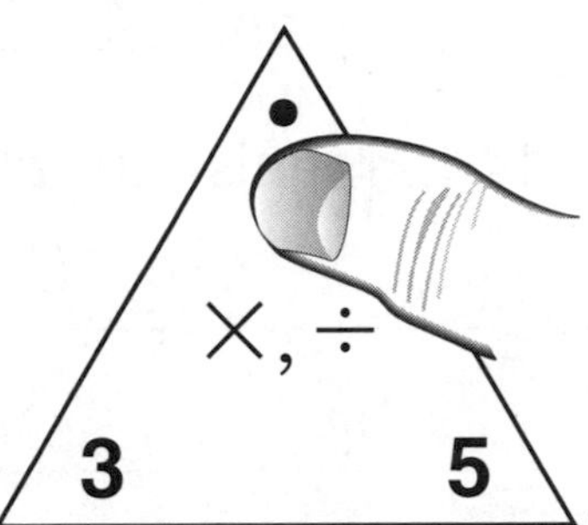

Your child should name one or two multiplication facts: $3 \times 5 = 15$, or $5 \times 3 = 15$.

To practice division, cover one of the smaller numbers.

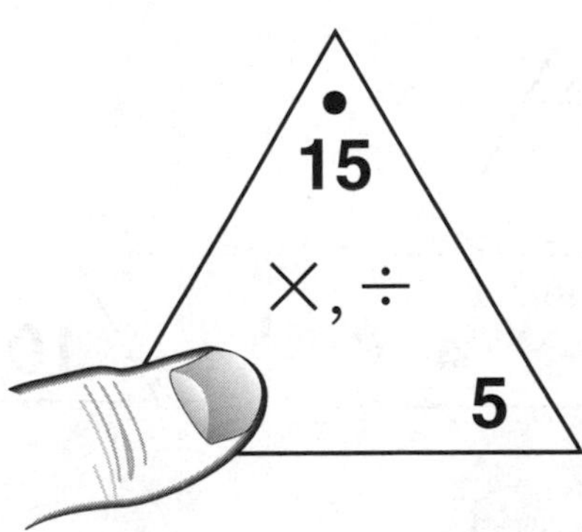

Your child should name the division fact $15 \div 5 = 3$.

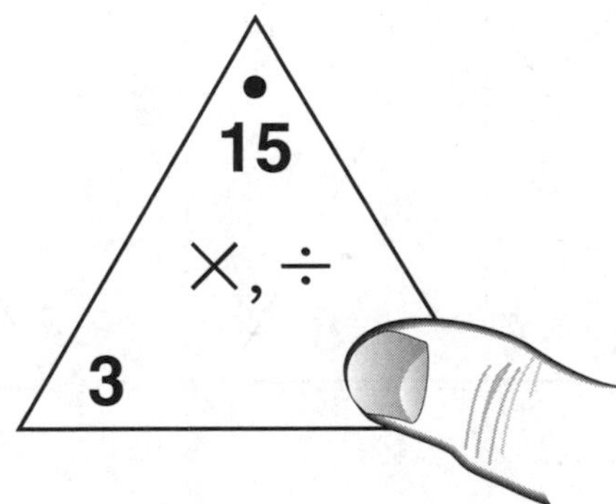

Your child should name the division fact $15 \div 3 = 5$.

If your child misses a fact, flash the other two problems and then return to the fact that was missed. *Example:* Ravi can't answer $15 \div 3$. Flash 3×5, and then $15 \div 5$, and finally $15 \div 3$ a second time.

Make this activity brief and fun. Spend about 10 minutes each night for the next few weeks, or until your child learns them all. The work you do at home will support the work we are doing at school.

SRB 54 55

Please return the ***second page*** *of this Home Link to school tomorrow.*

Copyright © Wright Group/McGraw-Hill

Name Date Time

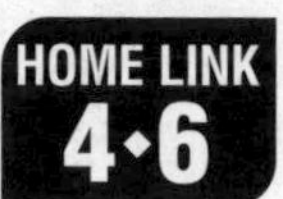

×, ÷ Fact Triangles *continued*

Tell someone at home about multiplication/division fact families.

1. The numbers 2, 5, and 10 form the following facts:

   $2 \times 5 =$ _____ _____ $\div 2 = 5$

   $5 \times 2 =$ _____ _____ $\div 5 = 2$

2. Knowing $6 \times 2 =$ _____ and $2 \times 6 =$ _____

   helps me know _____ $\div 2 = 6$ and _____ $\div 6 = 2$.

3. The numbers 2, 7, and 14 form this multiplication/division fact family:

   _____________ _____________

   _____________ _____________

Write the fact family for each ×, ÷ Fact Triangle.

4.

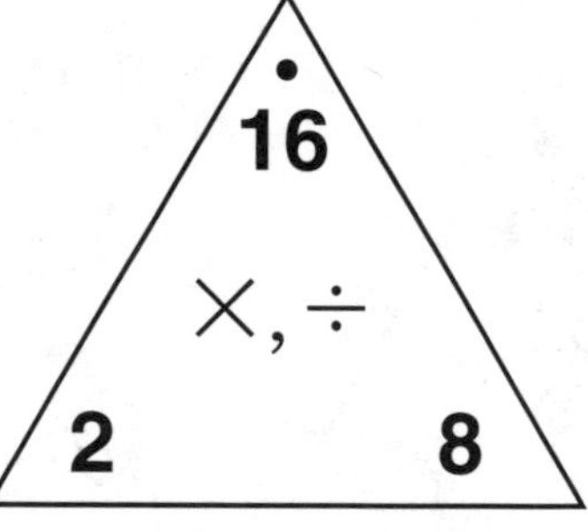

____

____

____

____

5.

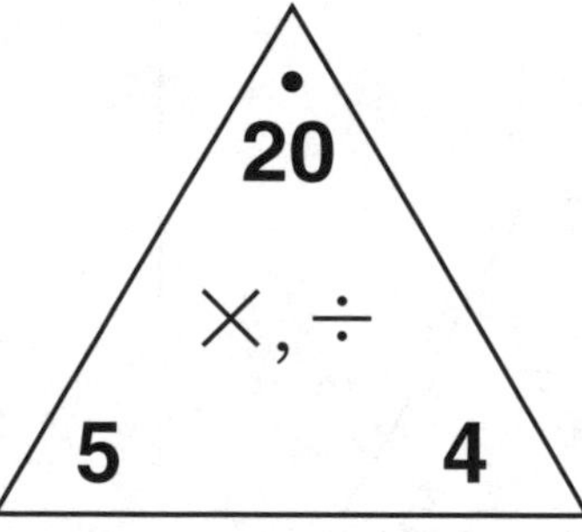

____

____

____

____

6.

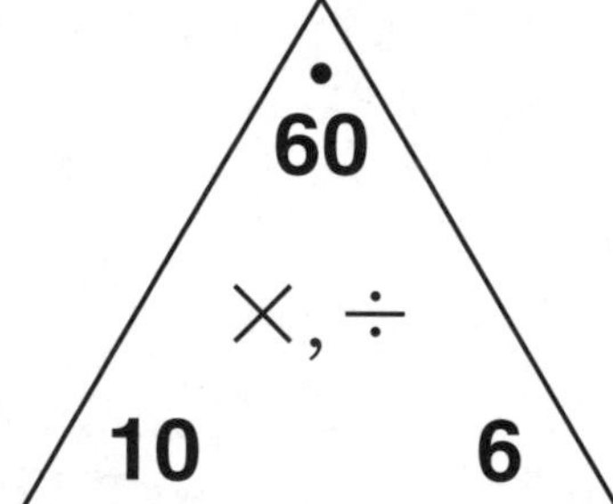

____

____

____

____

Copyright © Wright Group/McGraw-Hill

Name Date Time

LESSON 4•6

Multiplication/Division Fact Triangles 1

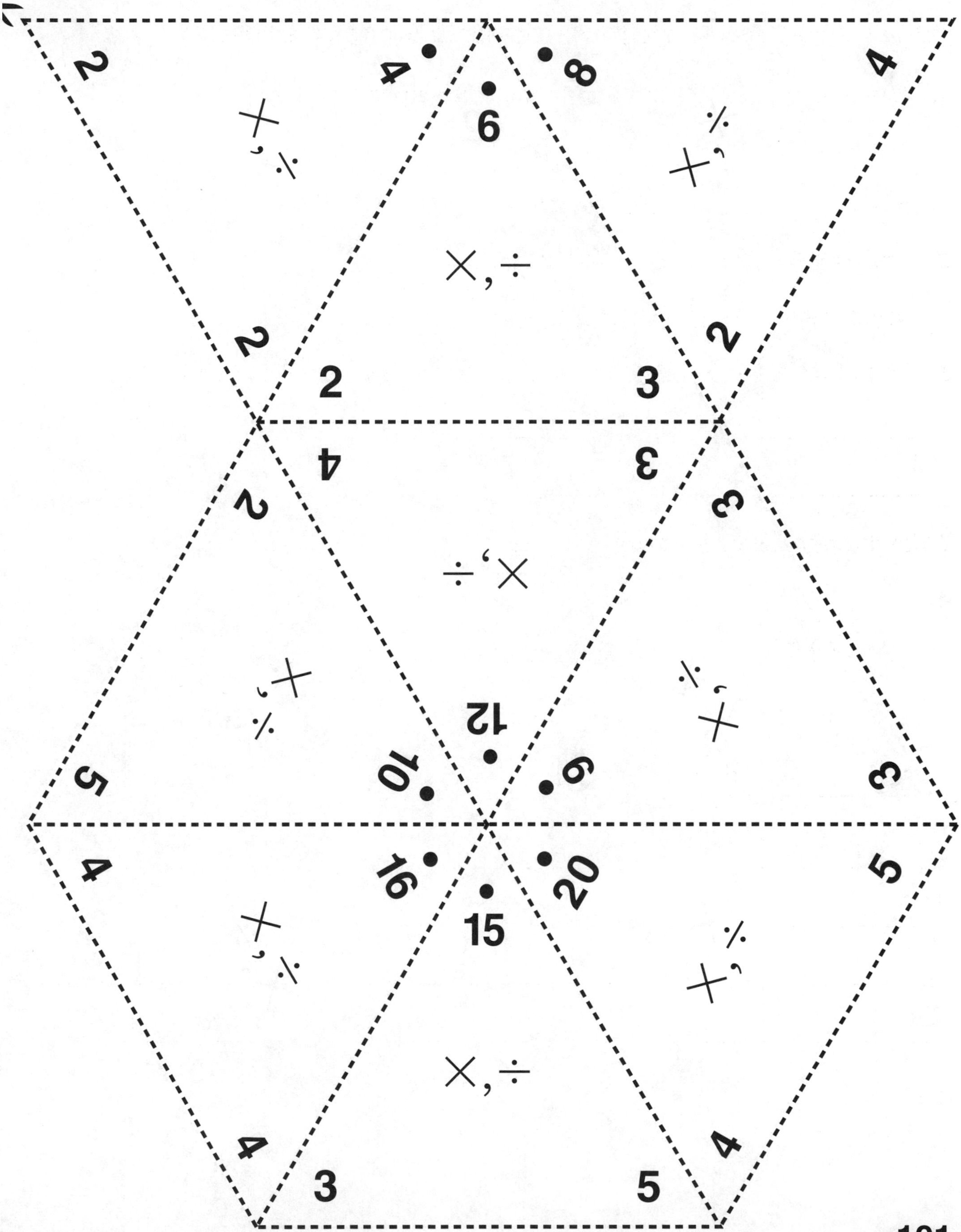

8 • 2 4 ×, ÷

4 • 2 2 ×, ÷

6 • 2 3 ×, ÷

12 • 4 3 ×, ÷

10 • 2 5 ×, ÷

9 • 3 3 ×, ÷

16 • 4 4 ×, ÷

15 • 3 5 ×, ÷

20 • 4 5 ×, ÷

Copyright © Wright Group/McGraw-Hill

Name Date Time

LESSON 4·6

Multiplication/Division Fact Triangles 2

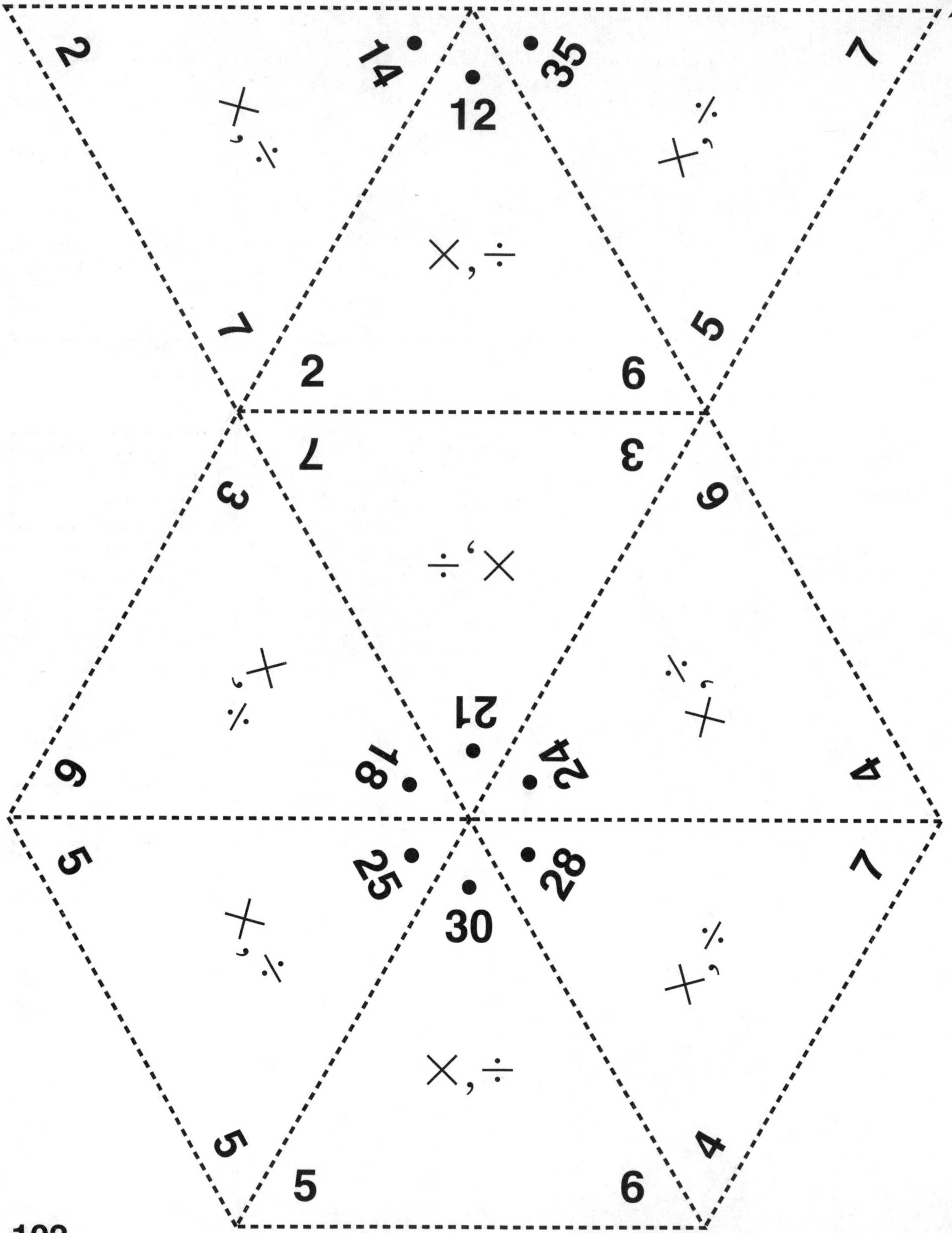

14, 2, 7 ×, ÷

12, 2, 6 ×, ÷

35, 5, 7 ×, ÷

21, 7, 3 ×, ÷

18, 3, 6 ×, ÷

24, 6, 4 ×, ÷

25, 5, 5 ×, ÷

30, 5, 6 ×, ÷

28, 4, 7 ×, ÷

Copyright © Wright Group/McGraw-Hill

Name Date Time

LESSON 4•6

Multiplication Facts & Calculator Counts

1. Use your calculator to count by 3s. Complete the table below.

One 3	Two 3s	Three 3s	Four 3s	Five 3s	Six 3s	Seven 3s	Eight 3s	Nine 3s	Ten 3s
3	6								30

2. Use your calculator to count by 4s. Complete the table below.

One 4	Two 4s	Three 4s	Four 4s	Five 4s	Six 4s	Seven 4s	Eight 4s	Nine 4s	Ten 4s
4	8								

3. Use your calculator to count by 6s. Complete the table below.

One 6	Two 6s	Three 6s	Four 6s	Five 6s	Six 6s	Seven 6s	Eight 6s	Nine 6s	Ten 6s
6	12								

4. How can counting on your calculator help you learn your multiplication facts?

Copyright © Wright Group/McGraw-Hill

Name Date Time

Fact Families

Family Note Your child continues to practice multiplication in school. You can help by stressing the relationship between multiplication and division: With the three nonzero numbers in a multiplication fact, two division facts can be formed. Fact Triangles are designed to help children understand this concept.

Please return this Home Link to school tomorrow.

Write the fact family for each Fact Triangle.

1.

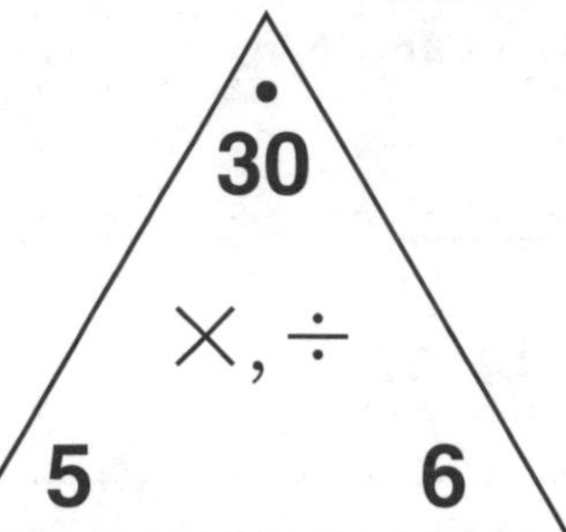

_____ × _____ = _____

_____ × _____ = _____

_____ ÷ _____ = _____

_____ ÷ _____ = _____

2.

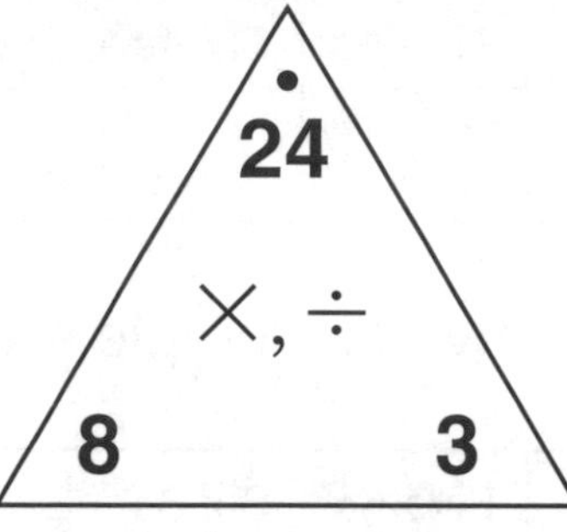

_____ × _____ = _____

_____ × _____ = _____

_____ ÷ _____ = _____

_____ ÷ _____ = _____

3.

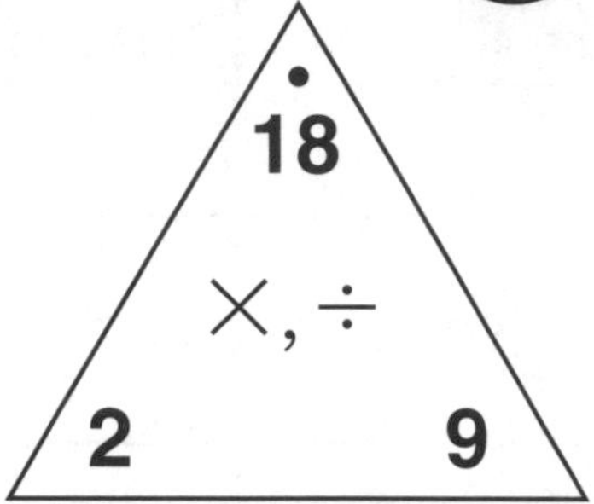

_____ × _____ = _____

_____ × _____ = _____

_____ ÷ _____ = _____

_____ ÷ _____ = _____

4.

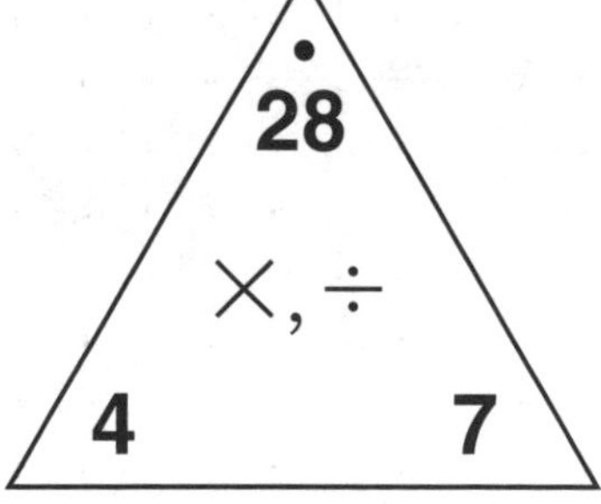

_____ × _____ = _____

_____ × _____ = _____

_____ ÷ _____ = _____

_____ ÷ _____ = _____

5.

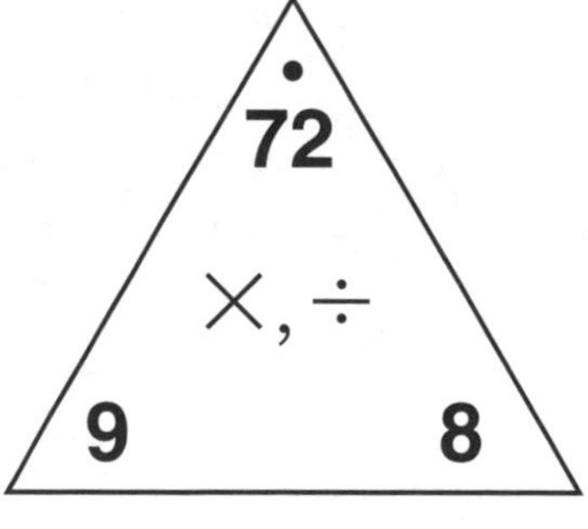

_____ × _____ = _____

_____ × _____ = _____

_____ ÷ _____ = _____

_____ ÷ _____ = _____

6.

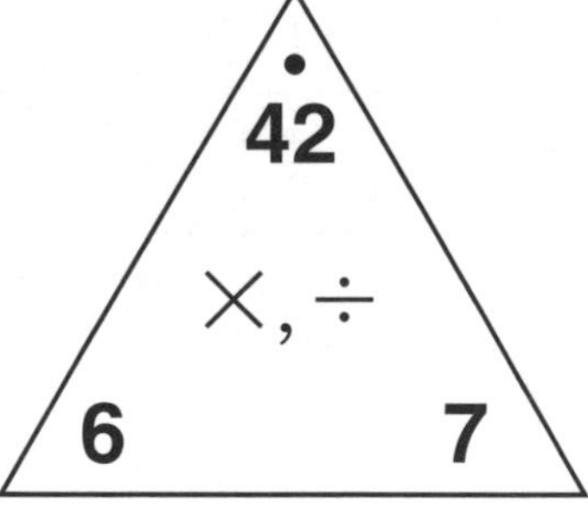

_____ × _____ = _____

_____ × _____ = _____

_____ ÷ _____ = _____

_____ ÷ _____ = _____

Copyright © Wright Group/McGraw-Hill

Name Date Time

LESSON 4•7

Practice with Facts and Arrays

List the times ______ facts. If you are not sure of a fact, draw an array with Os or Xs.

1. $2 \times$ ___ = ___
2. $3 \times$ ___ = ___
3. $4 \times$ ___ = ___
4. $5 \times$ ___ = ___
5. $6 \times$ ___ = ___
6. $7 \times$ ___ = ___
7. $8 \times$ ___ = ___
8. $9 \times$ ___ = ___
9. $10 \times$ ___ = ___

Talk to a partner about the patterns you find in your list.

Copyright © Wright Group/McGraw-Hill

Name Date Time

Exploration B: Setting Up Chairs

Materials ☐ *Math Journal 1,* page 93

☐ 35 pennies or other counters

Problem A teacher was setting up the chairs in his classroom for parent night. He wanted them to be in rows with the same number of chairs in each row. Use the clues to find out how many chairs were in the room.

Clues

1. When the teacher tried to set up the chairs in rows of 2, there was 1 leftover chair.
2. He also had 1 leftover chair when he tried to set them up in rows of 3.
3. One of his students suggested that he try rows of 4. There was still 1 leftover chair.
4. Finally, he tried rows of 5. This worked fine. There were no leftover chairs.
5. The number of chairs in the room was the smallest possible number that fits all of the clues.

What to Do

1. Experiment with counters to build rows. *Hint:* Could the answer be 5 chairs? 10 chairs (2 rows of 5 chairs each)? 15 chairs (3 rows of 5 chairs each)?
2. When you have found the answer, record it on journal page 93. Next, circle dots to show the chairs in rows of 2, 3, and 4, each with 1 chair left over. Then show the chairs in rows of 5.

Copyright © Wright Group/McGraw-Hill

Name Date Time

Exploration C: Fact Platters

Materials ☐ fact platter

☐ chalk

☐ eraser

Work with a partner at the board.

42

4 7 3 9 1 5 8 2 6 10

6×

30

1. Take turns. On your turn, pick a number from 1 to 10. Write it in the middle with a multiplication sign.
2. Your partner takes that number and multiplies it by each number on the circle, writing the products along the outside of the platter.
3. Check the products together. Make corrections.
4. Then, each of you writes one division fact for every multiplication fact around the circle.

   $42 \div 6 = 7$

5. Check each other's work.
6. Erase the board. Trade roles. Start again.
7. Keep going until each of you has had several turns picking a number for the center.

Copyright © Wright Group/McGraw-Hill

Name Date Time

Arrays and Areas

Family Note Your child uses the same procedure for finding the area of a rectangle that is used for finding the number of dots in an array. For Problem 3 it does not matter whether your child draws an array with 4 rows of 8 dots or 8 rows of 4 dots. What is important is that the array has two sides that have 4 dots and two sides that have 8 dots. The same concept is true for Problem 4.

Please return this Home Link to school tomorrow.

Make a dot inside each small square in one row. Then fill in the blanks.

1. Number of rows: _____

Number of squares in a row: _____

Number model: _____ × _____ = _____

Area: _____ square units

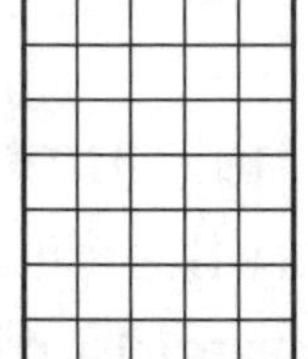

2. Number of rows: _____

Number of squares in a row: _____

Number model: _____ × _____ = _____

Area: _____ square units

Mark the dots to show each array. Then fill in the blanks.

3. Make a 4-by-8 array.

Number model: _____ × _____ = _____

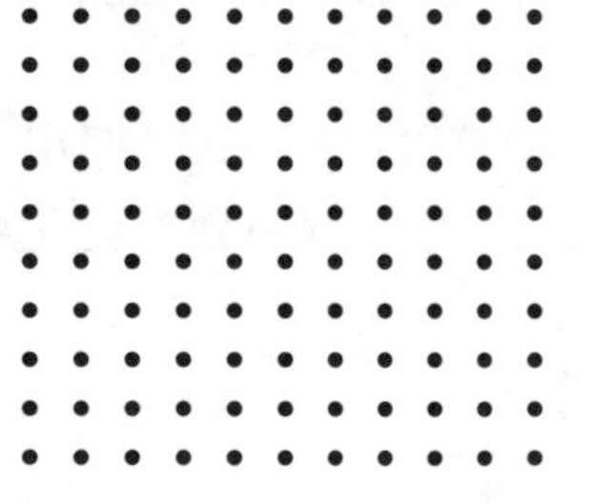

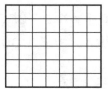

4. Make a 9-by-5 array.

Number model: _____ × _____ = _____

Copyright © Wright Group/McGraw-Hill

Name Date Time

One-Inch Segments

Copyright © Wright Group/McGraw-Hill

Name Date Time

Using a Map Scale

Family Note Your child is just learning how to use a map scale. He or she should use the scale to measure an as-the-crow-flies estimate for each problem. This expression refers to the most direct route between two points, disregarding road distance. Actual road distances are longer than these direct paths.

Please return this Home Link to school tomorrow.

For each question, circle all reasonable answers. (There may be more than one reasonable answer.) All distances are as the crow flies. Be sure to use the map scale on the next page.

1. About how many miles is it from New York to Los Angeles?

about 1,000 miles

more than the distance from Chicago to Dallas

about 2,400 miles

2. About how many miles is it from Chicago to Atlanta?

about 600 miles

more than the distance from Chicago to Seattle

less than the distance from Chicago to Denver

3. About how many miles is it from Seattle to Dallas?

about 2,600 miles

about 5,000 miles

more than the distance from New York to Chicago

4. About how many miles is it from New York to Atlanta?

less than the distance from Denver to Atlanta

more than the distance from New York to Portland

about 750 miles

Copyright © Wright Group/McGraw-Hill

Name Date Time

HOME LINK 4·9

Using a Map Scale *continued*

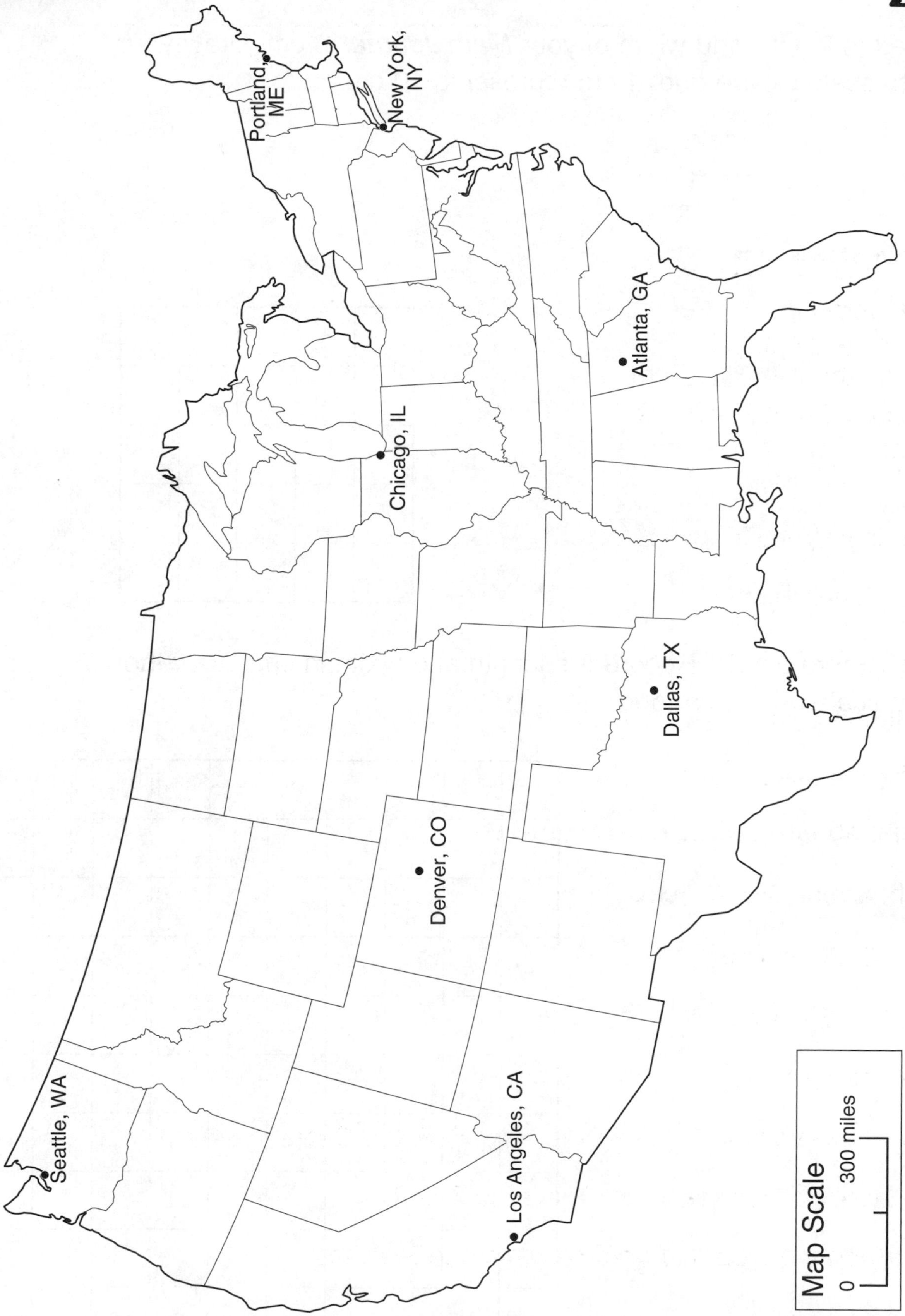

Portland, ME
New York, NY
Atlanta, GA
Chicago, IL
Dallas, TX
Denver, CO
Seattle, WA
Los Angeles, CA

Map Scale
0
300 miles

Copyright © Wright Group/McGraw-Hill

Name Date Time

Scale Drawings

Measure the length and width of your *Math Journal* in cm. Draw your journal to scale on the grid. 1 cm represents 10 cm.

Scale

1 cm : 10 cm

Scale: 1 cm represents 10 cm

1. *Math Journal*

length: about ______ cm

width: about ______ cm

Choose 1 more object. Record the length and width in cm. Draw the object to scale on the cm grid.

2. Object: ____________

length: about ______ cm

width: about ______ cm

Copyright © Wright Group/McGraw-Hill

Name Date Time

HOME LINK 4·10 A Fair Game?

Family Note The class is exploring probability. Play *Rock, Paper, Scissors* with your child. After 20 rounds, have your child decide whether the game is fair and tell you why or why not. (A game is fair if all players have an equal chance of winning or losing.)

Please return this Home Link to school tomorrow.

Play the game *Rock, Paper, Scissors* with someone at home. Play at least 20 times. Keep a tally of wins and losses.

Rock, Paper, Scissors

Materials ☐ players' hands

Players 2

Object of the Game To choose a hand position that beats your partner's choice.

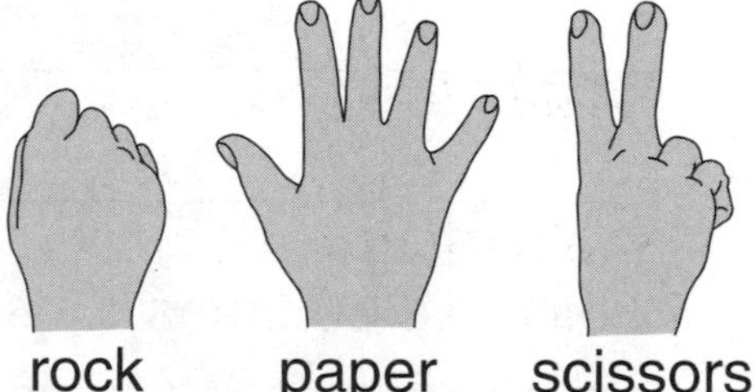

rock paper scissors

Directions

1. Each player hides one hand behind his or her back and puts it in the rock, paper, or scissors position.
2. One player counts, "One, two, three."
3. On "three," both players show their hand positions.
4. Players choose the winner according to these rules.

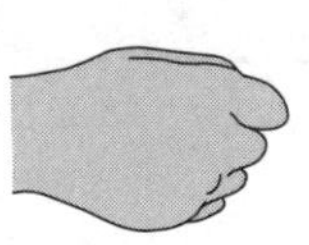
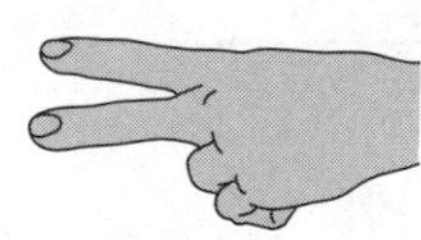

Rock dents scissors.

Rock wins.

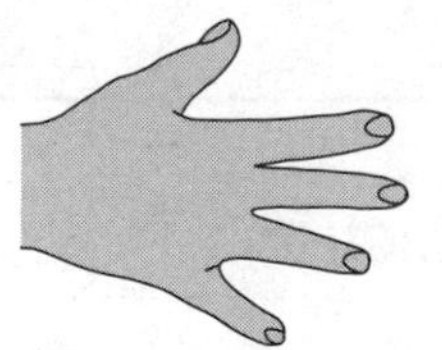
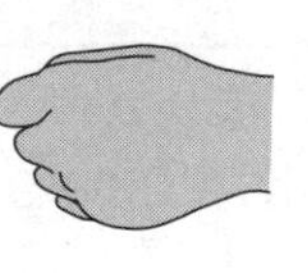

Paper covers rock.

Paper wins.

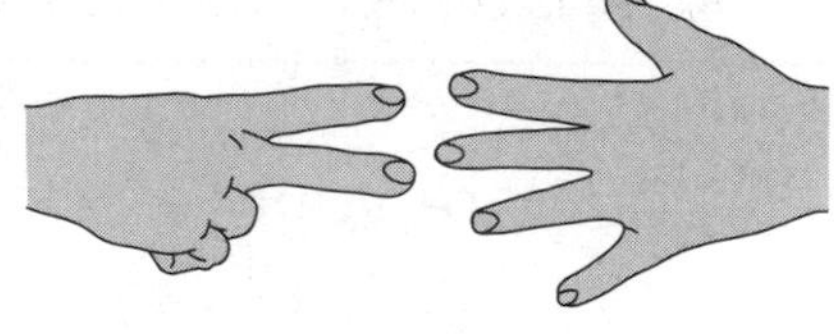

Scissors cut paper.

Scissors wins.

If both players show the same position, no one wins.

1. Is this a fair game? (*Fair* means each player has the same chance of winning.) _______
2. On the back of this paper, explain why or why not.

Copyright © Wright Group/McGraw-Hill

Name Date Time

LESSON 4•10

Making Predictions about Rolling Dice

Think about how you would know that a die is fair.

1. Make predictions. If you roll the die 30 times,

which number will come up the most? ______________________

How many times might you roll a 5? ______________________

Explain how you made your predictions.

____

____

2. Roll a die 30 times. Use tally marks to record your results in the table below.

Number	Times Rolled
1	
2	
3	
4	
5	
6	

3. Compare your results with your predictions.

____

4. Do you think your die is fair?

Explain. ______________________

____

Copyright © Wright Group/McGraw-Hill

Name Date Time

Unit 5: Family Letter

Place Value in Whole Numbers and Decimals

In Unit 5, children will review place value up to 5-digit whole numbers. They will read, write, compare, and order these numbers before they begin to explore larger numbers.

To understand real-life applications of larger numbers, children will study population data about U.S. cities. They will also approximate their own ages to the minute.

Seattle 563,374
Portland 529,121
San Francisco 776,733
San Jose 894,943
Las Vegas 478,434
Los Angeles 3,694,820
San Diego 1,223,400
Phoenix 1,321,045
Denver 554,636
Minneapolis 382,618
Milwaukee 596,974
Chicago 2,896,016
St. Louis 348,189
Indianapolis 791,926
Columbus 711,470
Detroit 951,270
Boston 589,141
New York 8,008,278
Philadelphia 1,517,550
Baltimore 651,154
Washington, D.C. 572,059
Charlotte 540,828
Memphis 650,100
Atlanta 416,474
Dallas 1,188,580
Austin 656,562
San Antonio 1,144,646
Houston 1,953,631
New Orleans 484,674
Jacksonville 735,617
Miami 362,470

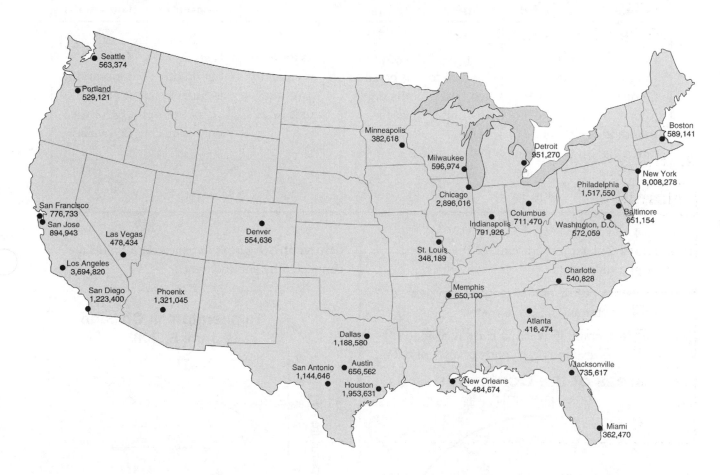

In second grade, children studied decimals by working with money. In this unit, they will gradually extend their knowledge of decimals in the following ways:

- through concrete models, such as base-10 blocks.
- by writing decimal values in three ways (0.1, one-tenth, $\frac{1}{10}$).
- by comparing and ordering numbers with symbols (<, >, =).

Decimal	Word	fraction
0.1	one-tenth	$\frac{1}{10}$
0.2	two-tenths	$\frac{2}{10}$
0.3	three-tenths	$\frac{3}{10}$
0.4	four-tenths	$\frac{4}{10}$

Please keep this Family Letter for reference as your child works through Unit 5.

Copyright © Wright Group/McGraw-Hill

Vocabulary

Important terms in Unit 5:

place value A system that gives a digit a value according to its position, or place, in a number. The value of each digit in a numeral is determined by its place in the numeral. This chart demonstrates the value of each digit in the numeral 4,815.904 (read as *four thousand, eight hundred fifteen, and nine hundred four thousandths*):

thousands	hundreds	tens	ones		tenths	hundredths	thousandths
4	8	1	5	.	9	0	4
Each thousand is equal to one thousand times the unit value.	Each hundred is equal to one hundred times the unit value.	Each ten is equal to ten times the unit value.	Each one is equal to the unit value.		Each tenth is equal to $\frac{1}{10}$ of the unit value.	Each hundredth is equal to $\frac{1}{100}$ of the unit value.	Each thousandth is equal to $\frac{1}{1,000}$ of the unit value.
4,000	800	10	5		$\frac{9}{10}$	$\frac{0}{100}$	$\frac{4}{1,000}$

maximum The largest amount, or the greatest number in a set of data.

millimeter A metric unit of length equivalent to $\frac{1}{10}$ of a centimeter and $\frac{1}{1,000}$ of a meter.

pie graph A graph in which a circle is divided into regions corresponding to parts of a set of data.

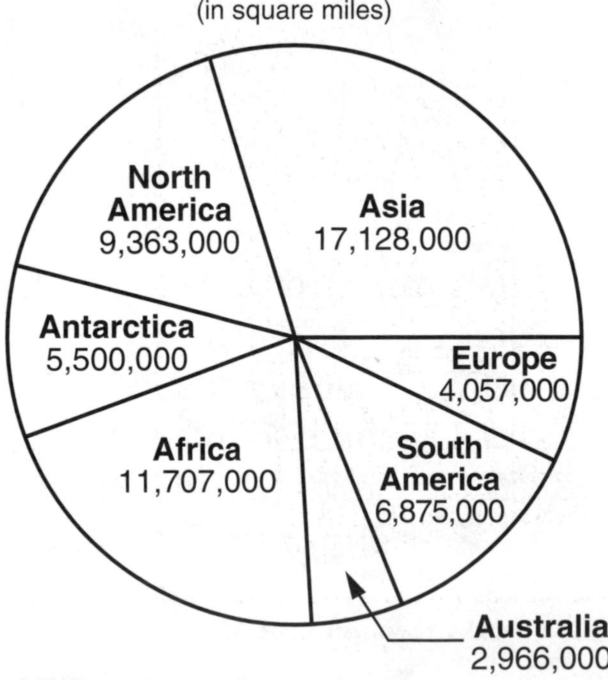

line graph A graph in which data points are connected by line segments.

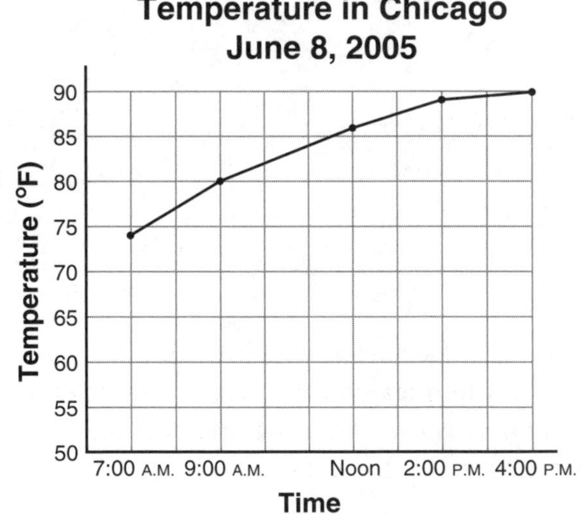

Copyright © Wright Group/McGraw-Hill

Do-Anytime Activities

To work with your child on the concepts taught in this unit and in previous units, try these activities:

1. Dictate large numbers for your child to write. *Examples:* 4,123; 10,032; 2,368,502.

2. Display similar multidigit numbers on a calculator for your child to read.

3. Together, write 5 multidigit numbers in order from smallest to largest.

4. Start at any whole number and, using a calculator, count on by increments of 0.01 or 0.1.

5. Use money on a family shopping trip; practice making change.

Building Skills through Games

In Unit 5, your child will practice numeration and computation skills by playing the following games. For detailed instructions, see the *Student Reference Book.*

Baseball Multiplication

Players use multiplication facts to score runs. Team members take turns pitching by rolling two dice to get two factors. Then players on the batting team take turns multiplying the two factors and saying the product.

Number Top-It

As players pick each card, they must decide in which place-value box (from ones to ten-thousands at first, and then on to hundred-thousands) to place the card so that they end up with the largest number.

Beat the Calculator

A Calculator (a player who uses a calculator) and a Brain (a player who solves the problem without a calculator) race to see who will be first to solve multiplication problems.

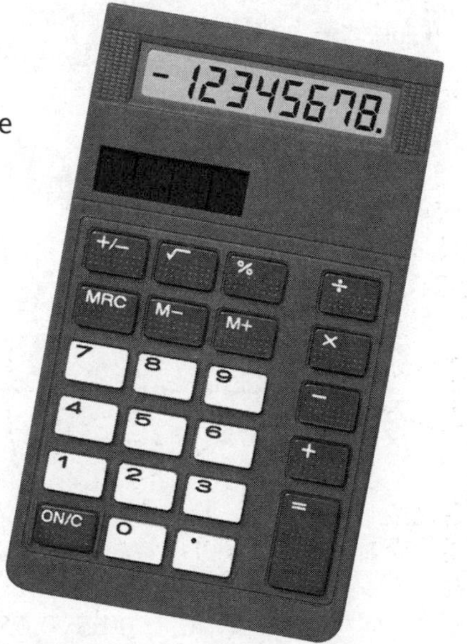

Division Arrays

Players make arrays with counters using number cards to determine the number of counters and a toss of a die to determine the number of rows.

Copyright © Wright Group/McGraw-Hill

HOME LINK 4•11 **Unit 5: Family Letter** *cont.*

As You Help Your Child with Homework

As your child brings home assignments, you may want to go over the instructions together, clarifying them as necessary. The answers listed below will guide you through this unit's Home Links.

Home Link 5•1

1. 8,879; 8,889; 8,899; 8,909; 8,919; 8,929
2. 8,789; 8,889; 8,989; 9,089; 9,189; 9,289
3. 7,889; 8,889; 9,889; 10,889; 11,889; 12,889

Home Link 5•2

1. < **2.** > **3.** <
4. < **5.** > **6.** <
7. 3,689 **8.** 9,863 **9.** Answers vary.
10. 51,100; 52,100 **11.** 56
12. 163 **13.** 796 **14.** 484

Home Link 5•3

1. largest: 7,654,321; smallest: 1,234,567
total: 8,888,888
3. 7,037,562; 7,000,007; 4,056,211; 104,719; 42,876; 25,086; 9,603; 784
4. 42,876 **5.** 7,037,562
6. 4,056,211 **7.** 7,000,007

Home Link 5•4

1. 7 continents **2.** Asia **3.** Australia
4. Antarctica, North America, and South America
5. Europe **6.** North America
7. Africa

Home Link 5•5

3,358	5,338
3,385	5,383
3,538	5,833
3,583	8,335
3,835	8,353
3,853	8,533

Home Link 5•7

1. $\frac{3}{10}$ or $\frac{30}{100}$; 0.3 or 0.30 **2.** $\frac{9}{100}$; 0.09
3. $\frac{65}{100}$; 0.65 **4.** 0.3; 0.65; 0.65
8. 0.04, 0.53, 0.8

Home Link 5•8

1. 57 hundredths; 5 tenths 7 hundredths
2. 70 hundredths; 7 tenths 0 hundredths
3. 4 hundredths; 0 tenths 4 hundredths
4. 0.23 **5.** 8.4 **6.** 30.20 **7.** 0.05
8. 0.4; 0.5; 0.6; 0.7; 0.8; 0.9
9. 0.04; 0.05; 0.06; 0.07; 0.08; 0.09
10. 503 **11.** 603

Home Link 5•9

1. 0.01; 0.02; 0.03; 0.04; 0.05; 0.06; 0.07; 0.08
2. 0.8; 0.9; 1.0; 1.1; 1.2; 1.3; 1.4

D A B C
0 1 2 3 4 5 6 7 8 9 10 11 12 13 14 15
cm

7. 27 **8.** 40 **9.** 0
10. 12 **11.** 9 **12.** 15

Home Link 5•10

1. a. 2 **b.** 10 **c.** 20 **d.** 100 **e.** 200 **f.** 600
2. a. 30 cm **b.** 0.3 m **c.** 300 mm
3. 49 **4.** 56 **5.** 63 **6.** 42

Home Link 5•11

1. < **2.** < **3.** > **4.** =
5. > **6.** < **7.** = **8.** <
9. hundredths, or 0.09 **10.** ones, or 3
11. 6.59; 6.60; 6.61 **12.** 1.03; 1.13; 1.23
13. 4.4 **14.** 4.17 **15.** 8.1 **16.** 5.53
17. 243 **18.** 782 **19.** 509

Home Link 5•12

1. 455 **2.** 455

Copyright © Wright Group/McGraw-Hill

Name Date Time

Math Message

Write the following numbers using digits:

1. two hundred fifty-six ______________
2. three thousand, four hundred eleven ______________
3. twenty-seven thousand, eight hundred fifty-three ______________
4. nine thousand, seventy ______________
5. thirty-five thousand, eight ______________

Copyright © Wright Group/McGraw-Hill

Name Date Time

Math Message

Write the following numbers using digits:

1. two hundred fifty-six ______________
2. three thousand, four hundred eleven ______________
3. twenty-seven thousand, eight hundred fifty-three ______________
4. nine thousand, seventy ______________
5. thirty-five thousand, eight ______________

Copyright © Wright Group/McGraw-Hill

Name Date Time

Frames and Arrows

Family Note Have your child read and solve the three Frames-and-Arrows problems. Review the rule that is being used in each puzzle. Ask your child to look for patterns in the frames. For example, which digit changes when adding or subtracting 10? *(tens digit and hundreds digit change when moving from the 8,800s to the 8,900s)* 100? *(hundreds digit and thousands digit change when moving from the 8,000s to the 9,000s)* 1,000? *(thousands digit and ten-thousands digit change when moving from the 9,000s to the 10,000s)*

Please return this Home Link to school tomorrow.

Solve each Frames-and-Arrows problem.

1.

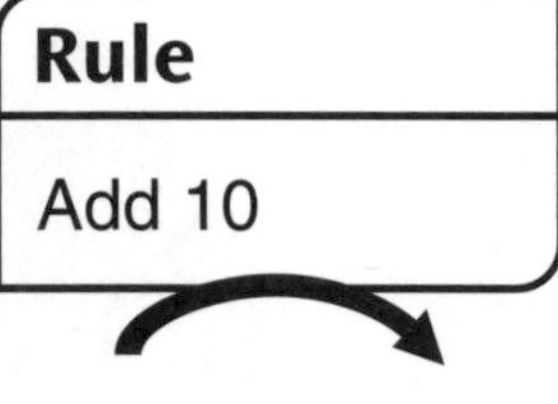

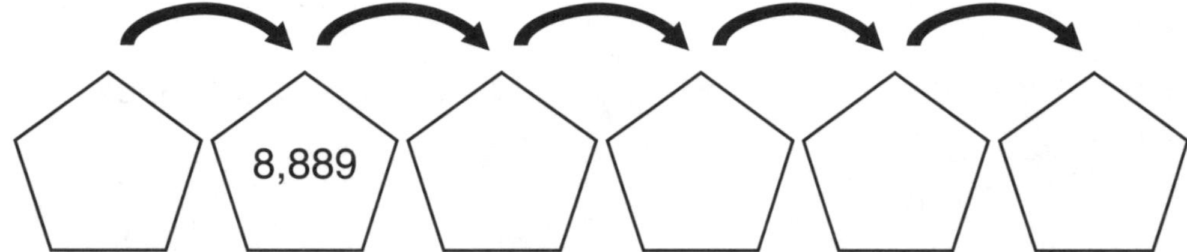

2.

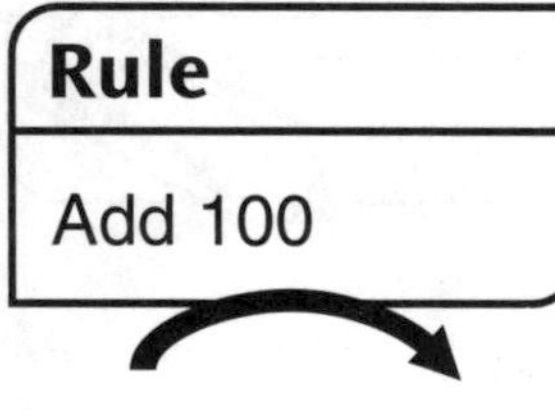

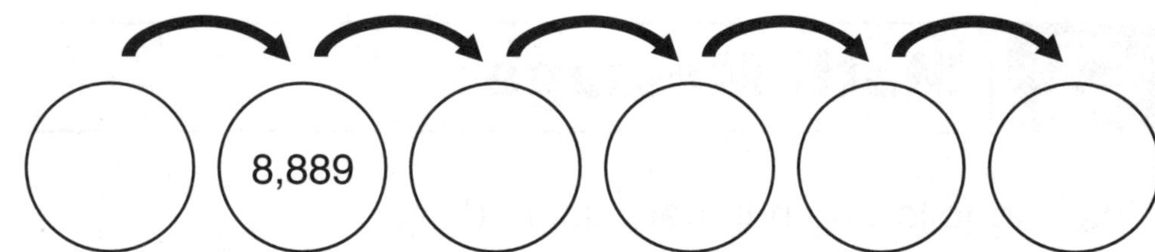

3.

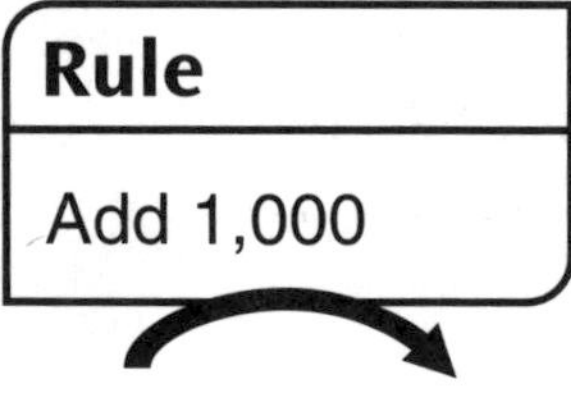

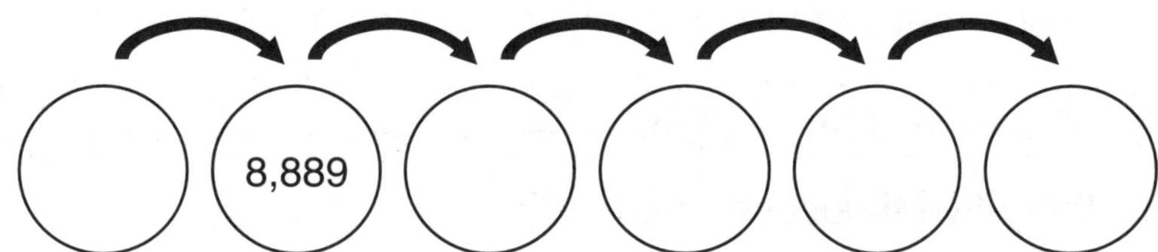

Copyright © Wright Group/McGraw-Hill

Name Date Time

LESSON 5•1 Patterns on a 100-Number Grid

									0
1	2	3	4	5	6	7	8	9	10
11	12	13	14	15	16	17	18	19	20
21	22	23	24	25	26	27	28	29	30
31	32	33	34	35	36	37	38	39	40
41	42	43	44	45	46	47	48	49	50
51	52	53	54	55	56	57	58	59	60
61	62	63	64	65	66	67	68	69	70
71	72	73	74	75	76	77	78	79	80
81	82	83	84	85	86	87	88	89	90
91	92	93	94	95	96	97	98	99	100

1. Which digit is used the greatest number of times on the 100-number grid? ______________________

2. Which digit is used the least number of times on the 100-number grid? ______________________

3. Is the digit 6 used more times in the ones place or in the tens place? ______________________

4. Use a calculator. Find the sum of two or three rows of the 100-number grid. How much more is the sum of the numbers in a row than the sum of the numbers in the row above it? Why?

____

____

____

5. On the back of this sheet, describe the strategies you used to answer Questions 1, 2, and 3. Try to find ways to answer the questions so that you do not need to count each digit.

Copyright © Wright Group/McGraw-Hill

Name _______________ Date _______________ Time _______________

LESSON 5•1

Place Value with Base-10 Blocks

Record each number. Then record how many of each block you used and how much those blocks are worth.

My number is ____________.

I used ____________ big cube(s), which is worth ____________.

I used ____________ flat(s), which is worth ____________.

I used ____________ long(s), which is worth ____________.

I used ____________ cube(s), which is worth ____________.

My number is ____________.

I used ____________ big cube(s), which is worth ____________.

I used ____________ flat(s), which is worth ____________.

I used ____________ long(s), which is worth ____________.

I used ____________ cube(s), which is worth ____________.

Copyright © Wright Group/McGraw-Hill

Name Date Time

Comparing Numbers

Family Note Review the meanings of the > and < relation symbols (see box below) before your child begins this page. When your child has completed the Home Link, ask him or her to read the numbers on the page to you.

The game *Number Top-It* gives children the opportunity to practice comparing 5-digit numbers. You may wish to play *Number Top-It* with your child. (See *Student Reference Book,* pages 302 and 303.)

Please return this Home Link to school tomorrow.

Write < or >.

1. 906 ________ 960

2. 5,708 ________ 599

3. 31,859 ________ 31,958

4. 10,006 ________ 10,106

5. 48,936 ________ 4,971

6. 76,094 ________ 76,111

< means *is less than*

> means *is greater than*

Use the digits 6, 8, 3, and 9.

7. Write the smallest possible number. ____________

8. Write the largest possible number. ____________

9. Write two numbers that are between the smallest and largest numbers.

________________________ ________________________

10. Fill in the missing numbers.

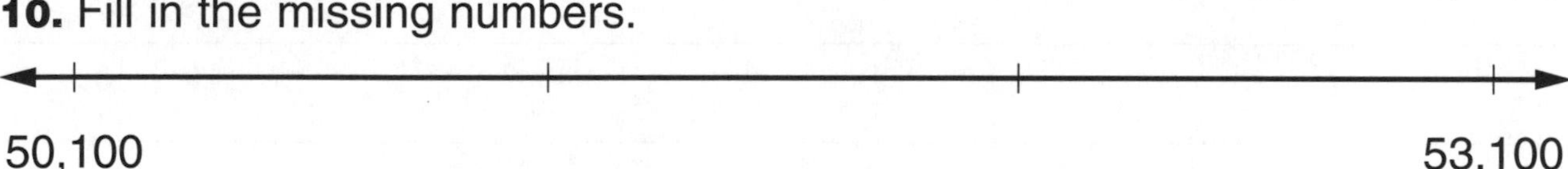

50,100 __________ __________ 53,100

Practice

Write these problems on the back of this page. Solve. Show your work.

11. 48 + 8

12. 86 +77

13. 717 + 79

14. 236 +248

Copyright © Wright Group/McGraw-Hill

Name Date Time

LESSON 5•2

Comparing 5-Digit Numbers

Write your 3 numbers on the lines below.

______________ ______________ ______________

1. Write a number that is greater than your largest number. ______________

2. Write a number that falls between your two largest numbers. ______________

3. Which of your numbers is closest to 50,000? ______________

How do you know?

____

____

4. Which of your numbers is closest to 10,000? ______________

How do you know?

____

5. Which 2 numbers are closest to each other?

____

How do you know?

____

____

6. Estimate the difference between your largest and smallest numbers.

____

What did you do to make your estimate?

____

____

Copyright © Wright Group/McGraw-Hill

Name Date Time

Comparing and Ordering Numbers

For each problem put an X about where you think the numbers will be on the number line. Then write the number above the X.

> is greater than
< is less than

1. Place these numbers on the number line: 73, 89, 99.

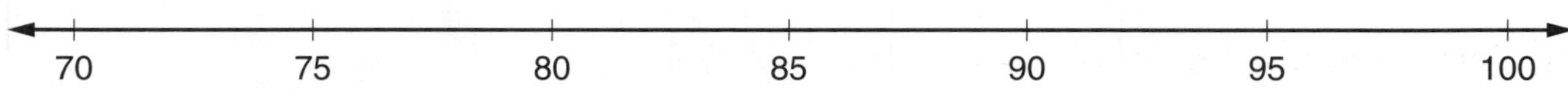

2. Place these numbers on the number line: 97, 108, 124.

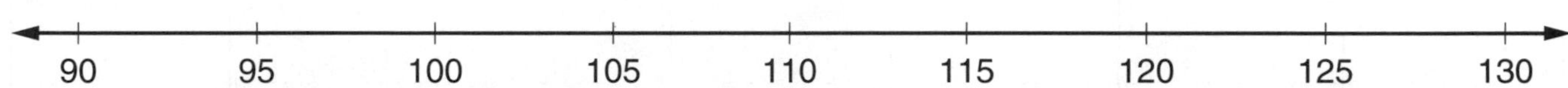

3. Place these numbers on the number line: 428, 441, 449.

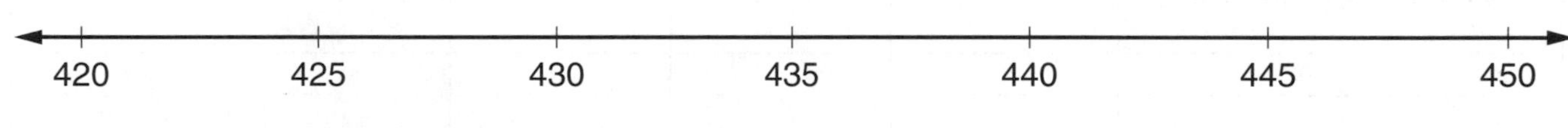

Try This

4. Place these numbers on the number line: 1,112; 1,138; 1,146.

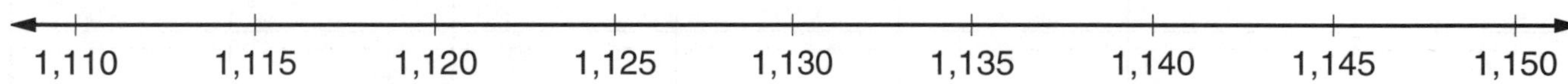

Copyright © Wright Group/McGraw-Hill

Name Date Time

7-Digit Place-Value Chart

Millions	, Hundred-Thousands	Ten-Thousands	Thousands	, Hundreds	Tens	Ones

Copyright © Wright Group/McGraw-Hill

Name Date Time

Number Diagram

___ ___ ___, ___ ___ ___, ___ ___ ___ (million, thousand) ___ ___ ___, ___ ___ ___, ___ ___ ___ (million, thousand)

___ ___ ___, ___ ___ ___, ___ ___ ___ (million, thousand) ___ ___ ___, ___ ___ ___, ___ ___ ___ (million, thousand)

___ ___ ___, ___ ___ ___, ___ ___ ___ (million, thousand) ___ ___ ___, ___ ___ ___, ___ ___ ___ (million, thousand)

___ ___ ___, ___ ___ ___, ___ ___ ___ (million, thousand) ___ ___ ___, ___ ___ ___, ___ ___ ___ (million, thousand)

___ ___ ___, ___ ___ ___, ___ ___ ___ (million, thousand) ___ ___ ___, ___ ___ ___, ___ ___ ___ (million, thousand)

___ ___ ___, ___ ___ ___, ___ ___ ___ (million, thousand) ___ ___ ___, ___ ___ ___, ___ ___ ___ (million, thousand)

___ ___ ___, ___ ___ ___, ___ ___ ___ (million, thousand) ___ ___ ___, ___ ___ ___, ___ ___ ___ (million, thousand)

Copyright © Wright Group/McGraw-Hill

Name Date Time

Practice with Place Value

Family Note Help your child use the seven digit squares to make the largest and smallest whole numbers possible out of all seven digits. *Number Top-It* (7-Digit Numbers) on *Student Reference Book,* page 304 provides practice comparing 7-digit numbers. You may wish to play this game with your child.

Please return this Home Link to school tomorrow.

SRB 304

1. Cut out the digit squares. Use all 7 digits to make the largest number and the smallest. Add the numbers and then read them to someone at home.

largest ____________

smallest ____________

Total ____________

2. Read the following numbers to someone at home:

784	25,086	4,056,211	42,876
9,603	7,000,007	7,037,562	104,719

3. Write the numbers above in order from the largest to the smallest.

____________ (largest)

____

____

____

____

____

____

____________ (smallest)

4. Which number is 1,000 less than 43,876?

____

5. Which number is 10,000 more than 7,027,562?

____

6. Which number is 10,000 less than 4,066,211?

____

7. Which number is 1,000,000 more than 6,000,007?

____

6 2 4 7 1 5 3

Copyright © Wright Group/McGraw-Hill

Name Date Time

Large Numbers

The world is full of large numbers. You can find them in many places: in newspapers, magazines, books, and encyclopedias, as well as on billboards and highway signs. Find some large numbers. List them below and write where you found them. Remember to write the units or labels. Then, write whether the numbers are estimates or exact.

Number and Where Found	**What it refers to** (count, label, location, measurement, and so on)	**Estimate or Exact**
778,000,000 km, Atlas	Jupiter's distance from sun	estimate

Copyright © Wright Group/McGraw-Hill

Name Date Time

LESSON 5•3

Find the Mystery Number

Read the clues. Use base-10 blocks to build the mystery number. Then use base-10 shorthand to show your work.

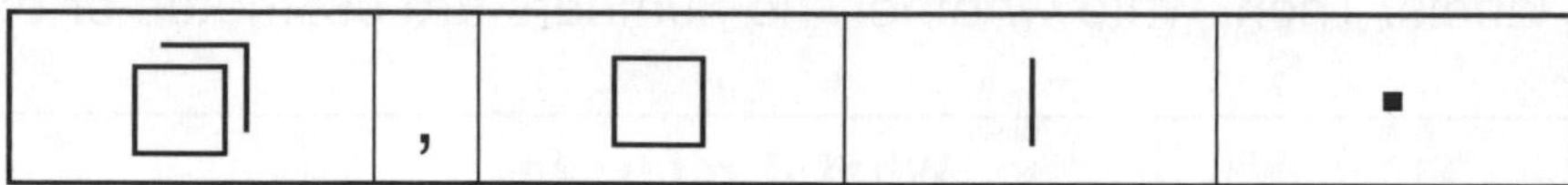

Example:

Clues: 12 ones and 3 tens

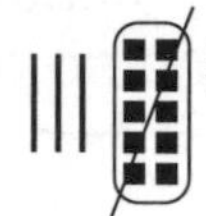

Mystery Number: 42

1. Clues: 18 ones and 4 tens

Mystery Number: ____________

2. Clues: 7 ones, 14 tens

Mystery Number: ____________

3. Clues: 2 ones, 16 tens

Mystery Number: ____________

4. Clues: 6 ones, 13 tens, 1 hundred

Mystery Number: ____________

5. Make up some clues for a mystery number. Give them to a partner to solve.

Clues: ____

Mystery Number: ________________________________

Copyright © Wright Group/McGraw-Hill

Name Date Time

Comparing Areas of Continents

Family Note Your child has been practicing reading and writing 6- and 7-digit numerals. Use the pie graph to help him or her answer the questions about the continents. Ask your child to read each of the areas of the continents aloud to you. Encourage rounding the areas to the nearest million when making the comparisons in Problems 5–7. Remember that working with numbers in the millions is a new skill for your child.

Please return this Home Link to school tomorrow.

SRB 194

Use the graph to answer the questions.

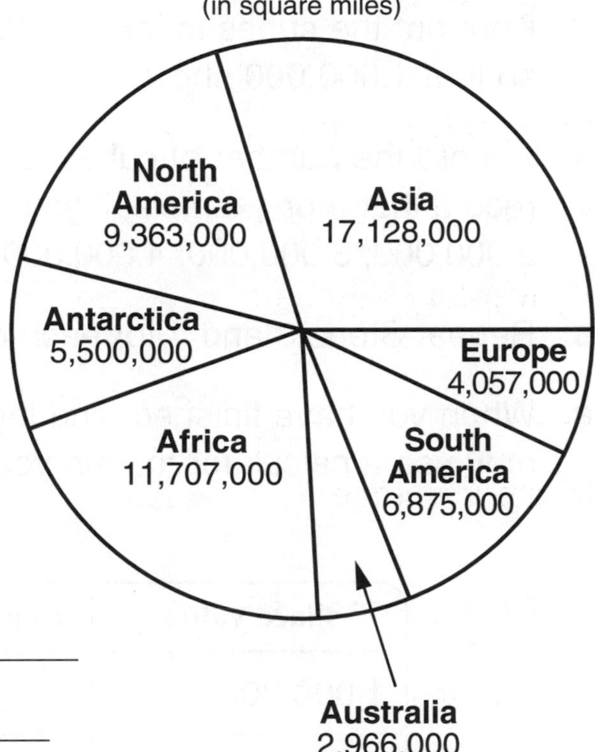

1. How many continents are there?

____

2. Which continent has the largest area?

____

3. Which continent has the smallest area?

____

4. Which continents have an area between 5 and 10 million square miles each?

____

____

5. Which continent is about 1 million square miles larger than Australia?

____

6. Which continent is a little more than half the size of Asia?

____

Try This

7. Which continent is a little less than 3 times the size of Europe?

____

Copyright © Wright Group/McGraw-Hill

Name Date Time

Making Large Numbers

You need a partner, 6 place-value bowls, 30 cubes, and a calculator. Follow these steps.

1. Without looking at the bottom of your place-value bowls, put some of your cubes into each bowl.
2. Now look at the bottom of the bowls and arrange them in order from the 1,000,000 on the left to 10 on the right.
3. Pour out the cubes in the "1,000,000" bowl and turn the bowl over so that 1,000,000 shows.
4. Record the number of cubes. Count the value of the cubes and record that. For example, if you have 4 cubes, count 1,000,000; 2,000,000; 3,000,000; 4,000,000. The value is 4,000,000.
5. Repeat Steps 3 and 4 for each of the place-value bowls.
6. When you have finished, find the total value of all your cubes. You may use a calculator to help you.

Place Value	Number of Cubes	Value of Cubes
1,000,000		
100,000		
10,000		
1,000		
100		
10		
Total Value of My Cubes: ____________		

Copyright © Wright Group/McGraw-Hill

Name Date Time

Working with Populations

1. Look at the map on *Student Reference Book,* pages 226 and 227. Nine cities on the map have populations greater than 1 million. List the cities and their populations in order from largest to smallest.

City	Population

2. Six cities on the map have populations less than 500,000. List the cities and their populations in order from largest to smallest.

City	Population

Copyright © Wright Group/McGraw-Hill

Name Date Time

LESSON 5•5

Math Message

1. 1 year = ________ weeks, or ________________ days
2. 1 day = ________ hours
3. 1 hour = ________ minutes
4. 1 minute = ________ seconds

Copyright © Wright Group/McGraw-Hill

Name Date Time

LESSON 5•5

Math Message

1. 1 year = ________ weeks, or ________________ days
2. 1 day = ________ hours
3. 1 hour = ________ minutes
4. 1 minute = ________ seconds

Copyright © Wright Group/McGraw-Hill

Name Date Time

LESSON 5•5

Math Message

1. 1 year = ________ weeks, or ________________ days
2. 1 day = ________ hours
3. 1 hour = ________ minutes
4. 1 minute = ________ seconds

Copyright © Wright Group/McGraw-Hill

Name Date Time

Writing and Ordering Numbers

Family Note Observe and encourage as your child makes 4-digit numbers using the digit squares, records the numbers, and then writes them in order from smallest to largest. Then listen as your child reads the numbers to you.

Please return this Home Link to school tomorrow.

Cut out the digit squares. Arrange them into 4-digit numbers in as many different ways as you can. Record each number you make. Then put the numbers in order from smallest to largest. Read your numbers to someone at home.

Record numbers here:	**Order** numbers here:
______________	______________ (smallest)
______________	______________
______________	______________
______________	______________
______________	______________
______________	______________
______________	______________
______________	______________
______________	______________
______________	______________
______________	______________
______________	______________ (largest)

Copyright © Wright Group/McGraw-Hill

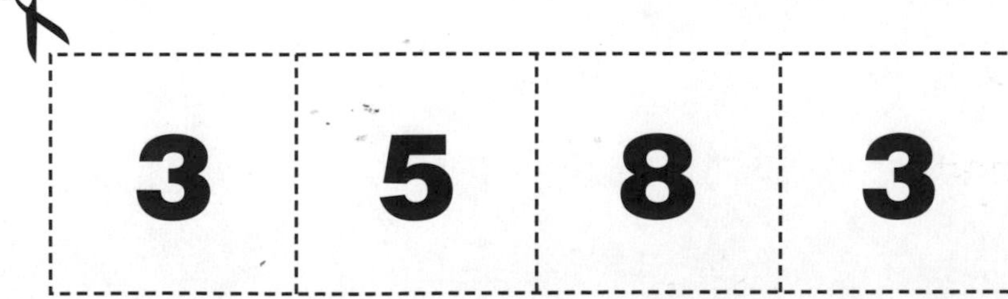

Name Date Time

LESSON 5•5

Units of Time

Answer the following questions. You may use counters, a calendar, your calculator, or any other math tool to help you.

1. The average American child watches television almost 20 hours per week.

   How much television does the average child watch in 2 weeks? ______________

   In 10 weeks? ______________

   In 15 weeks? ______________

2. The average time per week that children spend talking to their parents is about 40 minutes. In 3 weeks, they talk to their parents a total of about 2 hours.

   How much do they talk to their parents in 6 weeks? ______________

   In 15 weeks? ______________

3. About how much more time do they spend watching television in 15 weeks than talking to their parents in 15 weeks? ______________

More Facts about Television Watching:

- The average American watches more than 4 hours of TV per day.
- Hours per year the average American youth spends in school: 900
- Hours per year the average American youth watches television: 1,023

Facts collected by Real Vision at www.tvturnoff.org

Copyright © Wright Group/McGraw-Hill

Name _______________ Date _______________ Time _______________

HOME LINK 5•6

Stories with Large Numbers

Family Note Help your child write an addition and a subtraction story using 5-, 6-, or 7-digit numbers. Your child has been working with numbers as large as millions (7 digits), so this is a realistic expectation. However, it is acceptable for children to make up stories with 5- or 6-digit numbers.

Please return this Home Link to school tomorrow.

For each number story, try to think about large numbers of things. Share your stories with someone at home. If the numbers are too big for you to add or subtract, use a calculator or ask someone at home to help.

1. Write a number story that you solve by adding. **Workspace**

____

____

____

____

____

Answer: _______________
(unit)

2. Write a number story that you solve by subtracting.

____

____

____

____

____

Answer: _______________
(unit)

Copyright © Wright Group/McGraw-Hill

Name Date Time

Math Message

Write the following amounts using a dollar sign and a decimal point:

1. 3 dollar bills, 5 dimes, and 1 penny ______
2. 3 dimes and 6 pennies ______
3. 2 dollar bills and 7 dimes ______
4. 9 pennies ______

Copyright © Wright Group/McGraw-Hill

Name Date Time

Math Message

Write the following amounts using a dollar sign and a decimal point:

1. 3 dollar bills, 5 dimes, and 1 penny ______
2. 3 dimes and 6 pennies ______
3. 2 dollar bills and 7 dimes ______
4. 9 pennies ______

Copyright © Wright Group/McGraw-Hill

Name Date Time

Math Message

Write the following amounts using a dollar sign and a decimal point:

1. 3 dollar bills, 5 dimes, and 1 penny ______
2. 3 dimes and 6 pennies ______
3. 2 dollar bills and 7 dimes ______
4. 9 pennies ______

Copyright © Wright Group/McGraw-Hill

Name Date Time

Understanding Decimals

Family Note Your child has been using grids like the ones below to understand the meaning of decimals. The grid is made up of 100 squares. Each square is $\frac{1}{100}$ or 0.01 of the grid. Ten squares is $\frac{1}{10}$ or 0.10 of the grid. 0.8 is read as "eight-tenths." 0.04 is read as "four-hundredths." 0.53 is read as "fifty-three hundredths."

Please return this Home Link to school tomorrow.

If the grid is ONE, then what part of each grid is shaded?
Write a fraction and a decimal below each grid.

1.

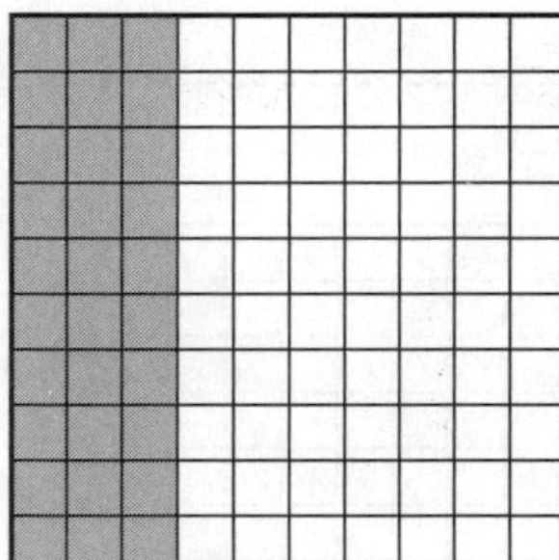

fraction: ____________

decimal: ____________

2.

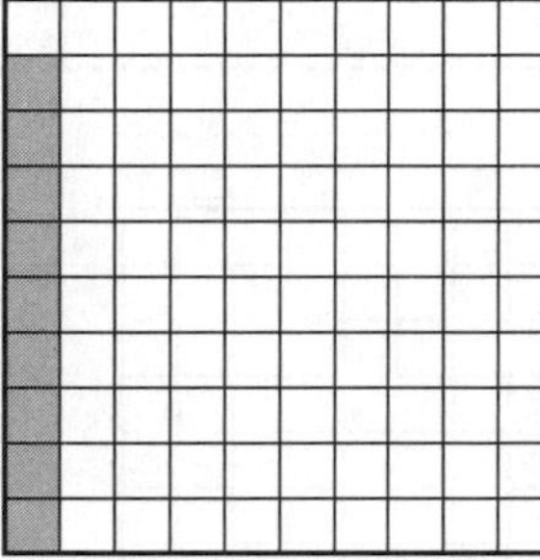

fraction: ____________

decimal: ____________

3.

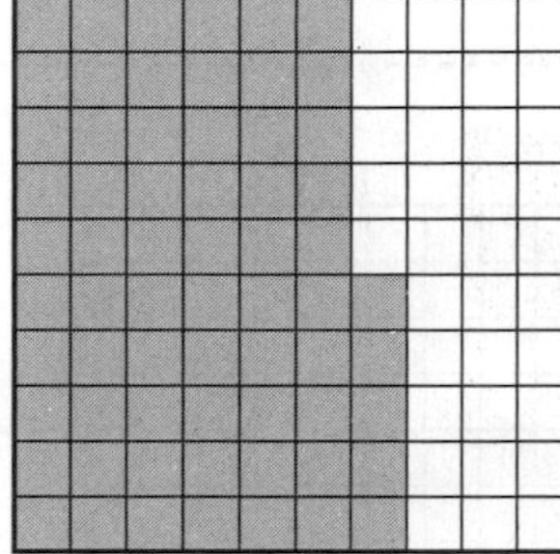

fraction: ____________

decimal: ____________

4. Which decimal is greater? Use the grids to help you.

0.3 or 0.09 ____________ 0.09 or 0.65 ____________ 0.3 or 0.65 ____________

5. Color 0.8 of the grid.

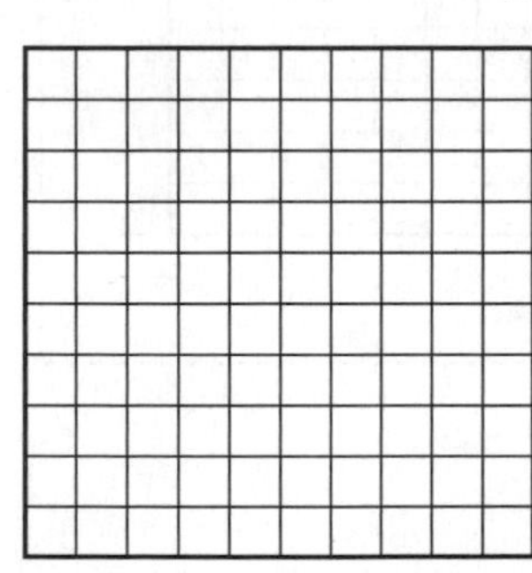

6. Color 0.04 of the grid.

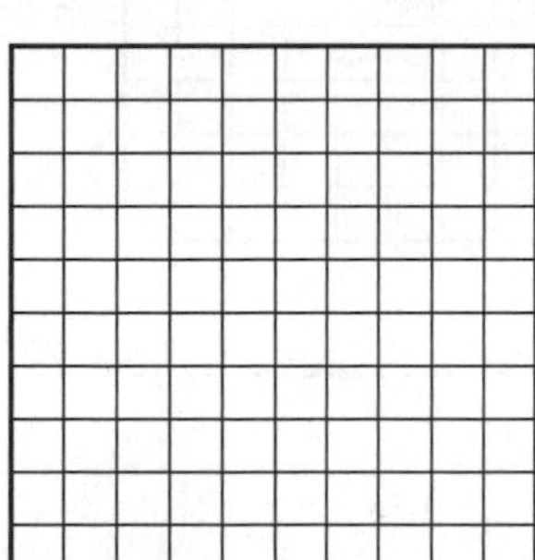

7. Color 0.53 of the grid.

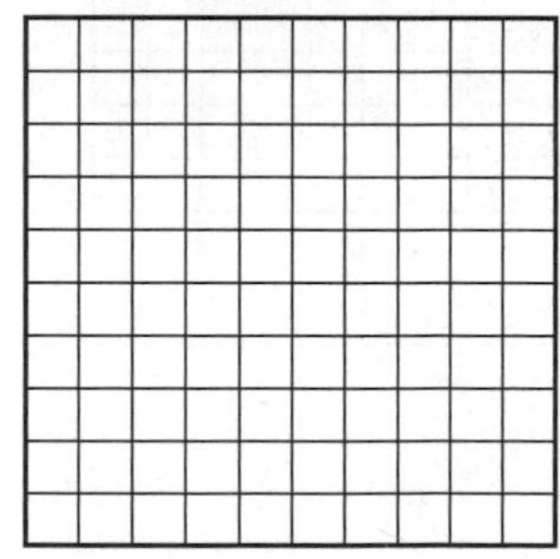

8. Write 0.8, 0.04, and 0.53 in order from smallest to largest.

Use the grids to help you. ________ ________ ________

Copyright © Wright Group/McGraw-Hill

Name Date Time

LESSON 5•7

Writing Names on Hundred Grids

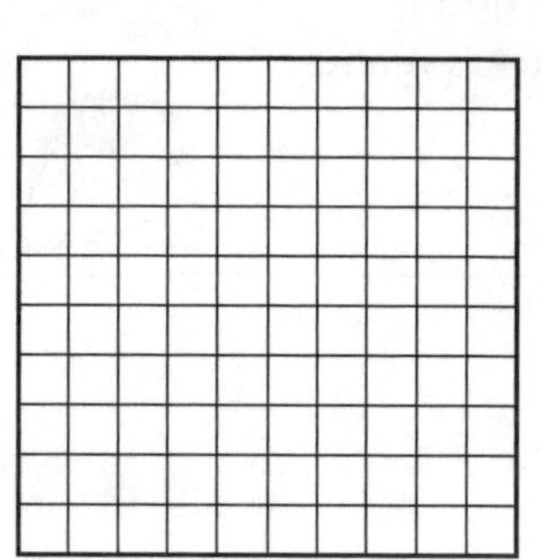
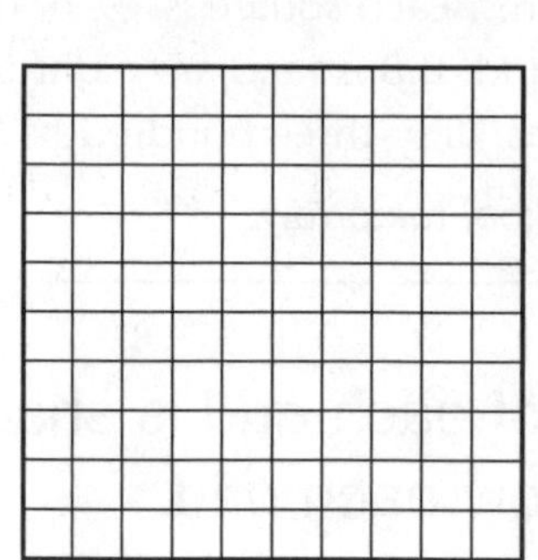
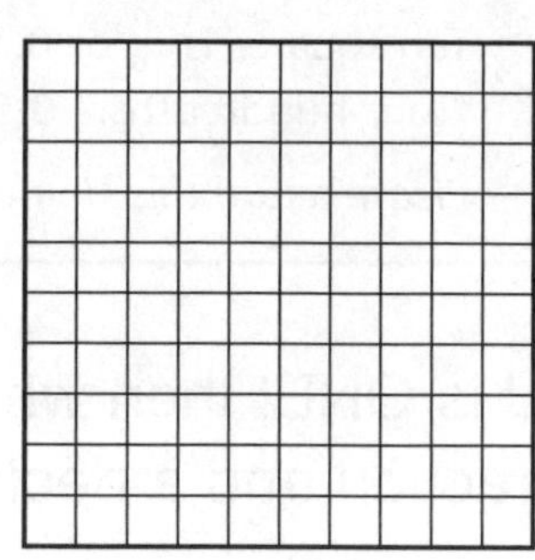

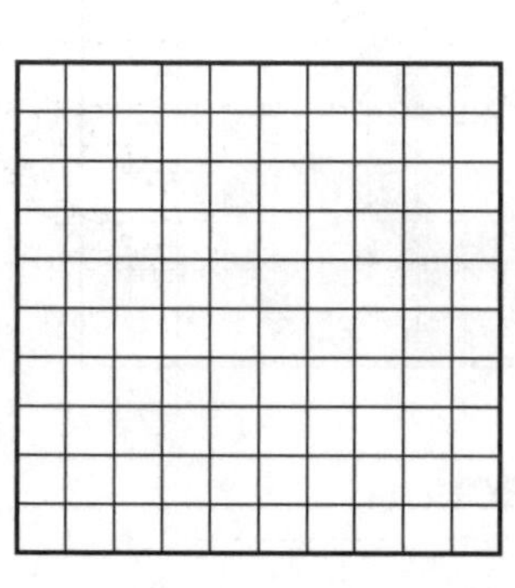
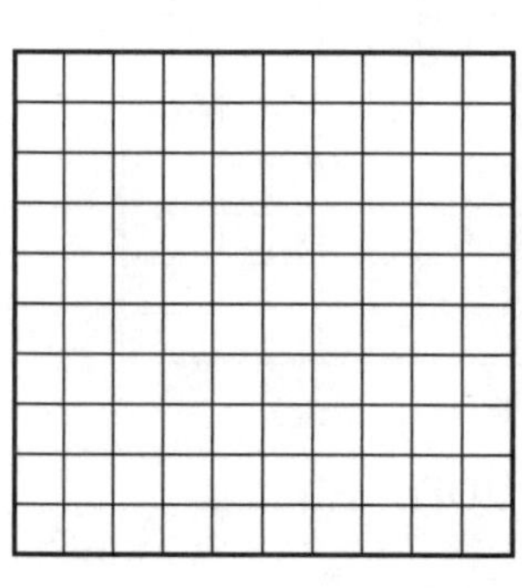
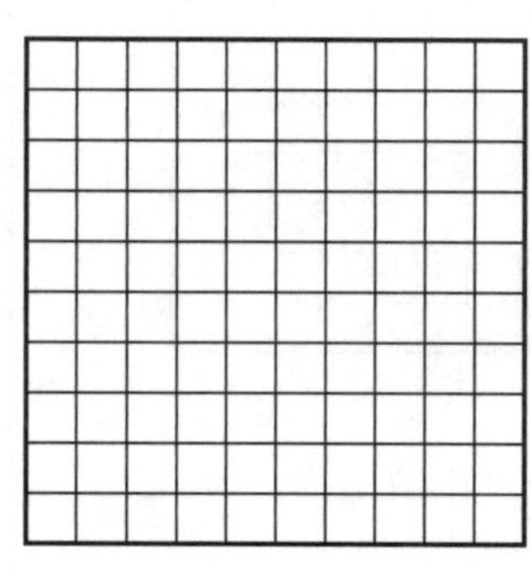

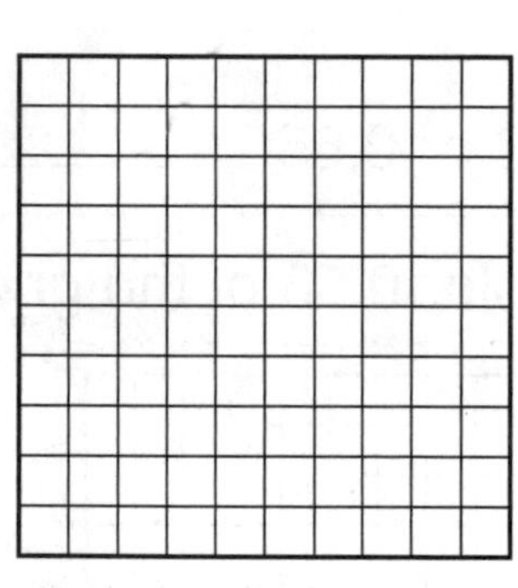
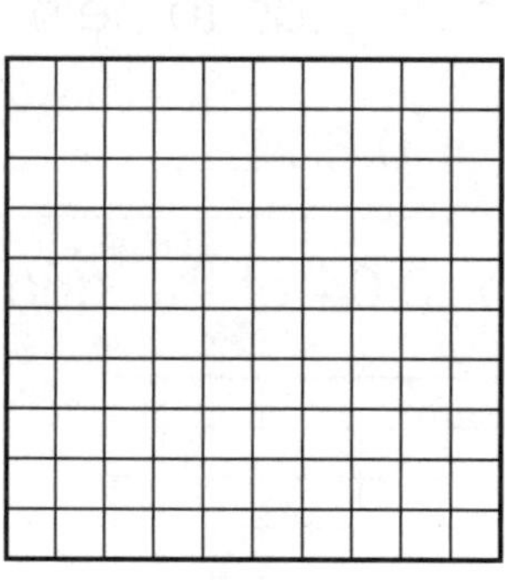
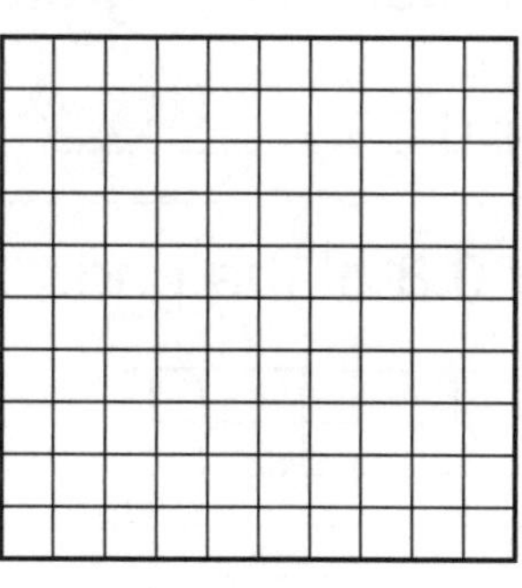

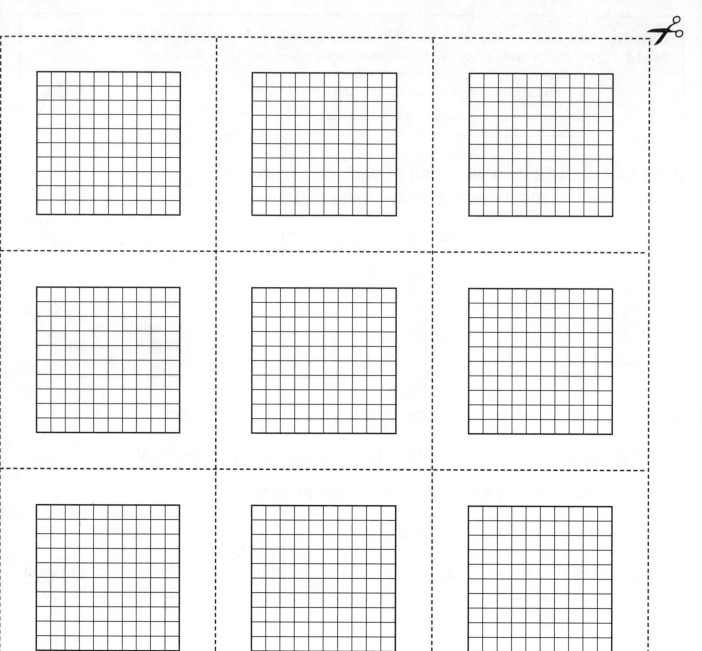

Copyright © Wright Group/McGraw-Hill

Name Date Time

Math Message

Write the following numbers with digits:

1. fourteen-hundredths ______
2. four-hundredths ______
3. four-tenths ______
4. four hundred ______

Copyright © Wright Group/McGraw-Hill

Name Date Time

Math Message

Write the following numbers with digits:

1. fourteen-hundredths ______
2. four-hundredths ______
3. four-tenths ______
4. four hundred ______

Copyright © Wright Group/McGraw-Hill

Name Date Time

Math Message

Write the following numbers with digits:

1. fourteen-hundredths ______
2. four-hundredths ______
3. four-tenths ______
4. four hundred ______

Copyright © Wright Group/McGraw-Hill

Name Date Time

LESSON 5·8

Exploring Decimals

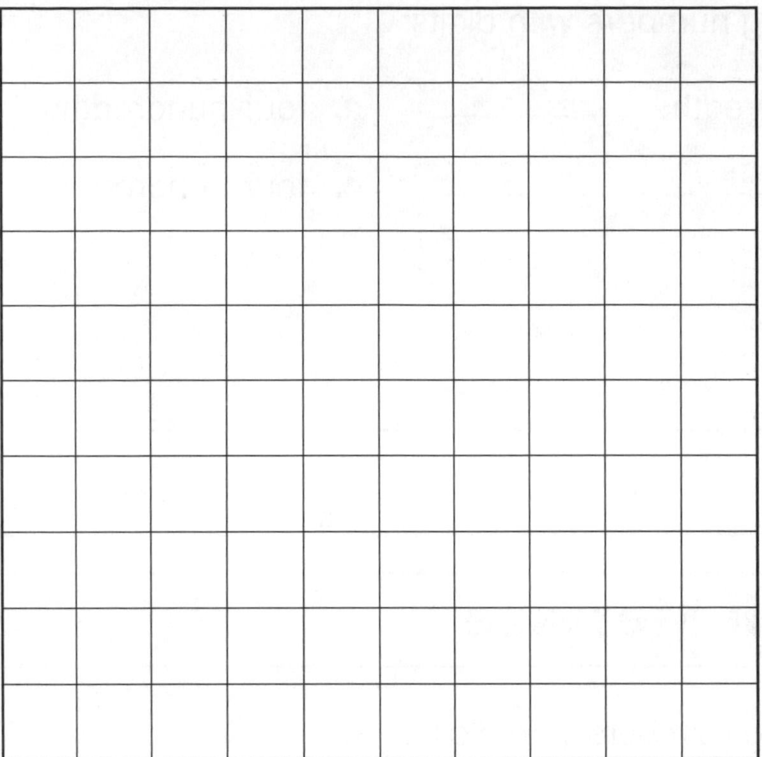

A	B	C	D
______ hundredths	______ tenths, ______ hundredths	0. ______	
______ hundredths	______ tenths, ______ hundredths	0. ______	
______ hundredths	______ tenths, ______ hundredths	0. ______	
______ hundredths	______ tenths, ______ hundredths	0. ______	
______ hundredths	______ tenths, ______ hundredths	0. ______	
______ hundredths	______ tenths, ______ hundredths	0. ______	
______ hundredths	______ tenths, ______ hundredths	0. ______	

Copyright © Wright Group/McGraw-Hill

Name _______________ Date _______________ Time _______________

Record Sheet for Exploring Decimals

A	B	C	D
27 hundredths	2 tenths, 7 hundredths	0. 27	$\frac{27}{100}$
_____ hundredths	_____ tenths, _____ hundredths	0. _____	
_____ hundredths	_____ tenths, _____ hundredths	0. _____	
_____ hundredths	_____ tenths, _____ hundredths	0. _____	
_____ hundredths	_____ tenths, _____ hundredths	0. _____	
_____ hundredths	_____ tenths, _____ hundredths	0. _____	
_____ hundredths	_____ tenths, _____ hundredths	0. _____	
_____ hundredths	_____ tenths, _____ hundredths	0. _____	
_____ hundredths	_____ tenths, _____ hundredths	0. _____	
_____ hundredths	_____ tenths, _____ hundredths	0. _____	
_____ hundredths	_____ tenths, _____ hundredths	0. _____	
_____ hundredths	_____ tenths, _____ hundredths	0. _____	
_____ hundredths	_____ tenths, _____ hundredths	0. _____	
_____ hundredths	_____ tenths, _____ hundredths	0. _____	

Copyright © Wright Group/McGraw-Hill

Name Date Time

HOME LINK 5•8

Tenths and Hundredths

Family Note Your child continues to work with decimals. Encourage him or her to think about ways to write money amounts. This is called dollars-and-cents notation. For example, $0.07 (7 cents), $0.09 (9 cents), and so on.

Please return this Home Link to school tomorrow.

Write what each diagram shows.

1. 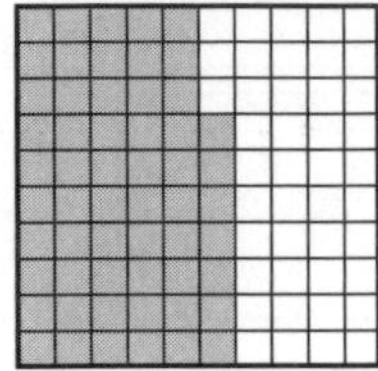

_____ hundredths

___ tenths ___ hundredths

2. 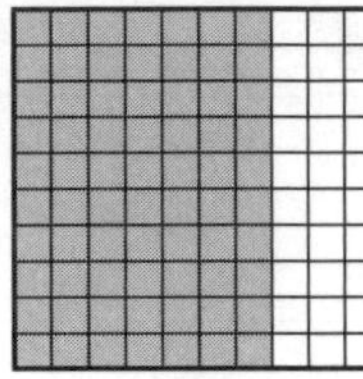

_____ hundredths

___ tenths ___ hundredths

3. 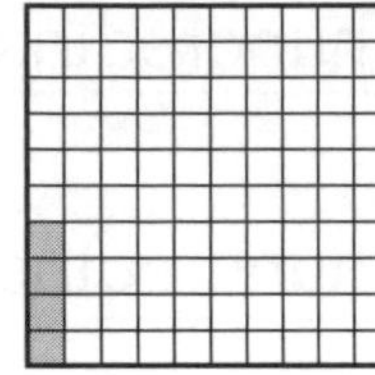

_____ hundredths

___ tenths ___ hundredths

Write the words as decimal numbers.

4. twenty-three hundredths

____

5. eight and four-tenths

____

6. thirty and twenty-hundredths

____

7. five-hundredths

____

Continue each pattern.

8. 0.1, 0.2, 0.3, ______, ______, ______, ______, ______, ______

9. 0.01, 0.02, 0.03, ______, ______, ______, ______, ______, ______

Practice

Write these problems on the back of this page. Solve. Show your work.

10. 621 − 118 = ______

11. 135 + 468 = ______

Copyright © Wright Group/McGraw-Hill

Name Date Time

Place-Value Mat

1 Ones Large cubes	0.1 Tenths Flats	0.01 Hundredths Longs	0.001 Thousandths Cubes

Copyright © Wright Group/McGraw-Hill

Name Date Time

LESSON 5•8

Place-Value Mat

$1.00 1	$0.10 0.1	$0.01 0.01
Dollars Ones Flats	**Dimes Tenths Longs**	**Pennies Hundredths Cubes**

Copyright © Wright Group/McGraw-Hill

Name Date Time

LESSON 5•9

A Shopping Trip

Use pages 215–217 in your *Student Reference Book.*

1. List at least 4 items you are buying in the space below. If you buy the same item 2 times, list it 2 times.

Item	Sale Price
◆ ______	◆ ______
◆ ______	◆ ______
◆ ______	◆ ______
◆ ______	◆ ______

2. Estimate how many dollar bills you need to pay for these items. ______

3. Give the clerk the dollar bills.

4. The clerk calculates the total cost. $ ______

5. The clerk calculates the change you should get. $ ______

6. Record your change. Use Ⓟ, Ⓝ, Ⓓ, Ⓠ. ______

Try This

Use Stock-Up Sale Poster #1 in your *Student Reference Book,* page 216.

7. Justin wants to buy 5 ballpoint pens. How much money will he save by buying them at the "5-or-More Sale"?

Regular price (for 5 ballpoint pens): $ ___.___

"5-or-More Sale" price: $ ___.___

Amount saved: $ ___.___

Copyright © Wright Group/McGraw-Hill

Name Date Time

HOME LINK 5•9

Practice with Decimals

Family Note Your child has been using the metric system to practice measurements and to convert centimeters to meters. The following equivalencies will assist you in helping your child solve Problems 3–6.

Please return this Home Link to school tomorrow.

1 cm = 10 mm
1 m = 100 cm
1 m = 1,000 mm

Fill in the missing numbers.

1.

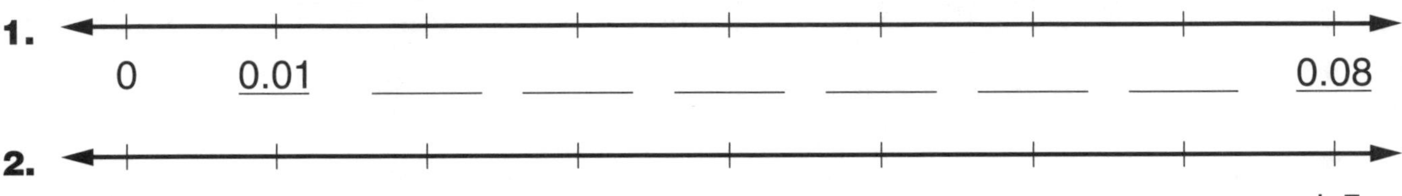

2.

Follow these directions on the ruler below.

3. Make a dot at 7 cm and label it with the letter *A.*

4. Make a dot at 90 mm and label it with the letter *B.*

5. Make a dot at 0.13 m and label it with the letter *C.*

6. Make a dot at 0.06 m and label it with the letter *D.*

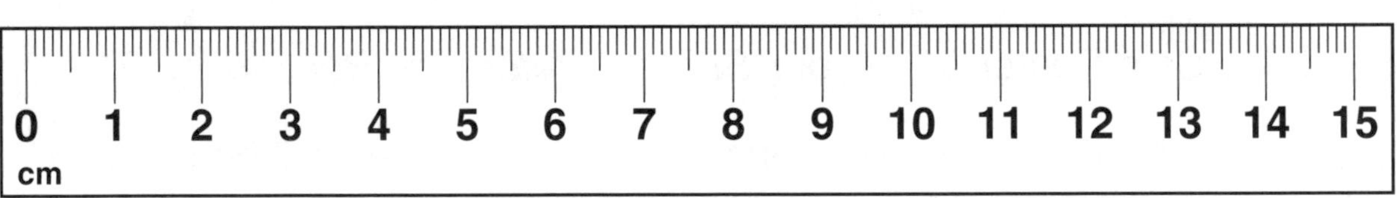

Practice

7. $3 \times 9 =$ ______ **8.** $5 \times 8 =$ ______ **9.** $0 \times 8 =$ ______

10. ______ $= 2 \times 6$ **11.** ______ $= 3 \times 3$ **12.** ______ $= 5 \times 3$

Copyright © Wright Group/McGraw-Hill

Name Date Time

Magnified View of 1 Centimeter

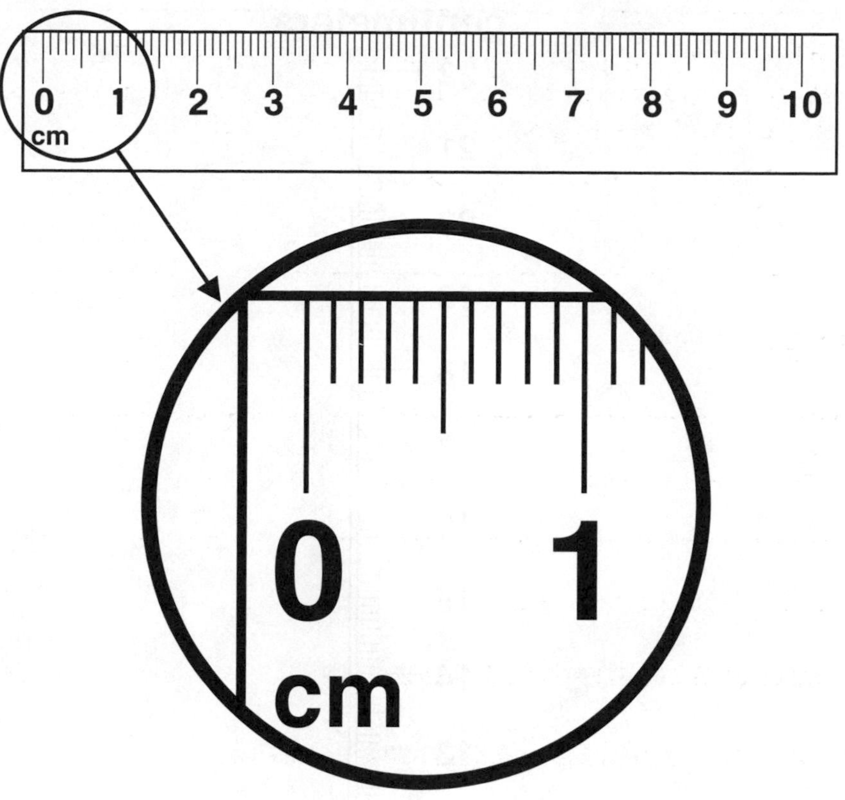

1 centimeter = 10 millimeters

Copyright © Wright Group/McGraw-Hill

Name Date Time

Rain Gauge

centimeters

22
21
20
19
18
17
16
15
14
13
12
11
10
9
8
7
6
5
4
3
2
1
0

Copyright © Wright Group/McGraw-Hill

Name Date Time

HOME LINK 5•10

Measuring with Millimeters

Family Note Your child has been using millimeters to learn about decimal place value. This page offers a way to practice with millimeters and other metric measurements. Have your child use the ruler at the bottom of the page to answer the questions.

Please return this Home Link to school tomorrow.

A queen termite is drawn above the ruler at the bottom of the page. It is 5 millimeters long.

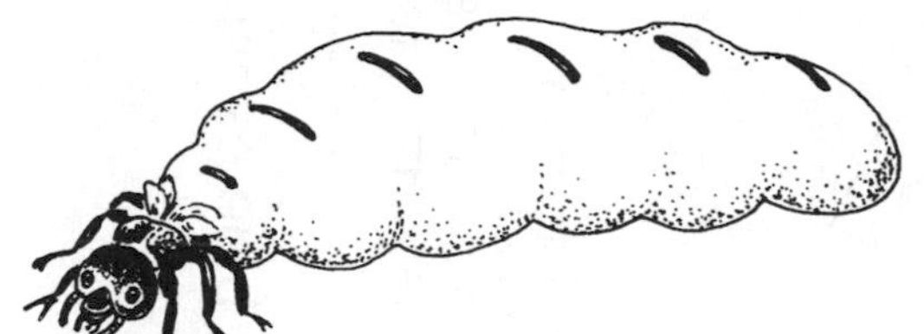

A queen termite shown larger than actual size

1 cm = 10 mm
1 m = 100 cm
1 m = 1,000 mm

1. How many termites would fit on:

a. 1 centimeter? ________ **b.** 5 centimeters? ________

c. 10 centimeters? ________ **d.** 50 centimeters? ________

e. 1 meterstick? ________ **f.** 3 metersticks? ________

2. What would be the length of a chain of 60 termites?

a. ________ centimeters **b.** ________ meters **c.** ________ millimeters

Practice

3. $7 \times 7 =$ ________ **4.** ________ $= 7 \times 8$

5. $9 \times 7 =$ ________ **6.** ________ $= 6 \times 7$

Copyright © Wright Group/McGraw-Hill

Name ______________ Date ______________ Time ______________

LESSON 5·10

Comparing Millimeters and Centimeters

Below is a picture of a centimeter strip. It has both centimeter (cm) and millimeter (mm) marks on it.

Use a red pencil to trace the line that marks each centimeter.

Underneath the number for each centimeter, there is a second, larger number.

This is the number of millimeters if you count them starting at 0. Try it. Count from the 0 mark to the mark labeled 1 cm or 10 mm.

cm:	0	1	2	3	4	5	6	7	8	9	10	11	12	13	14	15	16	17	18	19	20	21
mm:	0	10	20	30	40	50	60	70	80	90	100	110	120	130	140	150	160	170	180	190	200	210

Find each of the points below on the centimeter strip and mark them with a blue pencil.

Fill in the missing numbers.

2 cm = ________ mm 11 cm = ________ mm 1.4 cm = ________ mm

________ cm = 80 mm ________ cm = 65 mm ________ cm = 135 mm

Copyright © Wright Group/McGraw-Hill

Name Date Time

Place-Value Book

1. Cut each page along the dashed lines.

   Do NOT cut any of the solid lines!

2. Cut along the vertical dashed lines to separate the digits on each page.

3. Assemble with the pages in order.

4. Staple the assembled book across the top margin. (Ask your teacher for help if you need it.)

Name ______________________ page 1

page 2

0	0.	0	0	0

page 3

1	1.	1	1	1

Copyright © Wright Group/McGraw-Hill

Name Date Time

LESSON 5·11

Place-Value Book *continued*

page 4

2	2.	2	2	2

page 5

3	3.	3	3	3

page 6

4	4.	4	4	4

Copyright © Wright Group/McGraw-Hill

Name Date Time

Place-Value Book *continued*

page 7

5	5.	5	5	5

page 8

6	6.	6	6	6

page 9

7	7.	7	7	7

Copyright © Wright Group/McGraw-Hill

Name Date Time

Place-Value Book *continued*

page 10

8	8.	8	8	8

page 11

9	9.	9	9	9

page 12

Tens	Ones	Tenths	Hundredths	Thousandths

Copyright © Wright Group/McGraw-Hill

Name Date Time

Comparing Decimals

Family Note Ask your child to read the decimal numerals aloud. Encourage your child to use the following method:

1. Read the whole-number part.
2. Say *and* for the decimal point.
3. Read the digits after the decimal point as though they formed their own number.
4. Say *tenths, hundredths,* or *thousandths,* depending on the placement of the right-hand digit. Encourage your child to exaggerate the *ths* sound.

Please return this Home Link to school tomorrow.

Write $>$, $<$, or $=$.

$>$ means *is greater than*

$<$ means *is less than*

1. 2.35 ______ 2.57

2. 1.008 ______ 1.8

3. 0.64 ______ 0.46

4. 0.90 ______ 0.9

5. 42.1 ______ 42.09

6. 7.098 ______ 7.542

7. 0.4 ______ 0.400

8. 0.206 ______ 0.214

Example: The 4 in 0.47 stands for 4 tenths or 0.4.

9. The 9 in 4.59 stands for 9 ______________ or ________.

10. The 3 in 3.62 stands for 3 ________ or ________.

Continue each number pattern.

11. 6.56, 6.57, 6.58, ________, ________, ________

12. 0.73, 0.83, 0.93, ________, ________, ________

Write the number that is 0.1 more.

13. 4.3 ________

14. 4.07 ________

Write the number that is 0.1 less.

15. 8.2 ________

16. 5.63 ________

Practice

Solve these problems on the back of this page. Show your work.

17. $\begin{array}{r} 282 \\ -\ 39 \\ \hline \end{array}$

18. $\begin{array}{r} 811 \\ -\ 29 \\ \hline \end{array}$

19. $\begin{array}{r} 685 \\ -\ 176 \\ \hline \end{array}$

Copyright © Wright Group/McGraw-Hill

Name Date Time

LESSON 5•11

Decimals between Whole Numbers

Work with a partner. Follow the directions. Use base-10 blocks if needed.

1. Write three decimal numbers that are between 0 and 1.

______________ ______________ ______________

2. Place each decimal where it belongs on the number line.
Think: *Is your decimal closer to 0 or closer to 1?*

3. Explain how you knew where to place your decimals.

Copyright © Wright Group/McGraw-Hill

Name Date Time

LESSON 5•12

Length-of-Day Line Graph

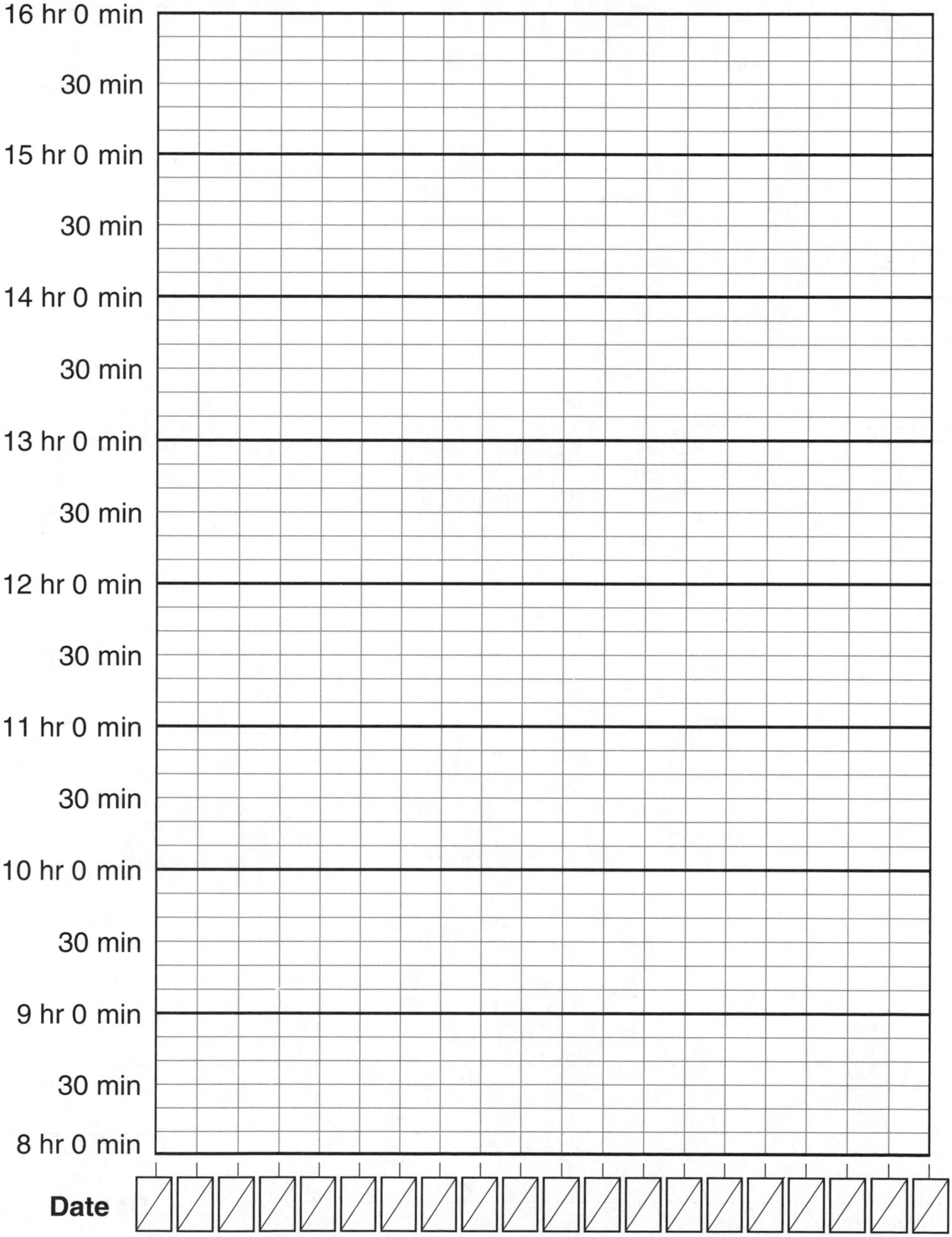

16 hr 0 min
30 min
15 hr 0 min
30 min
14 hr 0 min
30 min
13 hr 0 min
30 min
12 hr 0 min
30 min
11 hr 0 min
30 min
10 hr 0 min
30 min
9 hr 0 min
30 min
8 hr 0 min

Date

Copyright © Wright Group/McGraw-Hill

Name Date Time

LESSON 5•12

Length-of-Day Line Graph *continued*

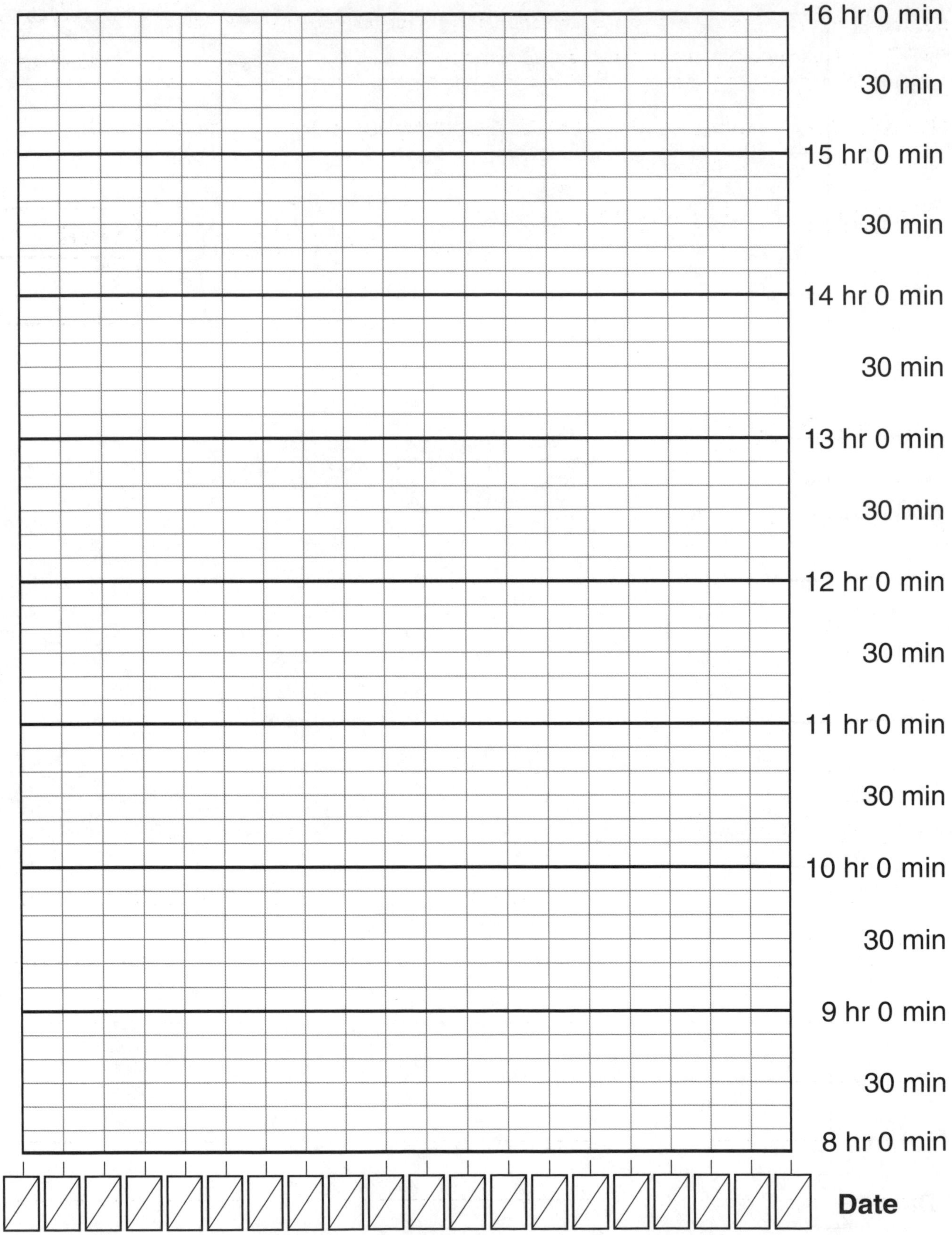

16 hr 0 min
30 min
15 hr 0 min
30 min
14 hr 0 min
30 min
13 hr 0 min
30 min
12 hr 0 min
30 min
11 hr 0 min
30 min
10 hr 0 min
30 min
9 hr 0 min
30 min
8 hr 0 min

Date

Copyright © Wright Group/McGraw-Hill

Name Date Time

HOME LINK 5•12

Subtraction & Multiplication Practice

Family Note Ask your child to explain the counting-up and trade-first subtraction methods.

Please return this Home Link to school tomorrow.

Make a ballpark estimate. Subtract and show your work. Check to see if your answer makes sense.

1. Use the counting-up method. ________________
(Ballpark estimate)

Unit

$$\begin{array}{r} 754 \\ -299 \\ \hline \end{array}$$

2. Use the trade-first method. ________________
(Ballpark estimate)

$$\begin{array}{r} 754 \\ -299 \\ \hline \end{array}$$

Multiplication. Write facts that you know.

3. × 2 facts

$4 \times 2 = 8$

4. × 3 facts

5. × 4 facts

Copyright © Wright Group/McGraw-Hill

Name Date Time

LESSON 5·12

World Population Growth

Use the data about world population on *Student Reference Book,* page 234 to help you answer the questions below.

1. About how many people were added to the world population between 1500 and 1804? ______________

   How many years is that? ______________

2. About how many people were added to the world population between 1804 and 1960? ______________

   How many years is that? ______________

3. About how many people were added to the world population between 1960 and 1999? ______________

   How many years is that? ______________

4. Compare your answers for Questions 1, 2, and 3. What do you notice about population growth?

   ____

   ____

5. Look at the World Population Graph. What does the line graph illustrate, or show, about world population?

   ____

   ____

   ____

6. Use the World Population Table to predict when the world population will reach 8,000,000,000. Explain. Use the back of this page, if needed.

   ____

   ____

   ____

   ____

Copyright © Wright Group/McGraw-Hill

Name Date Time

Unit 6: Family Letter

Geometry

Everyday Mathematics uses children's experiences with the everyday world to help them envision 3-dimensional (3-D) shapes. In previous grades, children were asked to identify 2-dimensional (2-D) shapes and their parts, such as sides and corners (vertices). They had several hands-on experiences with pattern blocks, geoboards, and templates. They also classified and named polygons, or closed figures consisting of line segments (sides) connected endpoint to endpoint.

In Unit 6, children will explore points, line segments, rays, lines, and the relationships among them, along with the geometric shapes that can be built from them. Children will construct angles, polygons, prisms, and pyramids.

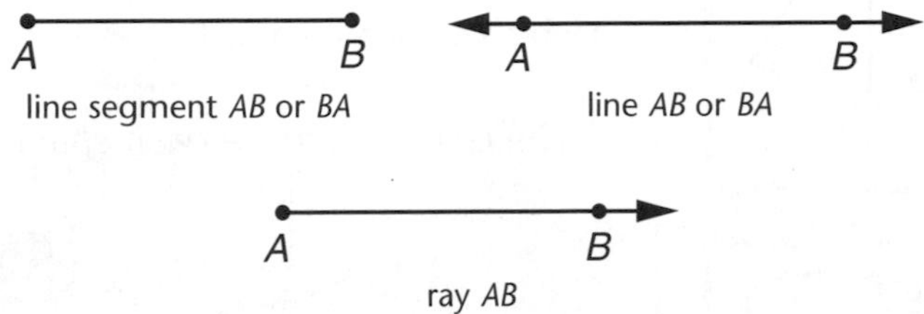

Children will also explore similarities and differences among 3-D shapes and regular polyhedrons within the context of a Shapes Museum. They will discover real-life examples of lines that are parallel, or lines that never meet, such as railroad tracks.

There is a great deal of vocabulary involved when working with geometry. However, the emphasis in this unit is not on memorizing the vocabulary, but rather on using it to examine relationships among classifications of geometric figures.

Please keep this Family Letter for reference as your child works through Unit 6.

Copyright © Wright Group/McGraw-Hill

Vocabulary

Important terms in Unit 6:

2-dimensional (2-D) shape A shape whose points are all in one plane, or flat surface, but not all on one line. A shape with length and width, but no thickness.

3-dimensional (3-D) shape A shape that does not lie completely within a plane, or flat surface; a shape with length, width, and thickness.

base of a 3-D shape A flat surface or face whose shape is the basis for naming some 3-dimensional objects.

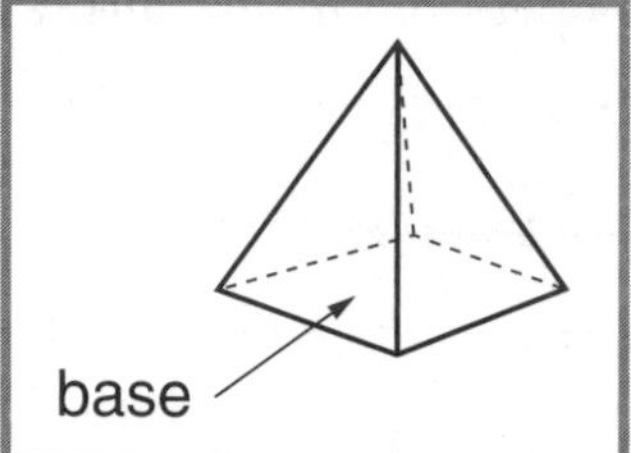

cone A 3-dimensional shape with a circular base, a curved surface, and one vertex, called the apex. An ice-cream cone is shaped like a cone.

sphere A 3-dimensional shape whose curved surface is, at all points, a given distance from its center point. A ball is shaped like a sphere.

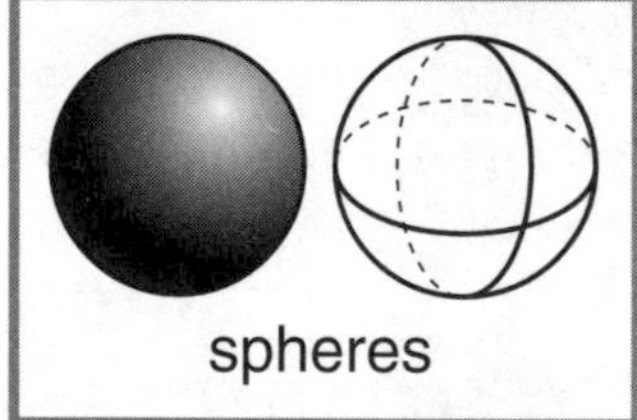

cylinder A 3-dimensional shape with two circular bases that are parallel and congruent and are connected by a curved surface. A soup can is shaped like a cylinder.

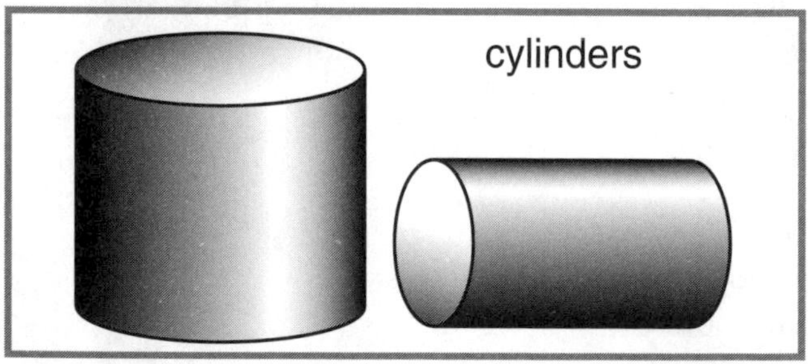

parallel Lines in a plane that never meet. Two parallel lines are always the same distance apart.

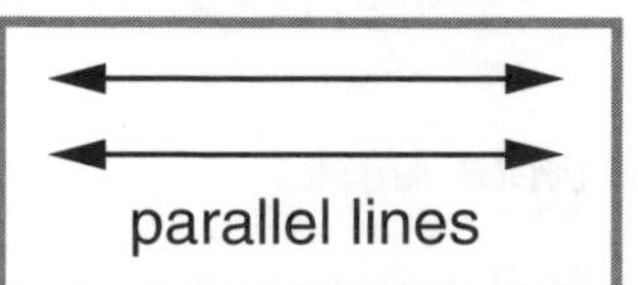

face In *Everyday Mathematics,* a flat surface on a 3-dimensional shape.

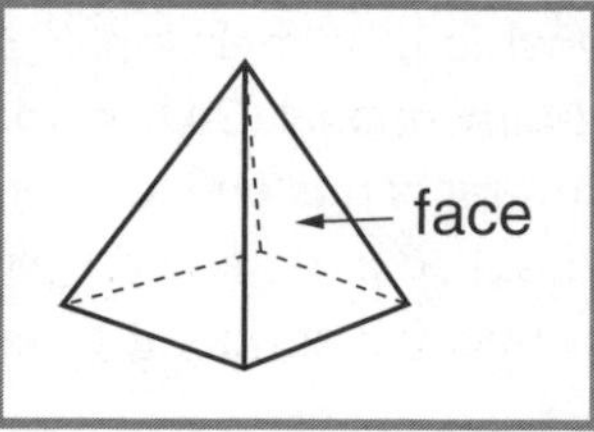

polyhedron A *3-dimensional shape* with polygons and their interiors for *faces.* Polyhedrons don't have any holes. Below are five regular polyhedrons, so called because all faces in each shape are identical.

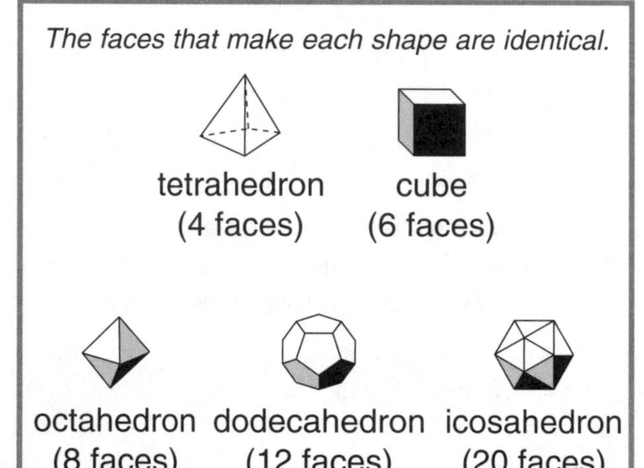

prism A *polyhedron* with two parallel *bases* that are the same size and shape. A prism is named for the shape of its base, and the other faces are all parallelograms.

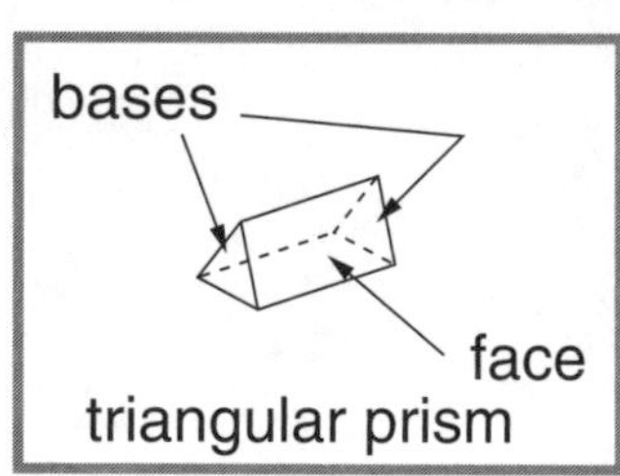

pyramid A *polyhedron* with a polygon for a *base* and the other faces are all triangles with a common vertex called the apex. A pyramid is named for the shape of its base.

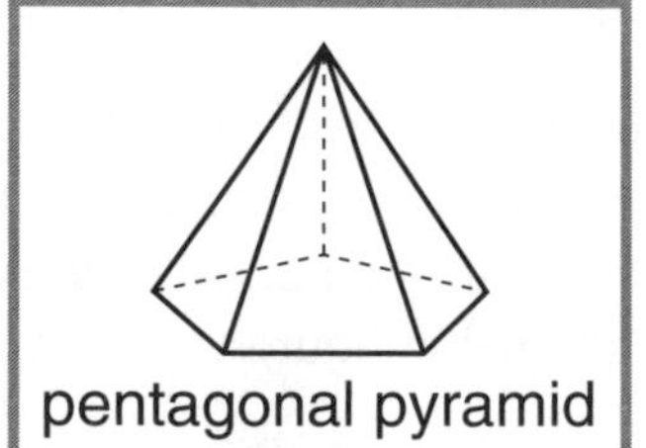

Copyright © Wright Group/McGraw-Hill

Do-Anytime Activities

To work with your child on the concepts taught in this unit and in previous units, try these interesting and rewarding activities:

1. Together, read the book *The Greedy Triangle,* by Marilyn Burns.
2. Begin a Shapes Museum at home. Label the shapes that your child collects.
3. Ask your child to identify 2-dimensional and 3-dimensional shapes inside and outside your home.
4. Measure objects to the nearest $\frac{1}{2}$ inch.

Building Skills through Games

In Unit 6, your child will practice numeration, multiplication, and geometry skills by playing the following games. For detailed instructions, see the *Student Reference Book.*

Number Top-It (Decimals)
As players pick each card, they must decide in which place-value box (from ones to thousandths) to place the card so that they end up with the largest number.

Beat the Calculator
A "Calculator" (a player who uses a calculator to solve the problem) and a "Brain" (a player who solves the problem without a calculator) race to see who will be first to solve multiplication problems.

Baseball Multiplication
Players use multiplication facts to score runs. Team members take turns "pitching" by rolling two dice to get two factors. Then players on the "batting" team take turns multiplying the two factors and saying the product.

Angle Race
Players build angles with rubber bands and "race" to see who will be first to complete the last angle exactly on the 360° mark.

Copyright © Wright Group/McGraw-Hill

HOME LINK 5•13 **Unit 6: Family Letter** *cont.*

As You Help Your Child with Homework

As your child brings home assignments, you may want to go over the instructions together, clarifying them as necessary. The answers listed below will guide you through this unit's Home Links.

Home Link 6•1

1. b, e, d, a, e or c **2.** B C

3. T O **4.** 568 **5.** 346

Home Link 6•2

Sample answers:

1. A B; Y Z

2. D, E, F, C

3. I, O, S, N

4.

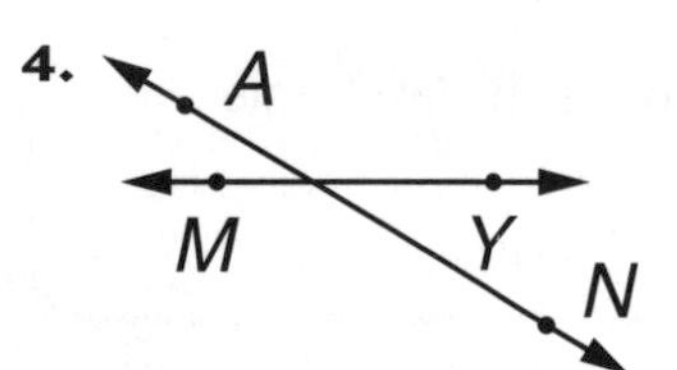

5. **6.**

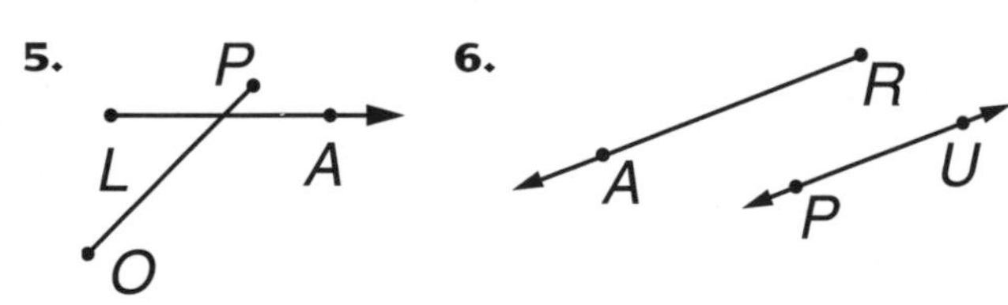

Home Link 6•4

5. 491 **6.** 289 **7.** 9

Home Link 6•5

1. right angles; equal; parallel

2. equal; parallel

3. equal; parallel

4. equal

5. 18 **6.** 12 **7.** 36

Home Link 6•6

Sample answers:

1. 4; kite; *XENA* **2.** 6; hexagon; *JORDAN*

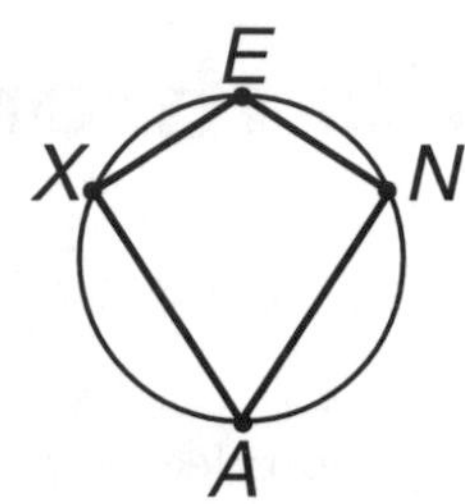

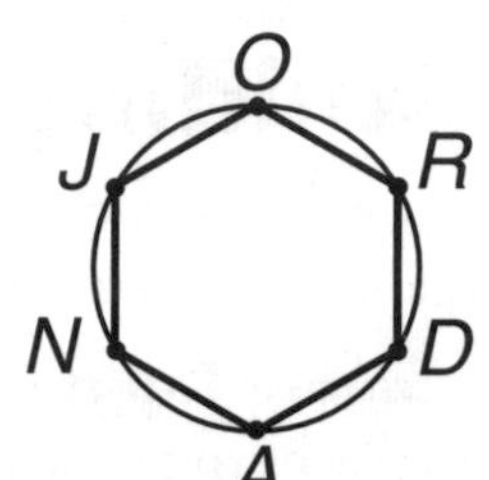

Home Link 6•8

1. *A* **2.** *D* **3.** *E*

4. *C* or *D* **5.** *A* or *B*

Home Link 6•9

1. a. triangle **b.** 2 sides **c.** 2 angles **d.** no

2. a. square **b.** yes **c.**

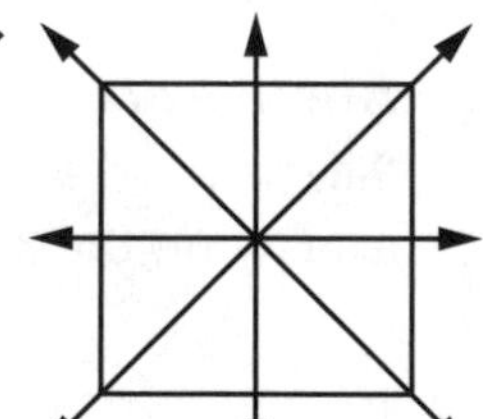

Home Link 6•11

1. (from left to right) prism; sphere; cylinder; cone; pyramid

4. 379 **5.** 25

Home Link 6•12

1. pentagonal prism **2.** pentagon

3. rectangle **4.** 15 edges

5. 10 vertices

Copyright © Wright Group/McGraw-Hill

Name Date Time

Line Segments, Rays, and Lines

Family Note Help your child match each name below with the correct drawing of a line, ray, or line segment. Then observe as your child uses a straightedge to draw and label figures. Pages 100 and 101 in the *Student Reference Book* discuss these figures.

Please return this Home Link to school tomorrow.

SRB 100 101

This line segment can be named $\overline{AB}$ or $\overline{BA}$.

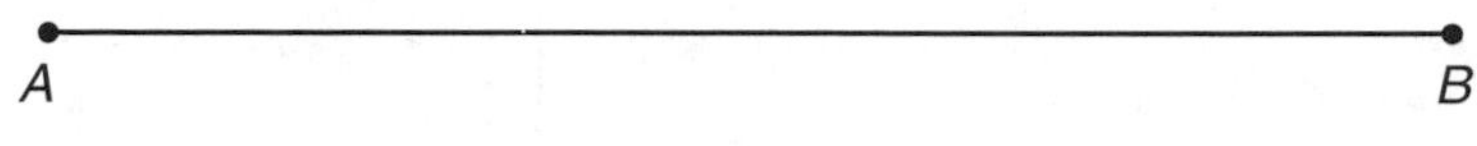

Each of these rays can be named $\overrightarrow{YZ}$.

This line can be named $\overleftrightarrow{AB}$, $\overleftrightarrow{BA}$, $\overleftrightarrow{AC}$, $\overleftrightarrow{CA}$, $\overleftrightarrow{BC}$, or $\overleftrightarrow{CB}$.

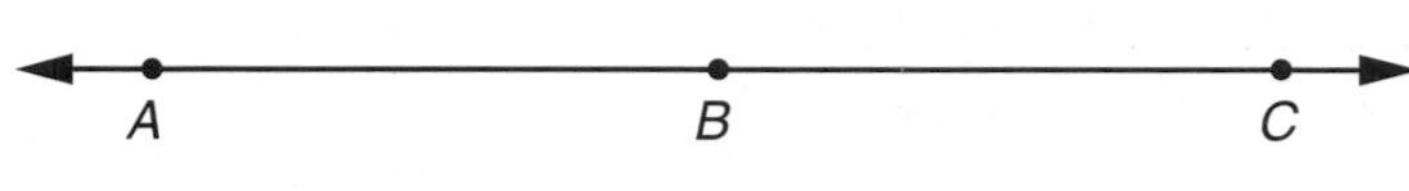

1. Match each drawing below with one of the names.

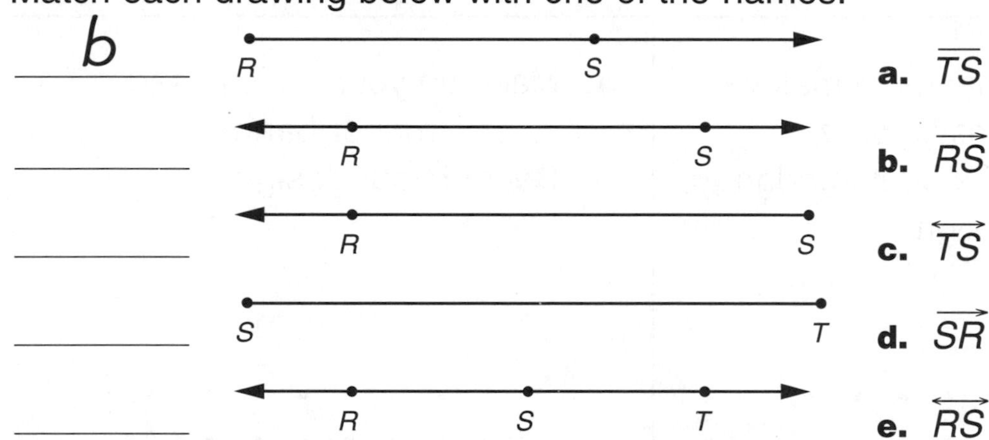

a. $\overline{TS}$

b. $\overrightarrow{RS}$

c. $\overleftrightarrow{TS}$

d. $\overrightarrow{SR}$

e. $\overleftrightarrow{RS}$

Follow the directions carefully. Use a straightedge.

2. Mark points *B* and *C*.
Draw a line segment, $\overline{BC}$.

3. Draw a ray, $\overrightarrow{TO}$.

Practice

Write these problems on the back of this page. Solve.

4. 479 + 89 = ______

5. 278 + 68 = ______

Copyright © Wright Group/McGraw-Hill

Geoboard Designs

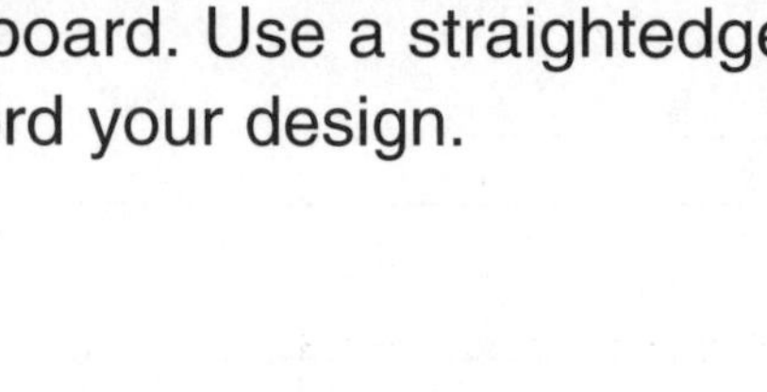

1. Use 3 rubber bands to make a shape or a design on a geoboard. Use a straightedge to record your design.

2. Use 6 rubber bands to make a shape or a design on a geoboard. Use a straightedge to record your design.

3. Use 8 rubber bands to make a shape or a design on a geoboard. Use a straightedge to record your design.

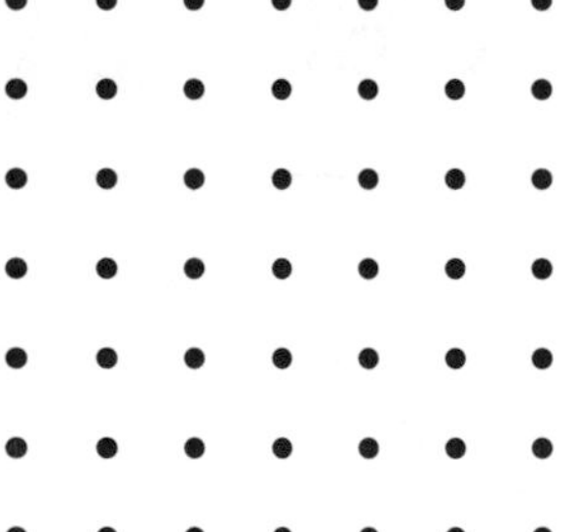

4. Make up your own. I used ______ rubber bands. Record your design.

Copyright © Wright Group/McGraw-Hill

Name Date Time

Diagonals of Polygons

1. Use the information from the polygons on *Math Journal 1,* page 128 to fill in the first three columns. Talk about the patterns you see with a partner.

number of points	3	4	5	6	7	8
number of line segments						

2. Can you guess the number of line segments in a 6-sided figure?
_____ line segments

3. Check your guess. Label 6 points. Draw line segments between each pair of points. How many line segments did you draw? Fill in the table.

4. Try it with 7 points. Try it with 8 points.

Copyright © Wright Group/McGraw-Hill

Name Date Time

Pattern-Block Template Shapes

Use your Pattern-Block Template to trace the shapes that have exactly 4 sides and 4 corners. Write their names. Describe your shapes to a partner.

________________	________________
________________	________________

Copyright © Wright Group/McGraw-Hill

Name Date Time

More Line Segments, Rays, and Lines

Family Note Refer to the following notations to help your child draw and label line segments, rays, and lines.

line segment *AB*	$\overline{AB}$	A B (segment)
ray *BA*	$\overrightarrow{BA}$	A B (ray)
line *AB*	$\overleftrightarrow{AB}$	A B (line)

Please return this Home Link to school tomorrow.

Use a straightedge and a sharp pencil to draw the following. Be sure to mark points and label the line segments, rays, and lines.

1. Draw line segment $\overline{YZ}$, that is parallel to $\overline{AB}$.

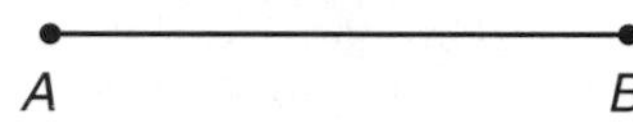

2. Draw a ray, $\overrightarrow{CD}$, that intersects $\overleftrightarrow{EF}$.

3. Draw two parallel rays, $\overrightarrow{IS}$ and $\overrightarrow{NO}$.

4. Draw two intersecting lines, $\overleftrightarrow{MY}$ and $\overleftrightarrow{AN}$.

5. Draw a line segment $\overline{PO}$ intersecting ray $\overrightarrow{LA}$.

6. Draw line $\overleftrightarrow{PU}$, parallel to ray $\overrightarrow{RA}$.

Copyright © Wright Group/McGraw-Hill

Name Date Time

LESSON 6•2

Parallel Possibilities

Each problem set tells you how many line segments to use and how many points of intersection to make. Use chenille sticks to figure out how to solve the problems. Record your solutions in the boxes provided.

Example:

2 Line Segments

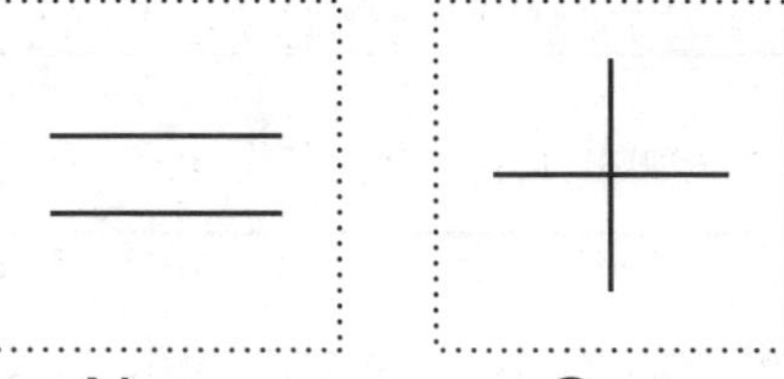

None One

3 Line Segments

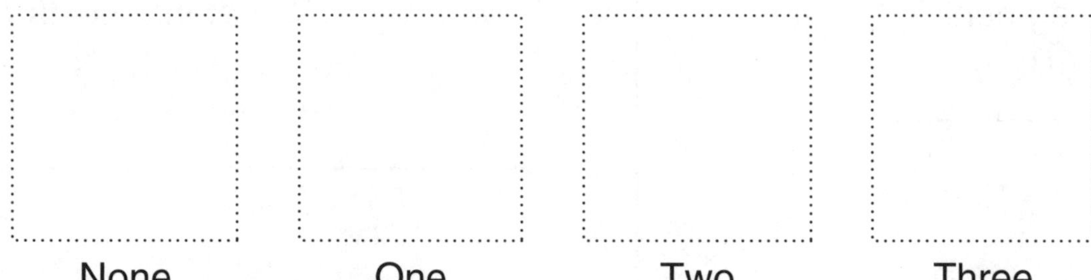

None One Two Three

Try This

4 Line Segments (*Hint:* One of these is not possible!)

None One Two Three

Four Five Six Seven

Copyright © Wright Group/McGraw-Hill

Name Date Time

Right Angles

Family Note Our class has been studying intersecting lines including lines that intersect at right angles. Help your child look for objects that have square corners or right angles—tables, pictures, the kitchen counter, a book, and so on.

Please return this Home Link to school tomorrow.

Find 4 things at home that have right angles (square corners).

Below, describe or draw a picture of each of these things. Bring your descriptions or your pictures to school to add to your Geometry Hunt.

Copyright © Wright Group/McGraw-Hill

Name Date Time

HOME LINK 6•4

Triangles

Family Note Your child has been learning about the properties of triangles. Watch as your child completes the page.

For each problem, use a straightedge to connect the three points with three line segments. Show someone at home that the triangles match their descriptions. To measure triangles 1–3, cut out and use the ruler at the right. To find the right angle in triangle 4, use the square corner of a piece of paper.

1. equilateral triangle

All sides and angles are equal.

A • B • C •

2. isosceles triangle

Two sides are equal.

D • F • E •

3. scalene triangle

No sides are equal.

G • I • H •

4. right triangle

The triangle has a right angle ($\frac{1}{4}$ turn).

K • J • L •

Copyright © Wright Group/McGraw-Hill

Practice

Solve the following problems on the back of this page.

5. 584 − 93 = ______ **6.** 823 − 534 = ______ **7.** ______ = 234 − 225

Name Date Time

Counting Triangles

Look at the large triangle below.

How many small triangles make up the large triangle? _____

How many triangles can you find all together? _____
(*Hint:* Look for different-size triangles that are made from smaller triangles.)

You might want to trace every triangle you find with a different color. (You don't have to trace the small ones or the largest one.) You can keep count by seeing how many colors you use.

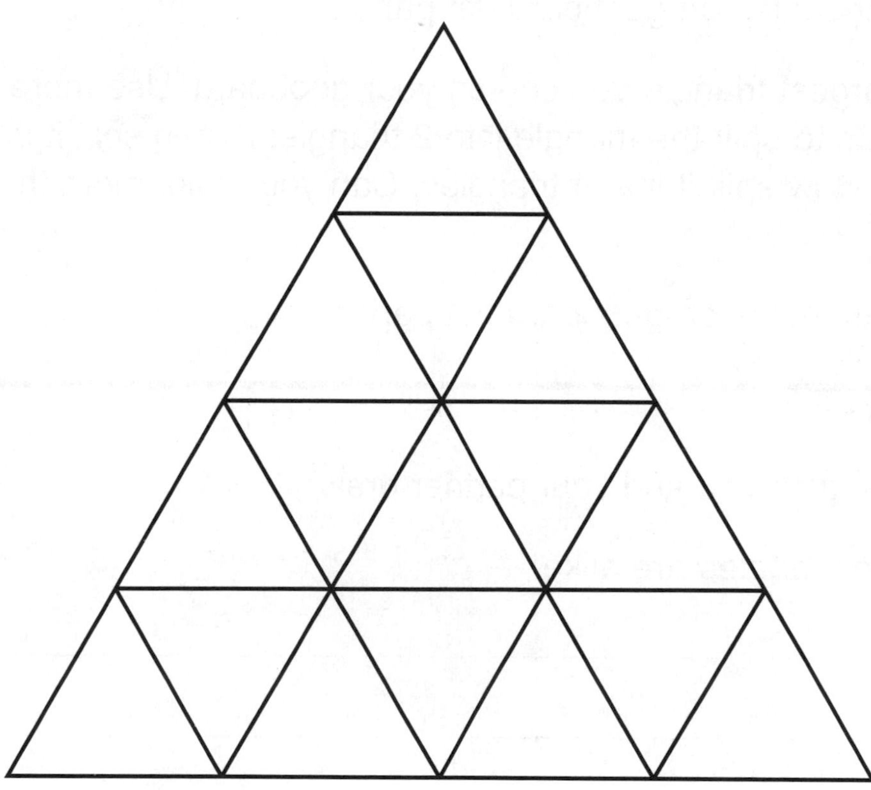

Copyright © Wright Group/McGraw-Hill

Name Date Time

Geoboard Triangles

Work with a partner or a small group.

Materials ☐ geoboard

☐ rubber bands

☐ geoboard dot paper (*Math Masters,* p. 429)

Directions

1. How many different-looking triangles can you make on your geoboard? Each partner or person in your group should try to find out.
2. Draw your triangles on geoboard dot paper.
3. Make the largest triangle you can on your geoboard. Use more rubber bands to split the triangle into 2 triangles. Then split it into 3 triangles. Now split it into 4 triangles. Can you make more than 4 triangles? Try.
4. Draw your triangles on geoboard dot paper.

Follow-Up

Look at the triangles you and your partner drew.

5. List how the triangles are alike.

____

____

____

6. List how the triangles are different.

____

____

____

Copyright © Wright Group/McGraw-Hill

Name Date Time

Quadrangles

Family Note Help your child complete the statements. A *right angle* is a square corner. *Parallel sides* are the same distance apart and will never meet. *Opposite sides* are directly across from each other. *Adjacent sides* meet at a vertex (corner).

Please return this Home Link to school tomorrow.

SRB 108 109

Fill in the blanks using the following terms: **equal** **parallel** **right angles**

1. Rectangle (Squares are special rectangles.)

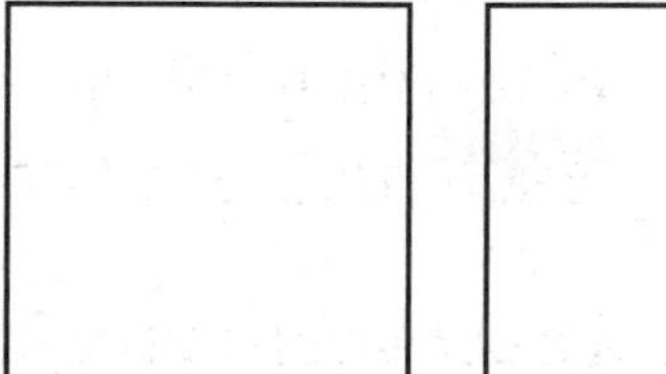

All angles are ________________.

Pairs of opposite sides are ________________ in length and ________________ to each other.

2. Rhombus (Squares are also rhombuses.)

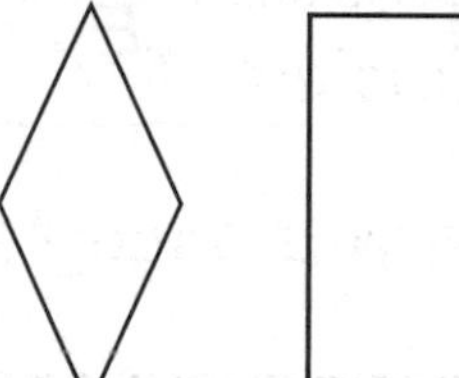

All sides are ________________ in length.

Opposite sides are ________________ to each other.

3. Parallelogram (Squares and rhombuses are also parallelograms.)

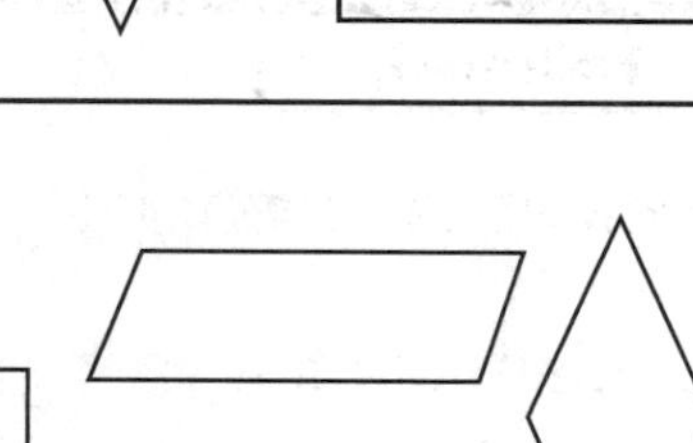

Opposite sides are ________________ in length.

Opposite sides are ________________ to each other.

4. Kite

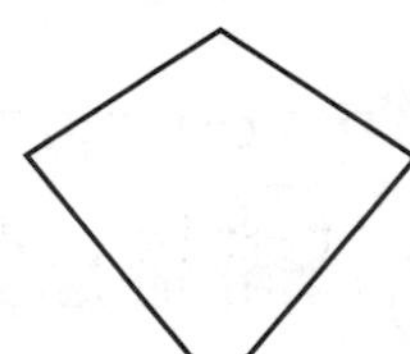

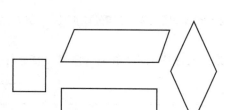

Opposite sides are not ________________ in length.

Practice

Solve.

5. $6 \times 3 =$ ____ **6.** ____ $= 3 \times 4$ **7.** $6 \times 6 =$ ____

Copyright © Wright Group/McGraw-Hill

Name Date Time

HOME LINK 6•6

Naming Polygons

Family Note Our class has been naming polygons. Help your child think of names with different numbers of letters, so that he or she can draw and name several different polygons.

Please return this Home Link to school tomorrow.

SRB 102 103

Think of names that have *different* letters. Use the letters to name points on each circle. Then use a pencil and a straightedge to connect the points to make a polygon. Count the number of sides. Name the polygon.

Example:

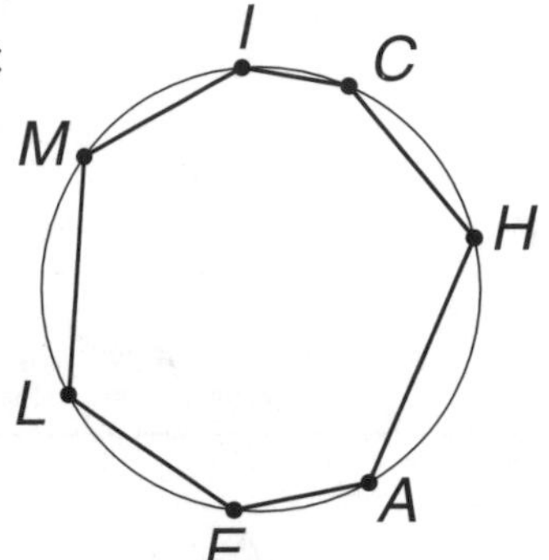

This polygon has 7 sides.

This polygon is a heptagon.

Its name is MICHAEL.

1.

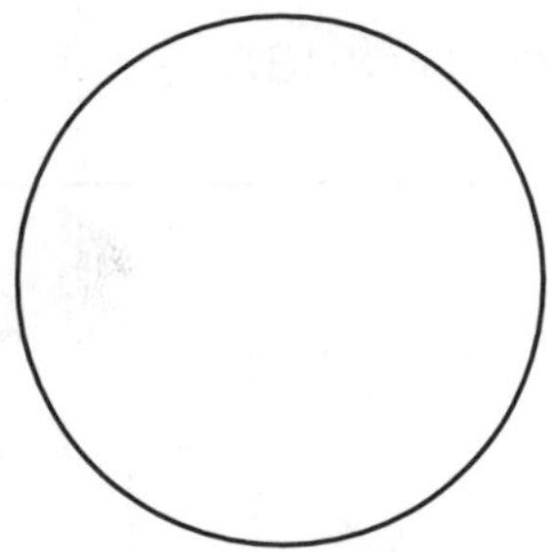

This polygon has ______________ sides.

This polygon is a ______________.

Its name is ______________.

2.

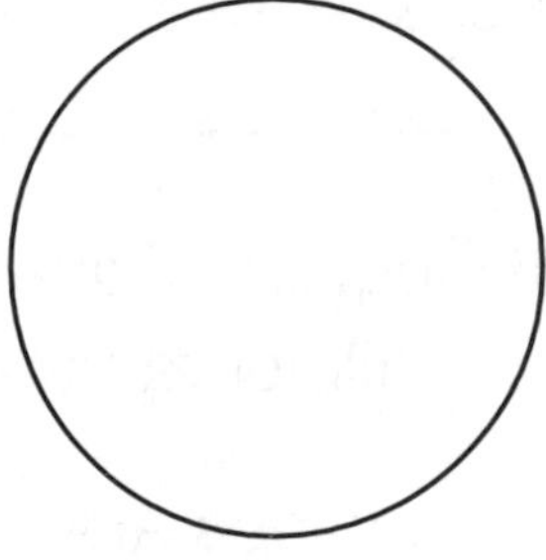

This polygon has ______________ sides.

This polygon is a ______________.

Its name is ______________.

3. Draw more circles and polygons on the back of this paper. Why do you think each letter in a polygon's name can be used only once?

____

____

Copyright © Wright Group/McGraw-Hill

Name Date Time

Sorting Geometry Vocabulary

Draw a picture for the word on each card. Cut out the cards and sort them into groups.

trapezoid	triangle	vertex (vertices)	side
angle	kite	rhombus	quadrangle
parallel sides	square	rectangle	adjacent sides
right triangle	equilateral triangle	regular polygon	polygons

Copyright © Wright Group/McGraw-Hill

Name Date Time

Geoboard Polygons

Work in a small group.

Materials ☐ geoboard ☐ rubber bands ☐ ruler

Directions Each person uses a geoboard to make the following polygons. Copy each polygon below.

1. Make a triangle in which each side touches exactly 3 pins.

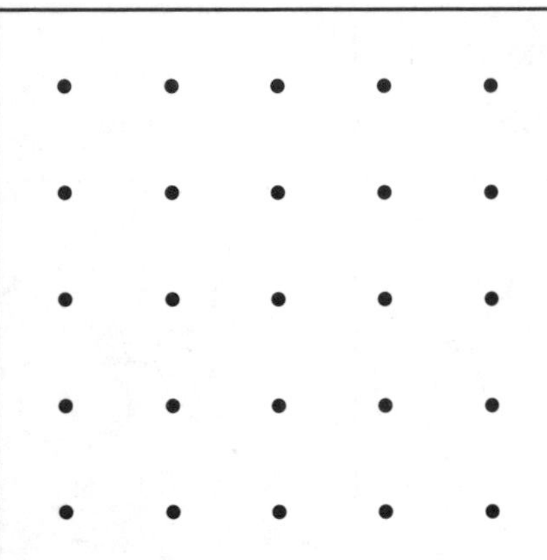

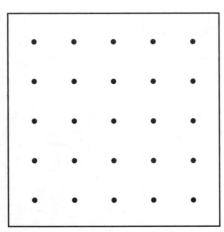

2. Make a quadrangle in which each side touches exactly 4 pins.

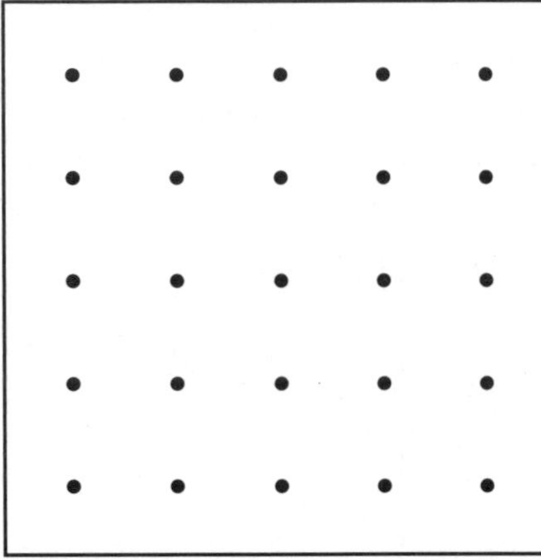

3. Make a pentagon that touches at least 5 pins.

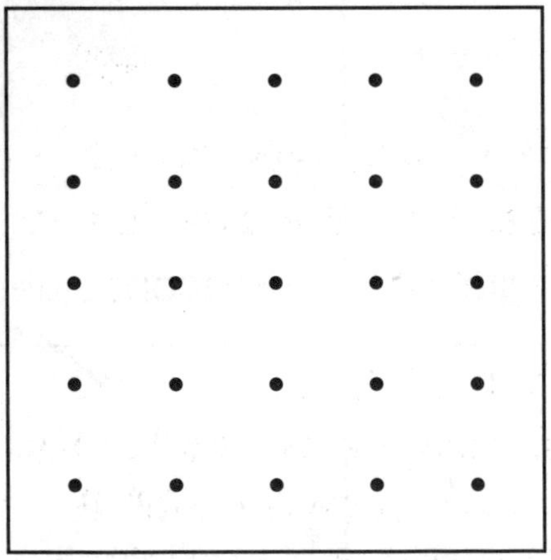

4. Make a hexagon whose sides touch exactly 6 pins in all.

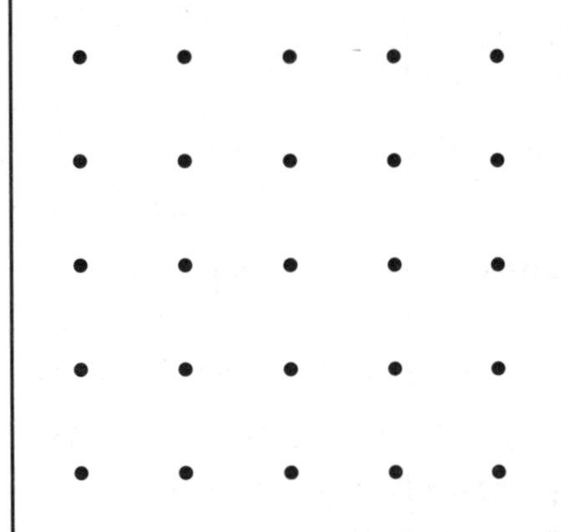

5. Compare your polygons with those of others in your group. Talk about how the polygons are alike and different. Use your ruler to check which of the polygons have sides that are equal in length.

Copyright © Wright Group/McGraw-Hill

Name Date Time

Turns

Family Note If your child needs help with the following problems, consider putting up signs in a room in your home to indicate the directions *north, south, east,* and *west.* Do the turns with your child.

Please return this Home Link to school tomorrow.

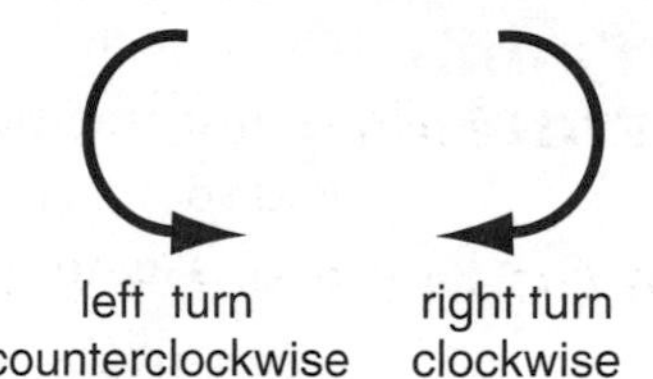

Make the turns described below. Show which way you face after each turn.

- Draw a dot on the circle.
- Label the dot with a letter.

Example: Face north.

Do a $\frac{1}{2}$ turn counterclockwise.

On the circle, mark the direction you are facing with the letter *A*.

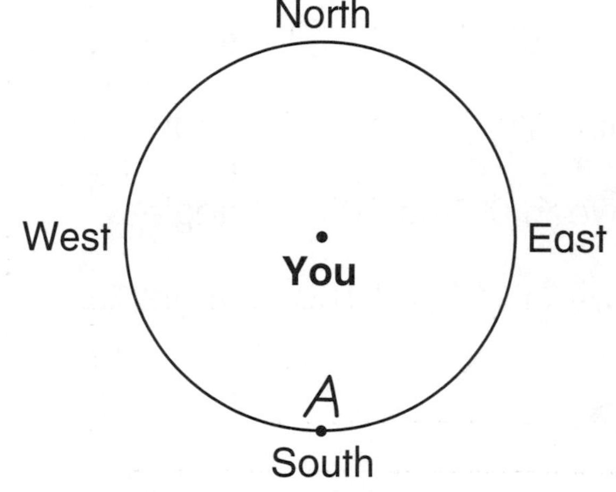

1. Face north. Do a $\frac{1}{4}$ turn clockwise. Mark the direction you are facing with the letter *B*.
2. Face north. Do a $\frac{3}{4}$ turn clockwise. Mark the direction you are facing with the letter *C*.
3. Face east. Do a $\frac{1}{4}$ turn counterclockwise. Mark the direction you are facing with the letter *D*.
4. Face west. Make less than a $\frac{1}{4}$ turn clockwise. Mark the direction you are facing with the letter *E*.
5. Face north. Make a clockwise turn that is more than a $\frac{1}{2}$ turn, but less than a $\frac{3}{4}$ turn. Mark the direction you are facing with the letter *F*.
6. Face north. Make a counterclockwise turn that is less than a $\frac{1}{2}$ turn, but more than a $\frac{1}{4}$ turn. Mark the direction you are facing with the letter *G*.

Copyright © Wright Group/McGraw-Hill

Name Date Time

HOME LINK 6•8

Degree Measures

Family Note Our class has been learning about turns, angles, and angle measures. A full turn can be represented by an angle of 360°, a $\frac{1}{2}$ turn by an angle of 180°, a $\frac{1}{4}$ turn by an angle of 90°, and so on. Help your child match the measures below with the angles pictured. (It is not necessary to measure the angles with a protractor.)

Please return this Home Link to school tomorrow.

Tell which angle has the given measure.

1. about 180° angle ______

2. about 90° angle ______

3. about 270° angle ______

4. between 0° and 90° angle ______

5. between 90° and 180° angle ______

Rotation	Degrees
$\frac{1}{4}$ turn	90°
$\frac{1}{2}$ turn	180°
$\frac{3}{4}$ turn	270°
full turn	360°

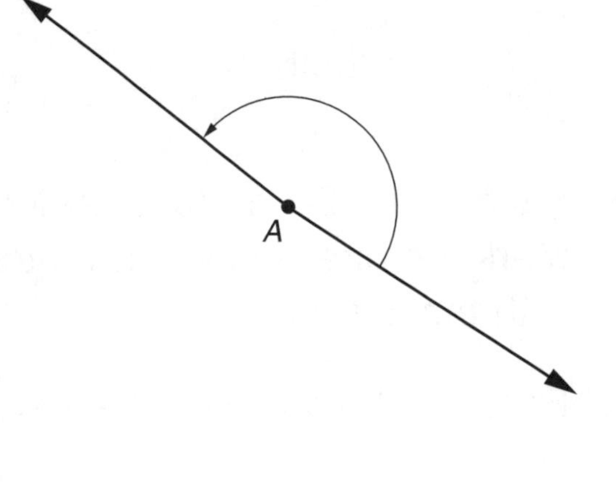

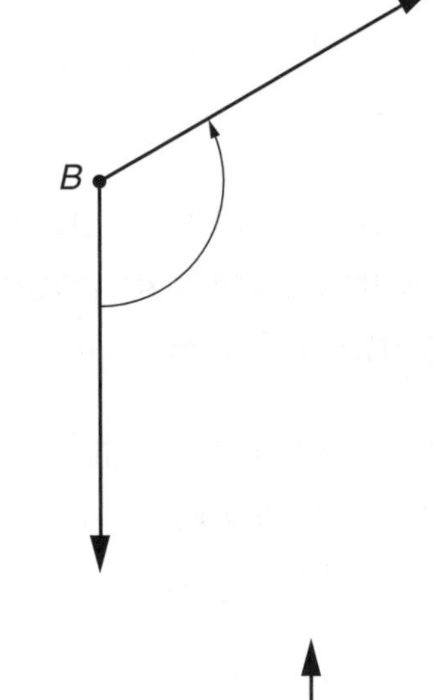

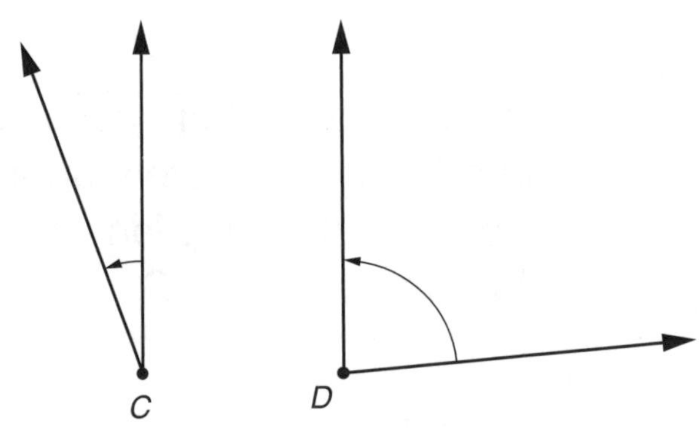

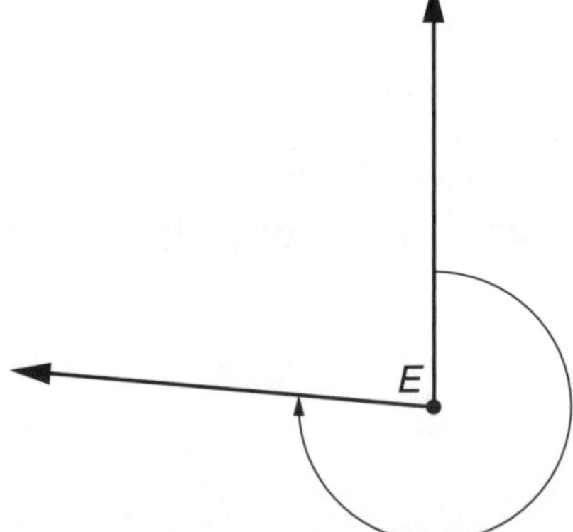

Copyright © Wright Group/McGraw-Hill

Name _______________ Date _______________ Time _______________

LESSON 6•8

Clock Angles

1. How many *minutes* does the minute hand take to move ...

from 10:00 to 11:00? _______________

from 4:00 to 4:30? _______________

from 6:00 to 6:15? _______________

from 9:00 to 9:05? _______________

2. Through how many *degrees* does the minute hand move ...

from 10:00 to 11:00? _______________

from 4:00 to 4:30? _______________

from 6:00 to 6:15? _______________

from 9:00 to 9:05? _______________

3. Through how many *degrees* does the hour hand move ...

in 3 hours? _______________

in 2 hours? _______________

in 1 hour? _______________

Make up your own clock-angle problems.

4. Through how many *degrees* does the _______________ hand move ...

in _______________? _______________

in _______________? _______________

Copyright © Wright Group/McGraw-Hill

Name Date Time

LESSON 6•8

Modeling Angles on a Clock Face

Connect 2 straws with a twist-tie.

- Model the movement of the minute hand as suggested in each problem on *Math Masters,* page 183.
- Refer to your angle measurer to help you figure out the measurements in Problems 2 and 3.

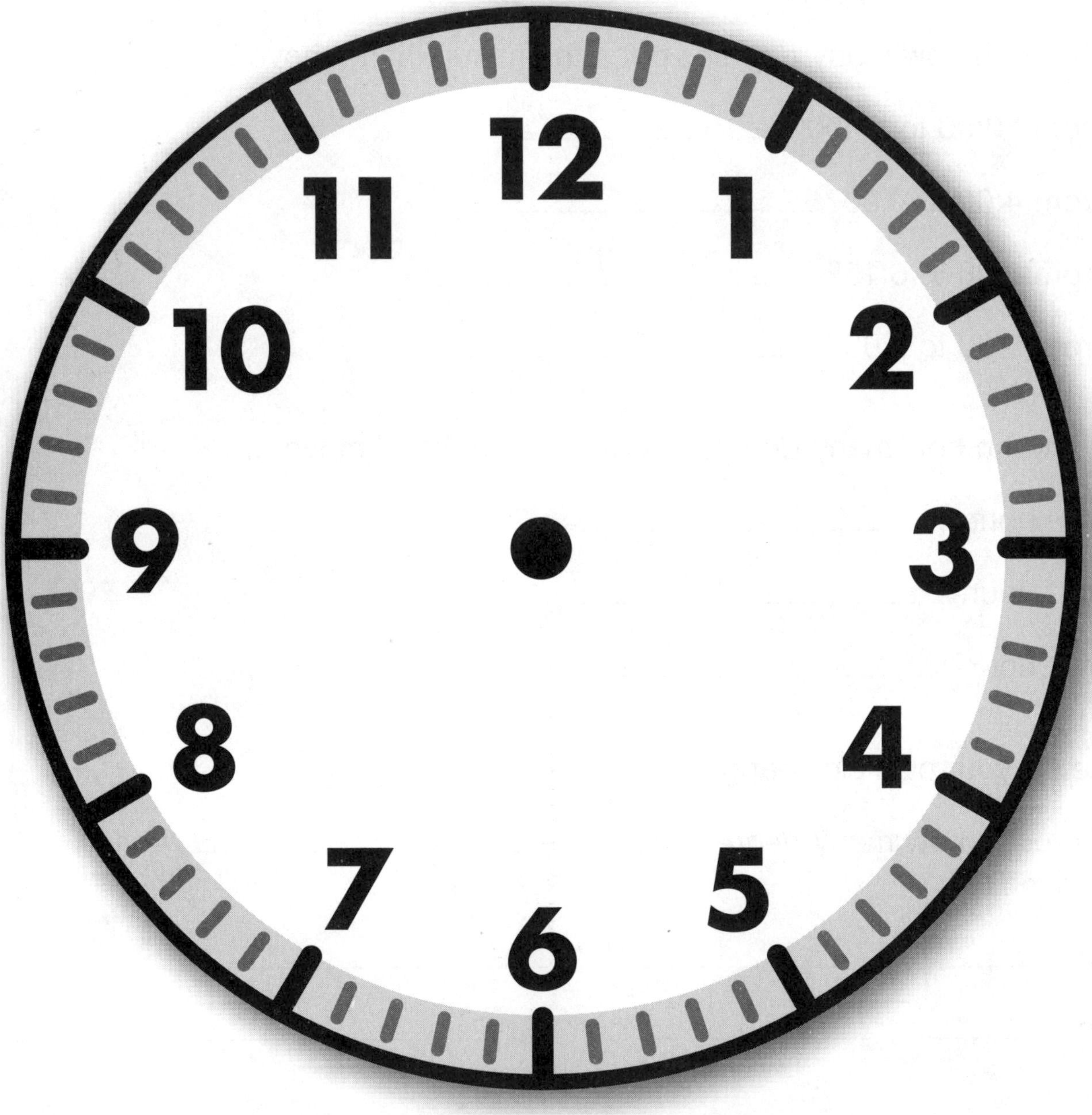

12 1 2 3 4 5 6 7 8 9 10 11

Copyright © Wright Group/McGraw-Hill

Mirror Image

B

A

D

C

G

E

F

I

H

J

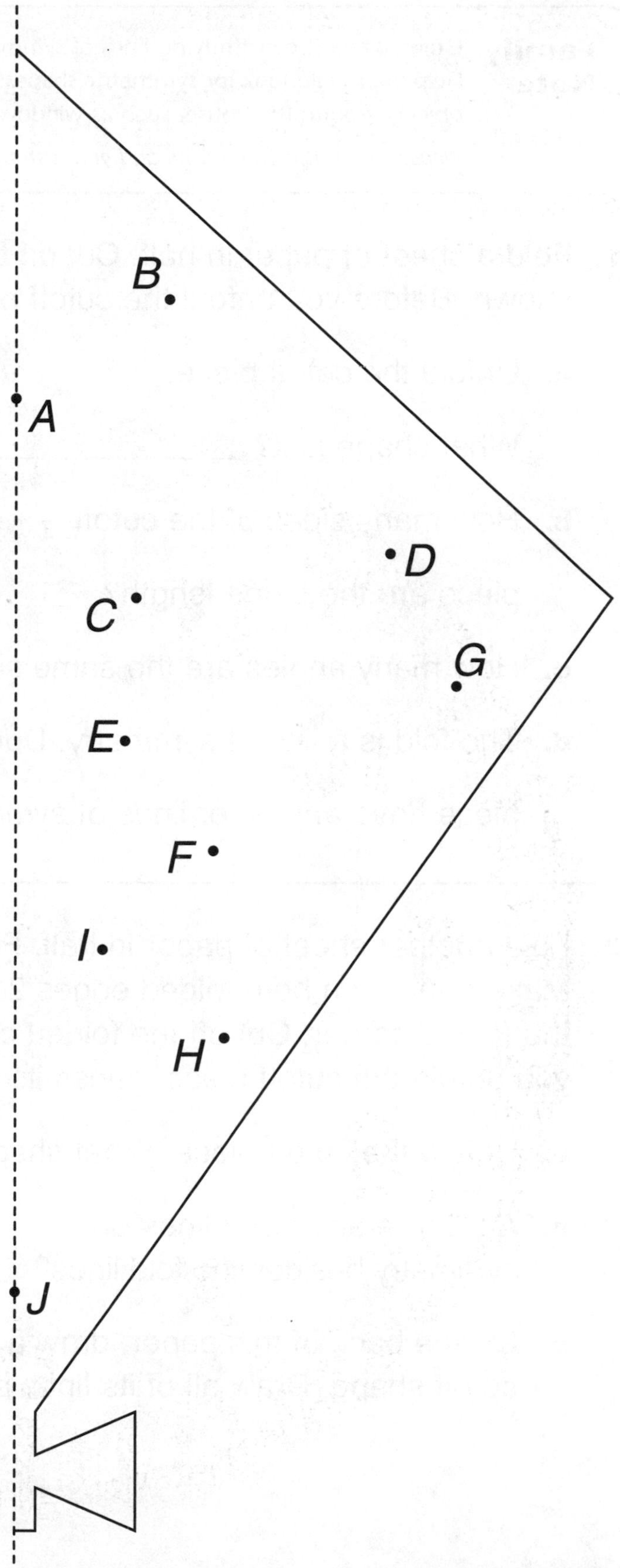

Copyright © Wright Group/McGraw-Hill

Name Date Time

Symmetric Shapes

Family Note Our class has been studying lines of symmetry—lines that divide figures into mirror images. Help your child look for symmetric shapes in books, newspapers, and magazines, and in objects around the house, such as windows, pieces of furniture, dishes, and so on.

Please return this Home Link and your cutouts to school tomorrow.

SRB 122 123

1. Fold a sheet of paper in half. Cut off the folded corner, as shown. Before you unfold the cutoff piece, guess its shape.

a. Unfold the cutoff piece.

What shape is it? _______________

b. How many sides of the cutoff piece are the same length? _______________

c. How many angles are the same size? _______________

d. The fold is a line of symmetry. Does the cutoff piece have any other lines of symmetry? _______________

---

2. Fold another sheet of paper in half. Fold it in half again. Make a mark on both folded edges 2 inches from the folded corner. Cut off the folded corner. Before you unfold the cutoff piece, guess its shape.

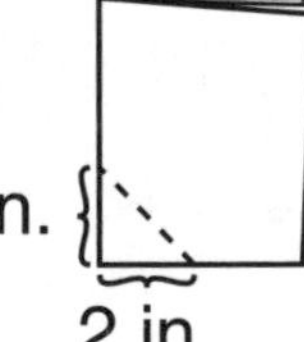

a. Unfold the cutoff piece. What shape is it? _______________

b. Are there any other lines of symmetry besides the fold lines? _______________

c. On the back of this paper, draw a picture of the cutoff shape. Draw all of its lines of symmetry.

Copyright © Wright Group/McGraw-Hill

Name Date Time

LESSON 6·9

Pattern-Block Symmetry Riddles

Use your Pattern-Block Template to record your solution to each problem on another piece of paper. Check that each solution works for all the clues in the problem.

1. Build a symmetrical shape using these clues:

- ◆ Use exactly 2 red trapezoids and put them together to make a hexagon.
- ◆ Use exactly 6 green triangles around the outside of the hexagon.
- ◆ Use exactly 8 blocks.

2. Build a symmetrical shape using these clues:

- ◆ Use exactly 2 red trapezoids.
- ◆ Use exactly 5 tan rhombuses.
- ◆ Use exactly 7 blocks.

3. Build a symmetrical shape using these clues:

- ◆ Build a large triangle.
- ◆ Use a yellow hexagon in the center at the bottom of the large triangle.
- ◆ Use at least 3 different colors of blocks.

Try This

4. Build a shape that has more than 1 line of symmetry using these clues:

- ◆ Use exactly 2 red trapezoids.
- ◆ Do not use yellow hexagons.
- ◆ The longer sides of the red trapezoids touch and line up together.
- ◆ Use a green triangle at the top and at the bottom of the shape.
- ◆ Use exactly 10 blocks.

Copyright © Wright Group/McGraw-Hill

Name Date Time

LESSON 6•10 Congruent Shapes

Exploration A:

You need:

- ☐ *Math Masters,* p. 189
- ☐ 1 trapezoid and 2 triangle pattern blocks
- ☐ Scissors and tape
- ☐ Pattern-Block Template
- ☐ Construction paper
- ☐ Unlined paper

1. Carefully cut out the shapes on *Math Masters,* page 189.
2. Match the congruent shapes to make 3 sets of shapes. They may be turned or flipped.
3. Tape the shapes in sets onto a piece of construction paper.
4. Use 1 trapezoid and 2 triangle pattern blocks. Place the blocks onto one of the congruent shapes. Use your template or trace around the blocks to show what you did.
5. Use the same pattern blocks in different arrangements to cover each of the remaining shapes, one at a time. Use your template or trace around the blocks to show what you did each time.

Example:

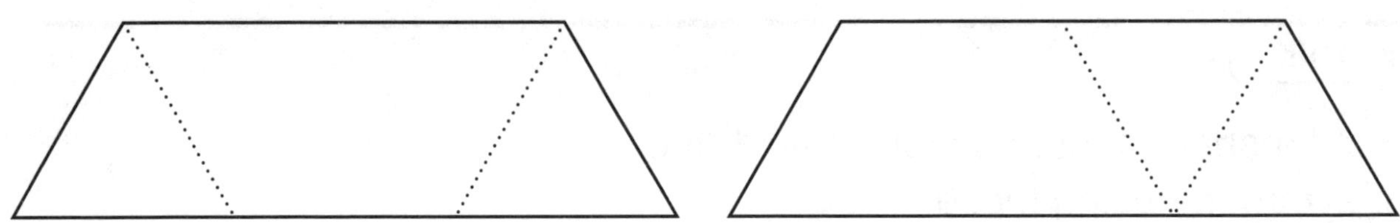

6. For each congruent set, make as many different arrangements with the 3 pattern blocks as you can.
7. Trace the blocks onto blank paper. Cut out the shapes and tape them in the set where they belong on your construction paper.

Copyright © Wright Group/McGraw-Hill

Name Date Time

Congruent Shapes *continued*

Exploration A:

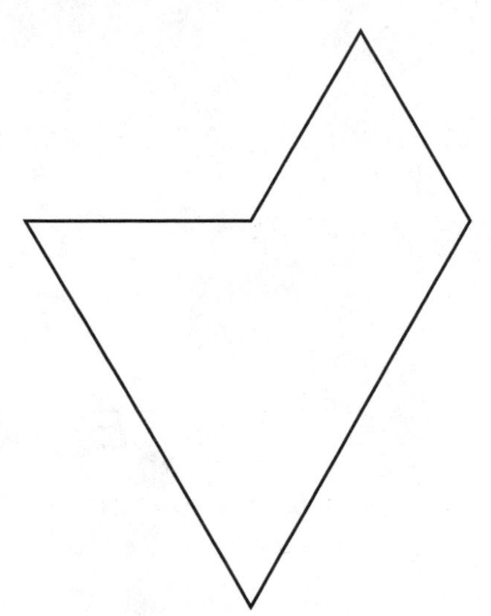

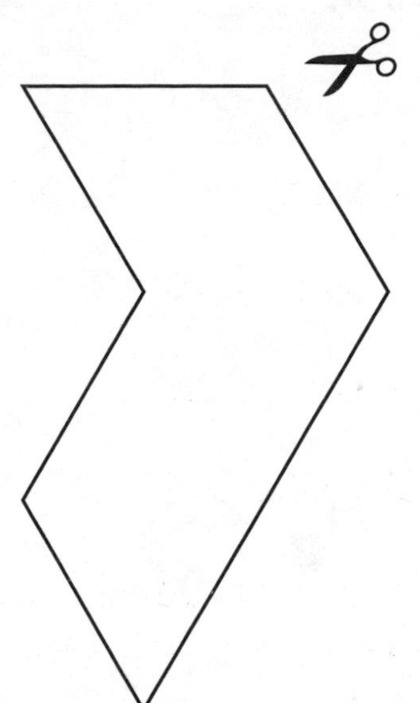

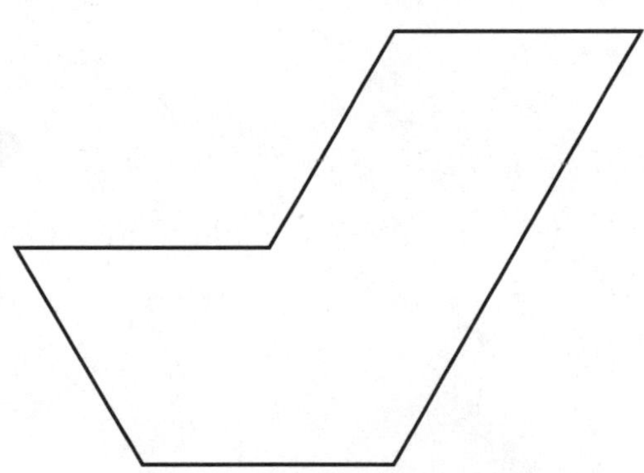

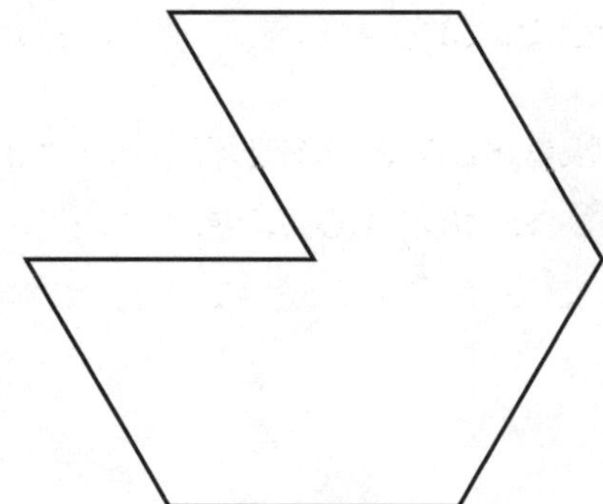

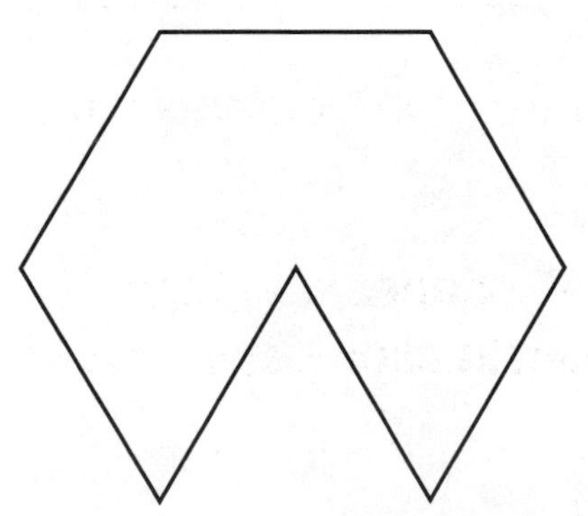

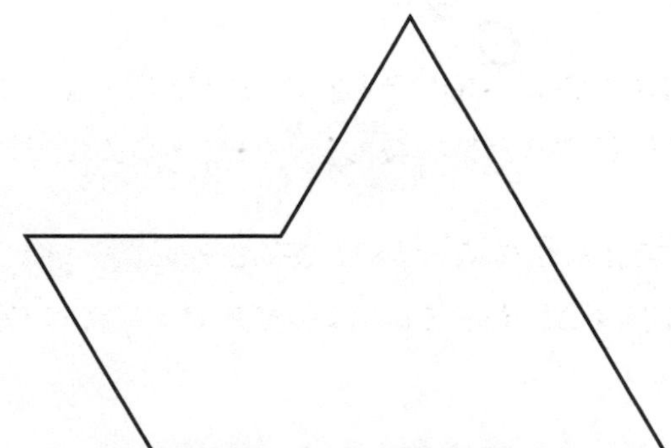

Copyright © Wright Group/McGraw-Hill

Name Date Time

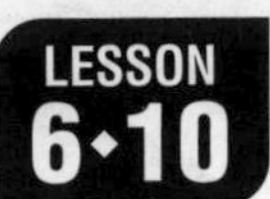

An 8-Point Design

Exploration B:

A

H E

D B

G F

C

Copyright © Wright Group/McGraw-Hill

Name Date Time

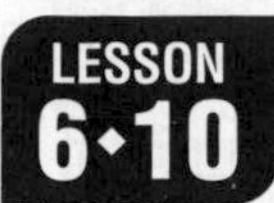

An 8-Point Design *continued*

Exploration B:

Materials ☐ straightedge and crayons or coloring pencils

☐ *Math Masters,* page 190

Directions

1. Look at *Math Masters,* page 190.

   Use your straightedge to draw a line segment from point *A* to each of the other points.

   How many line segments did you draw? ______________

2. Draw a line segment from point *B* to each of the other points. You have already drawn the line segment that connects points *A* and *B.*

3. Draw line segments from points *C* and *D* to each of the other points. Some segments have already been drawn.

4. Count the number of line segments that meet at points *A, B, C,* and *D.* There should be 7 line segments that meet at each of these points.

   Count the number of line segments that meet at points *E, F, G,* and *H.* There should be 4 line segments that meet at each of these points.

5. Draw a line segment from point *E* to each of the other points.

   Some of these segments have already been drawn. Then draw line segments from points *F, G,* and *H* to each of the other points.

6. Count the number of line segments that meet at each of the points *E, F, G,* and *H.*

   There should be 7 line segments that meet at each of these points.

7. Make a design by coloring the pattern you made. Use several different colors.

Copyright © Wright Group/McGraw-Hill

Name Date Time

Congruent Figures

Family Note If your child has difficulty determining the congruent shapes just by looking, encourage her or him to cut out the first shape. Your child can then rotate or flip the shape to find a congruent shape.

Please return this Home Link to school tomorrow.

SRB 120 121

Two figures that are exactly the same size and shape are called **congruent** figures. In each of the following, circle the shape or shapes that are congruent to the first shape. Explain to someone at home why the other shape or shapes are *not* congruent to the first.

1.

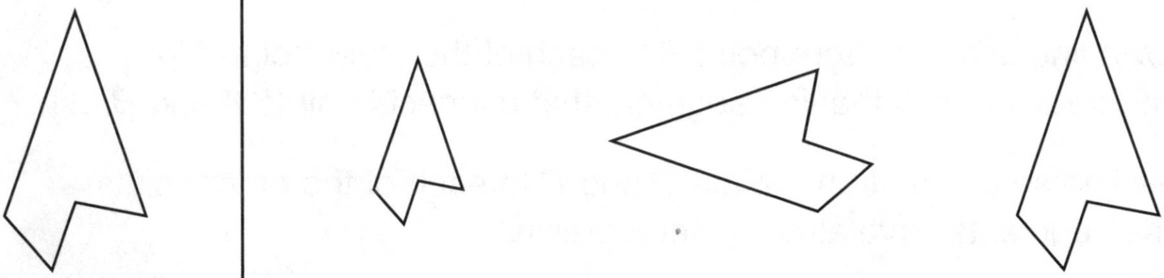

2.

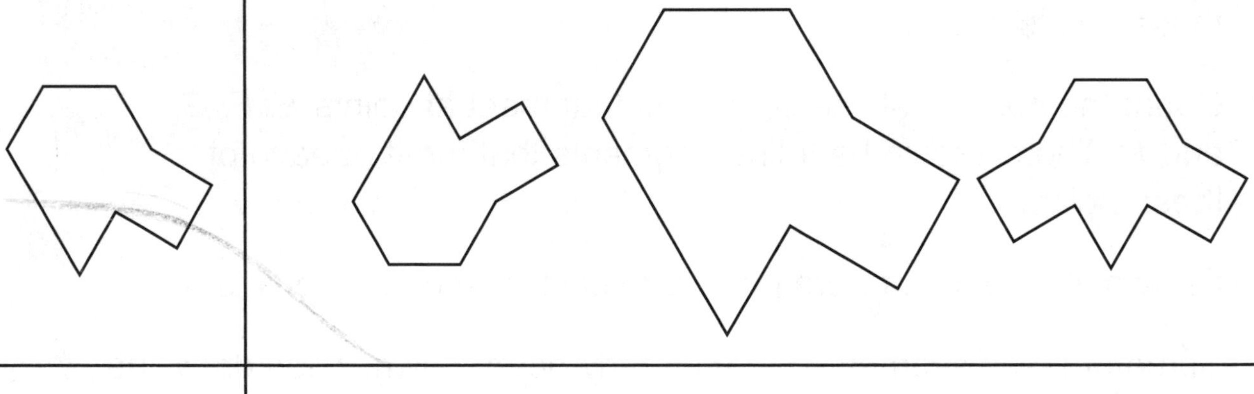

3.

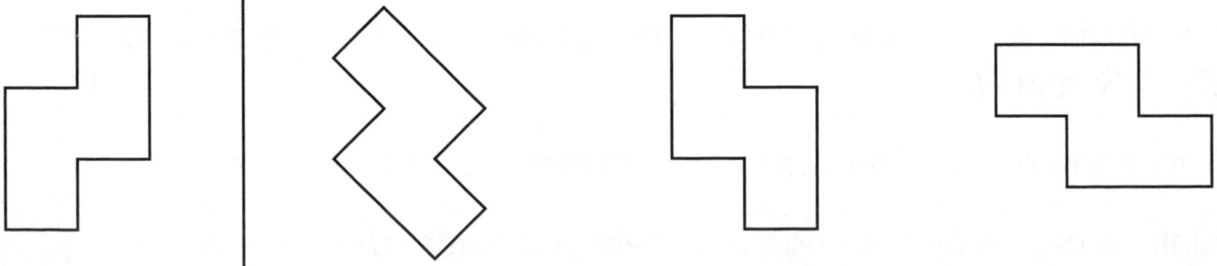

Copyright © Wright Group/McGraw-Hill

Name Date Time

Congruent Figures

Math Message:

Look at the examples of pairs of figures that are **congruent** and those pairs that are **not congruent.** Talk to a partner about the meaning of *congruent*.

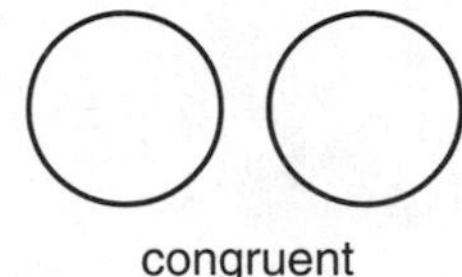

congruent

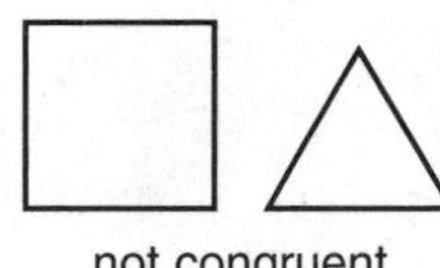

not congruent

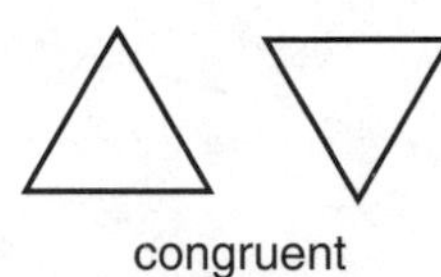

congruent

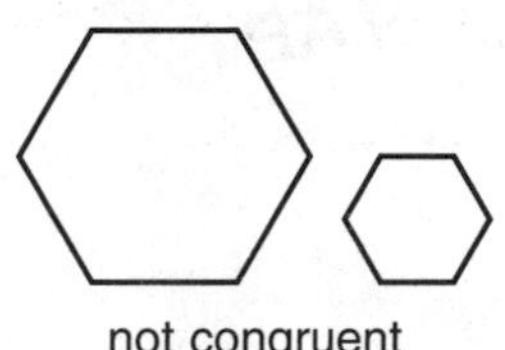

not congruent

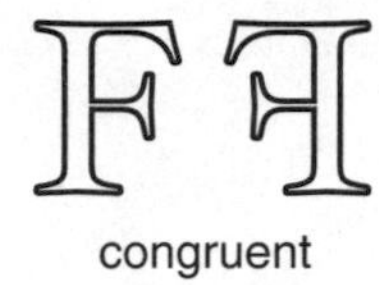

congruent

not congruent

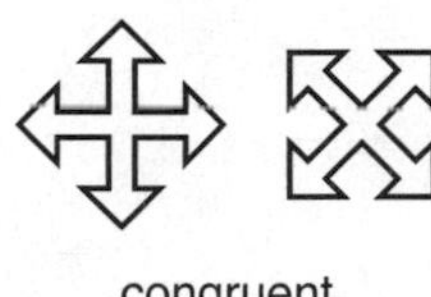

congruent

not congruent

Draw a pair of congruent squares.

Copyright © Wright Group/McGraw-Hill

Name Date Time

Constructing a Square Pyramid

Cut on the dashed lines.

Fold on the dotted lines.

Tape or glue each TAB inside or outside the pyramid.

TAB

TAB

TAB

TAB

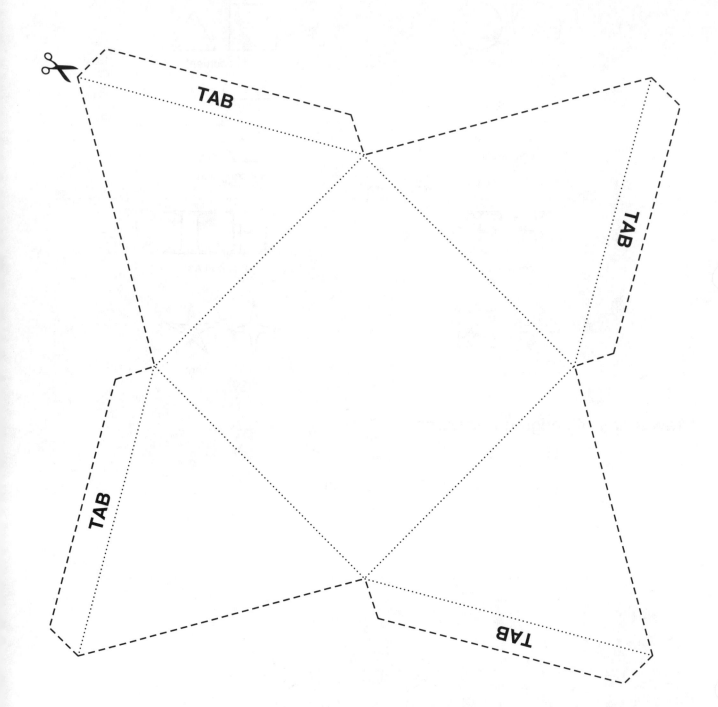

Copyright © Wright Group/McGraw-Hill

Name Date Time

LESSON 6•11

Constructing a Triangular Prism

Cut on the dashed lines.

Fold on the dotted lines.

Tape or glue each TAB inside or outside the prism.

TAB

TAB

TAB

TAB

TAB

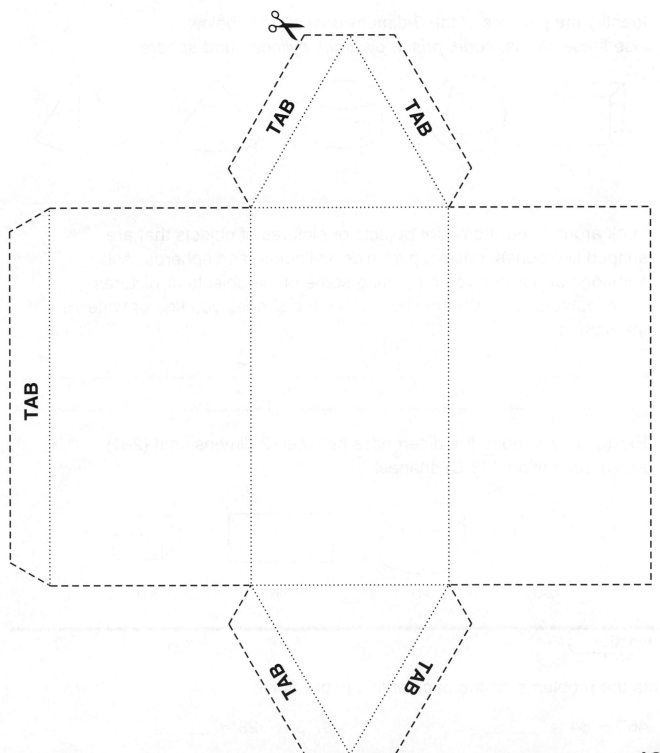

Copyright © Wright Group/McGraw-Hill

Name Date Time

3-Dimensional Shapes

Family Note Have your child identify 3-dimensional shapes. Then help search for 3-D objects (or pictures of objects) around your home for your child to bring to school. Pages 112–119 in the *Student Reference Book* discuss 3-D shapes.

SRB 112–119

Please return this Home Link to school tomorrow.

1. Identify the pictures of the 3-dimensional shapes below. Use these words: *cone, prism, pyramid, cylinder,* and *sphere.*

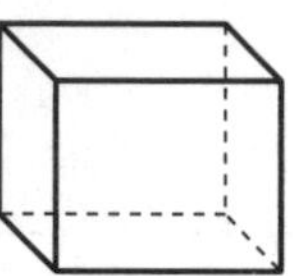  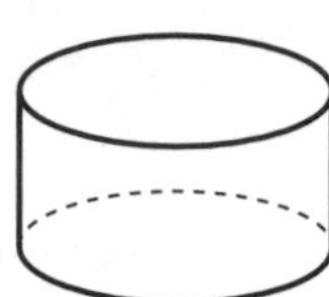 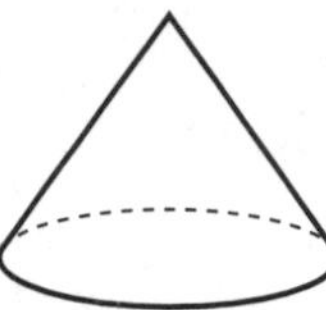 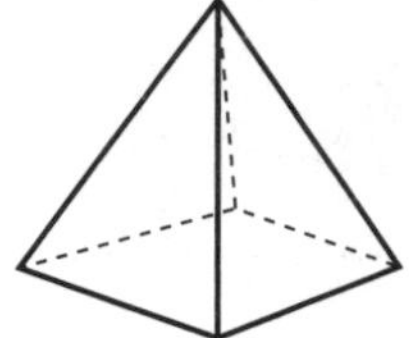

______ ______ ______ ______ ______

2. Look around your home for objects or pictures of objects that are shaped like cones, prisms, pyramids, cylinders, and spheres. Ask someone at home if you may bring some of the objects or pictures to school to share with the class. Draw the shapes you find or write the names.

______

______

3. Explain to someone the differences between 2-dimensional (2-D) and 3-dimensional (3-D) shapes.

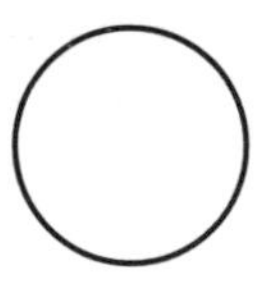

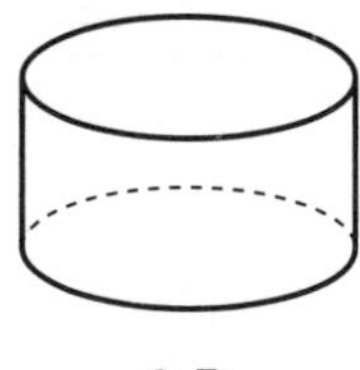
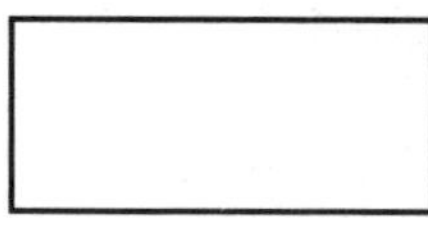
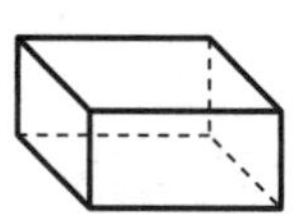

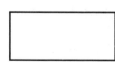

2-D 3-D 2-D 3-D

Copyright © Wright Group/McGraw-Hill

Practice

Write the problems on the back of this page. Solve.

4. 463 − 84 = ______ **5.** 54 − 29 = ______

Name Date Time

LESSON 6•11

Polygons

Use straws and twist-ties to make the following polygons. Draw the polygons. Then record the number of sides, vertices, and angles for each polygon.

1. Make a square.

Number of sides ______

Number of vertices ______

Number of angles ______

---

2. Make a triangle.

Number of sides ______

Number of vertices ______

Number of angles ______

---

3. Make a hexagon.

Number of sides ______

Number of vertices ______

Number of angles ______

---

4. Make a polygon of your choice.

Number of sides ______

Number of vertices ______

Number of angles ______

Copyright © Wright Group/McGraw-Hill

Name Date Time

Faces on a Cube

Ingrid built a large cube from cm cubes. The large cube had 3 small cm cubes along each edge. She painted the 6 faces of the large cube. Then she took it apart so it was broken up into small cm cubes again.

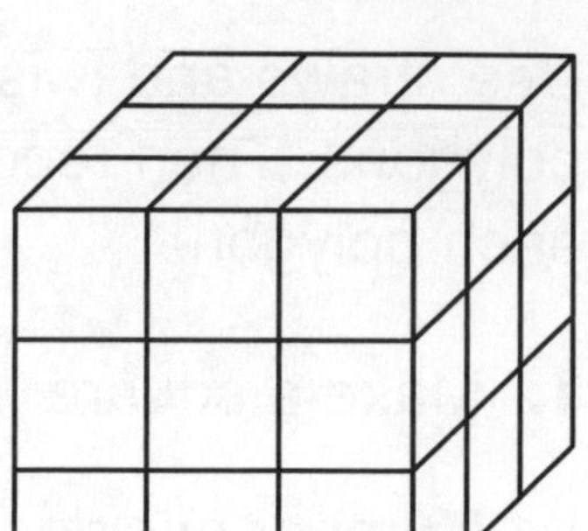

Answer the questions about Ingrid's cubes. Use cm cubes and draw pictures to help.

How many cm cubes had no paint on them? ____________

How many cm cubes had paint on 1 side? ____________

How many cm cubes had paint on 2 sides? ____________

How many cm cubes had paint on 3 sides? ____________

Try This

Build a cube like Ingrid's that has 5 cm cubes on each edge.

How many cm cubes would have no paint on them? ____________

How many cm cubes would have paint on 1 side? ____________

How many cm cubes would have paint on 2 sides? ____________

How many cm cubes would have paint on 3 sides? ____________

Copyright © Wright Group/McGraw-Hill

Name Date Time

HOME LINK 6·12

Making a Solid Shape

Family Note Our class has been exploring the characteristics and parts of various 3-dimensional shapes—especially prisms. The pattern on this page can be used to make one type of prism. Prisms are named for the shapes of their bases.

Please return this Home Link to school tomorrow.

SRB 117

Cut on the dashed lines. Fold on the dotted lines. Tape or paste each TAB inside or outside the shape.

Discuss the following questions with someone at home:

1. What is this 3-D shape called? ______________________

2. What is the shape of the bases? ______________________

3. What is the shape of the other faces? ______________________

4. How many edges does the shape have? ______________________

5. How many vertices does the shape have? ______________________

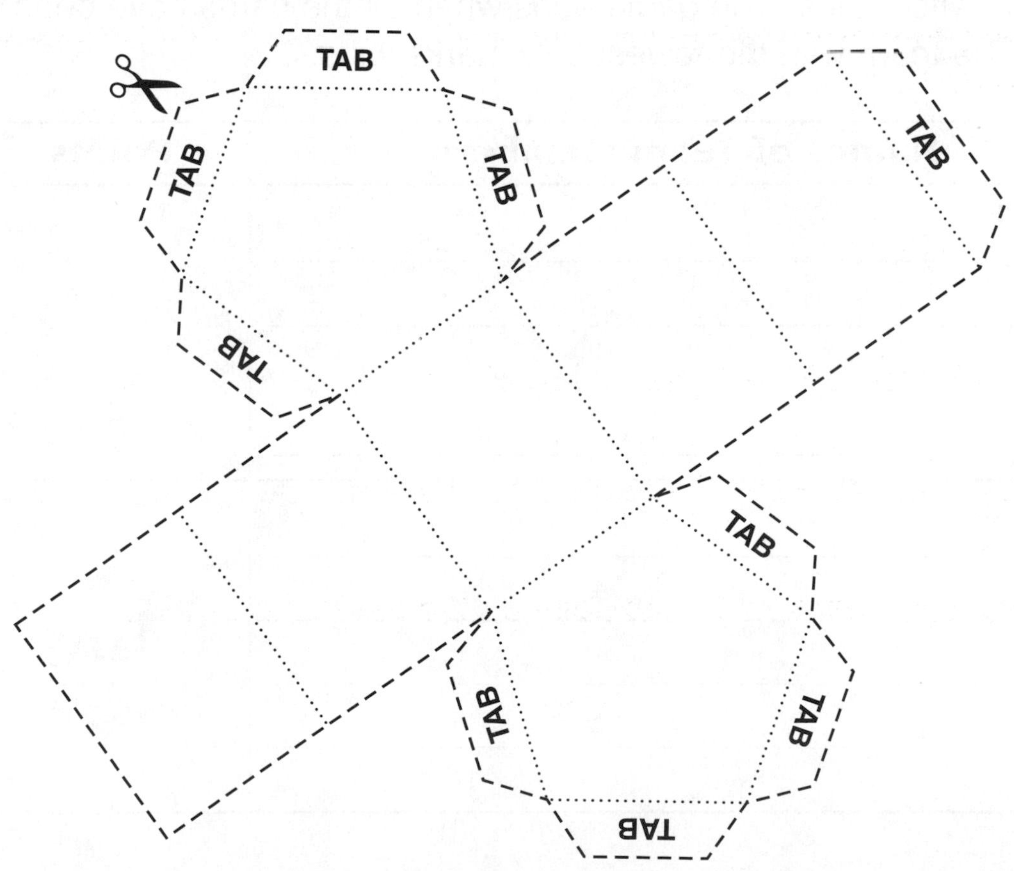

Copyright © Wright Group/McGraw-Hill

Name Date Time

Geometry Riddles

1. Work in teams of 2 to 4.
2. Cut out the Geometry Riddles cards from *Math Masters,* page 201 and place them facedown on the playing surface.
3. The team of readers chooses a card and silently reads all the clues. They write the answer to the riddle on a slate without showing it to the other team, the guessers. Then they read only the **first** clue **aloud** to the guessers. The guessers discuss the clue and guess the shape. If their guess is correct, the turn is over. If it is not correct, the readers read the second clue. Continue until the guessers name the shape on the card. Then switch roles.
4. Readers assign one tally mark for every clue needed. Record the tallies on the chart below.
5. If teams disagree on an answer to a riddle, they may use the *Student Reference Book* section on Geometric Solids, pages 112–119.
6. Teams switch roles. The game ends when all the cards have been used. The team with the fewest tally marks wins.

Names of Team Members	Points
Team 1: ____ ____ ____ ____	
Team 2: ____ ____ ____ ____	

Copyright © Wright Group/McGraw-Hill

Name Date Time

Geometry Riddles Cards

1. I am a geometric solid.
2. I have 2 surfaces.
3. My base is formed by a circle.
4. I have a point at the top.

What am I?

1. I am a geometric solid.
2. I have only 1 surface.
3. My 1 surface is curved.
4. I have no base.

What am I?

1. I am a polyhedron.
2. I have 2 triangular bases.
3. I have 3 other faces.
4. My other faces are rectangles.

What am I?

1. I am a polyhedron.
2. I have the fewest number of faces of all the polyhedrons.
3. All of my faces are triangles.
4. I come to a point at the top.

What am I?

1. I am a polyhedron.
2. I have 5 faces.
3. Four of my faces are triangles.
4. My base is a square.

What am I?

1. I am a polyhedron.
2. I have 6 faces.
3. All of my faces are congruent.
4. All of my faces are squares.

What am I?

Copyright © Wright Group/McGraw-Hill

Name Date Time

Unit 7: Family Letter

Multiplication and Division

In Unit 7, children will focus on learning the multiplication and division facts. Many of the same strategies that were used in previous grades for addition and subtraction will also be used for multiplication and division.

Children will review multiplication by 0, by 1, and by 10; multiplication facts having square products, such as $5 \times 5 = 25$ and $2 \times 2 = 4$; and the turn-around rule, which shows that $2 \times 5 = 10$ is the same as $5 \times 2 = 10$.

Children will also continue to work with fact families and Fact Triangles as they learn the multiplication and division facts.

$7 \times 8 = 56$

$8 \times 7 = 56$

$56 \div 7 = 8$

$56 \div 8 = 7$

Fact family for the numbers 7, 8, and 56

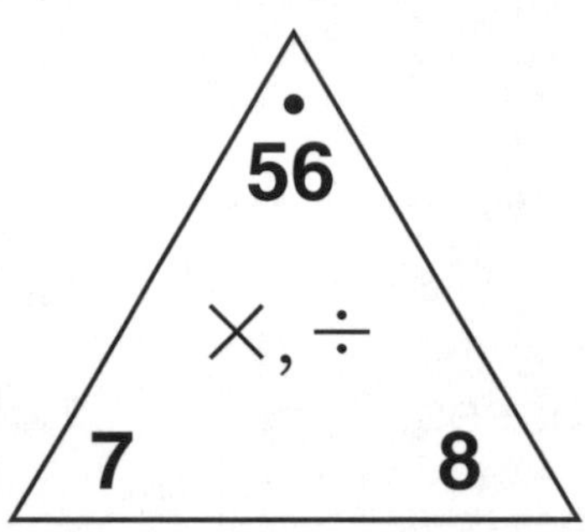

Fact Triangle

The goal is for children to demonstrate automaticity with × 0, × 1, × 2, × 5, and × 10 multiplication facts and to use strategies to compute remaining facts up to 10×10 by the end of the year.

Please keep this Family Letter for reference as your child works through Unit 7.

Copyright © Wright Group/McGraw-Hill

Vocabulary

Important terms in Unit 7:

factor Each of 2 or more numbers in a product. For example, $4 \times 3 = 12$; so 12 is the product, and 4 and 3 are the factors.

$$4 \times 3 = 12$$

factors — product

product The result of multiplying 2 numbers, called factors. For example, in $4 \times 3 = 12$, the product is 12.

square number The product of a counting number and itself. For example, 25 is a square number, because $5 \times 5 = 25$.

estimate (1) An answer close to, or approximating, an exact answer. (2) To make an estimate.

parentheses ( ) Grouping symbols used to indicate which parts of an expression should be done first.

extended multiplication fact A multiplication fact involving multiples of 10, 100, and so on. In an extended multiplication fact, each factor has only one digit that is not 0. For example, 60×7, 70×6, and 60×70 are extended facts.

Building Skills through Games

In Unit 7, your child will practice multiplication and division skills by playing the following games. For detailed instructions, see the *Student Reference Book.*

Baseball Multiplication

Players use multiplication facts to score runs. Team members take turns pitching by rolling two dice to get two factors. Then players on the batting team take turns multiplying the two factors and saying the product.

Multiplication Bingo

Players take turns calling out the product of two numbers. If that number appears on their *Multiplication Bingo* cards, they put a penny on that number. The first player to get 4 pennies in a row, column, or diagonal calls out "Bingo!" and wins the game.

Name That Number

Players turn over a card to find a number they must rename using any combination of five faceup cards. They may add, subtract, multiply, or divide the numbers on 2 or more of the 5 cards that are number-side up.

The number 15 can be renamed using 3 cards as $\mathbf{3} \times \mathbf{7} = 21$

$21 - \mathbf{6} = 15$

Copyright © Wright Group/McGraw-Hill

Do-Anytime Activities

To work with your child on the concepts taught in this and previous units, try these interesting and rewarding activities:

1. Practice multiplication facts by playing games and by working with Fact Triangles.

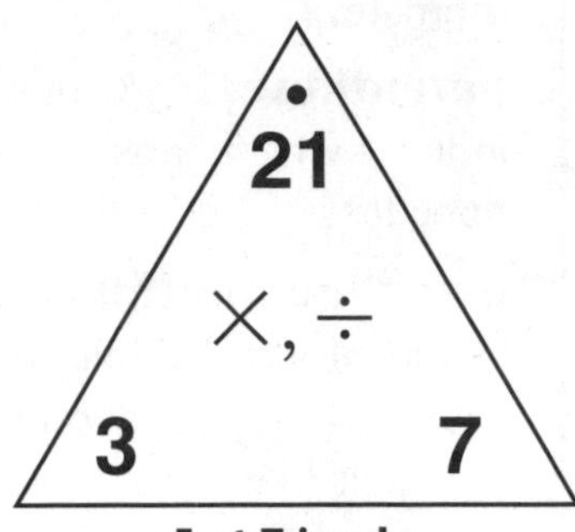

Fact Triangle

$3 \times 7 = 21$

$7 \times 3 = 21$

$21 \div 7 = 3$

$21 \div 3 = 7$

Fact families for the numbers 3, 7, and 21

2. Ask your child to count by certain intervals.
   For example: Start at zero and count by 6s.
3. Provide your child with problems with missing factors for multiplication practice.
   For example: 6 times what number equals 18?
4. Ask your child to estimate costs at the store.
   For example: One loaf of bread costs \$1.49. Two loaves are about \$3.00.
5. Ask questions that involve equal sharing.
   For example: Eight children share 64 paperback books. How many books does each child get?
6. Ask questions that involve equal groups.
   For example: Pencils are packaged in boxes of 8. There are 3 boxes. How many pencils are there in all?

Child's drawing of equal groups

Copyright © Wright Group/McGraw-Hill

HOME LINK 6·13

Unit 7: Family Letter *cont.*

As You Help Your Child with Homework

As your child brings home assignments, you may want to go over the instructions together, clarifying them as necessary. The answers listed below will guide you through this unit's Home Links.

Home Link 7·2

1.

Factor	Factor	Product
3	5	15
7	2	14
4	10	40
8	8	64
4	8	32
864	1	864
10	10	100
0	999	0
1	48	48
243	0	0

5. 14,189

6. 3,166

Home Link 7·4

1a. (17 − 10) + 3 = 10 **1b.** 17 − (10 + 3) = 4

2a. (26 − 7) × 2 = 38 **2b.** 26 − (7 × 2) − 12

3a. (24 − 17) − 6 = 1 **3b.** 24 − (17 − 6) = 13

4a. 3 × (6 + 13) = 57 **4b.** (3 × 6) + 13 = 31

7. The parentheses are placed incorrectly.
The number model should be (8 × 4) + 4 = 36.

Home Link 7·5

Scoring 15 Basketball Points

Number of 3-point baskets	Number of 2-point baskets	Number of 1-point baskets	Number models
5	0	0	(5 × 3) + (0 × 2) + (0 × 1) = 15
0	5	5	(0 × 3) + (5 × 2) + (5 × 1) = 15
3	3	0	(3 × 3) + (3 × 2) + (0 × 1) = 15
4	0	3	(4 × 3) + (0 × 2) + (3 × 1) = 15
2	3	3	(2 × 3) + (3 × 2) + (3 × 1) = 15
1	6	0	(1 × 3) + (6 × 2) + (0 × 1) = 15

1. 186 **2.** 509 **3.** 24

Home Link 7·6

1. 8 × 200 = 1,600
200 × 8 = 1,600
1,600 ÷ 8 = 200
1,600 ÷ 200 = 8

2. 9 × 30 = 270
30 × 9 = 270
270 ÷ 9 = 30
270 ÷ 30 = 9

3. 6 × 40 = 240
40 × 6 = 240
240 ÷ 6 = 40
240 ÷ 40 = 6

Home Link 7·7

2. b. 1,750 **c.** 1,251 **f.** 545 **g.** 614
i. 522

Home Link 7·8

5. a. 1,200 **b.** 1,400 **c.** 400 **d.** 800
e. 2,000 **f.** 200 **g.** 2,000 **h.** 1,000
i. 0 Total = 9,000

Sample answers:

6. a. 10 × 10 **b.** 3 × 50
c. 30 × 3 **d.** 40 × 4

a 100 +	**b** 150	= 250
c 90 +	**d** 160	= 250
	Total	500

Home Link 7·9

Mystery Numbers:

100; 199; 70; 44; 1,000; and 998

Copyright © Wright Group/McGraw-Hill

Name Date Time

Which Way Out?

Family Note Today your child explored patterns in square products, such as 3 × 3 and 4 × 4. The activity below provides practice in identifying square products. Have your child start at the picture of the Minotaur and use a pencil so he or she can erase wrong turns. If it would be helpful, suggest that your child mark each square product before attempting to find a path.

Please return this Home Link to school tomorrow.

According to Greek mythology, there was a monster called the Minotaur that was half bull and half human. The king had a special mazelike dwelling built, from which the Minotaur could not escape. The dwelling, called a **labyrinth** (la buh rinth), had many rooms and passageways that formed a puzzle. Whoever went in could not find their way out without help. One day, a Greek hero, Theseus, decided to slay the monster. To find his way out of the labyrinth, his friend Ariadne gave him a very, very long ball of string to unwind as he walked through the passageways. After Theseus slew the Minotaur, he followed the string to escape.

Pretend you are Theseus. To find your way out, you may go through only those rooms numbered with square products. Start at the Minotaur's chambers and draw a path to the exit.

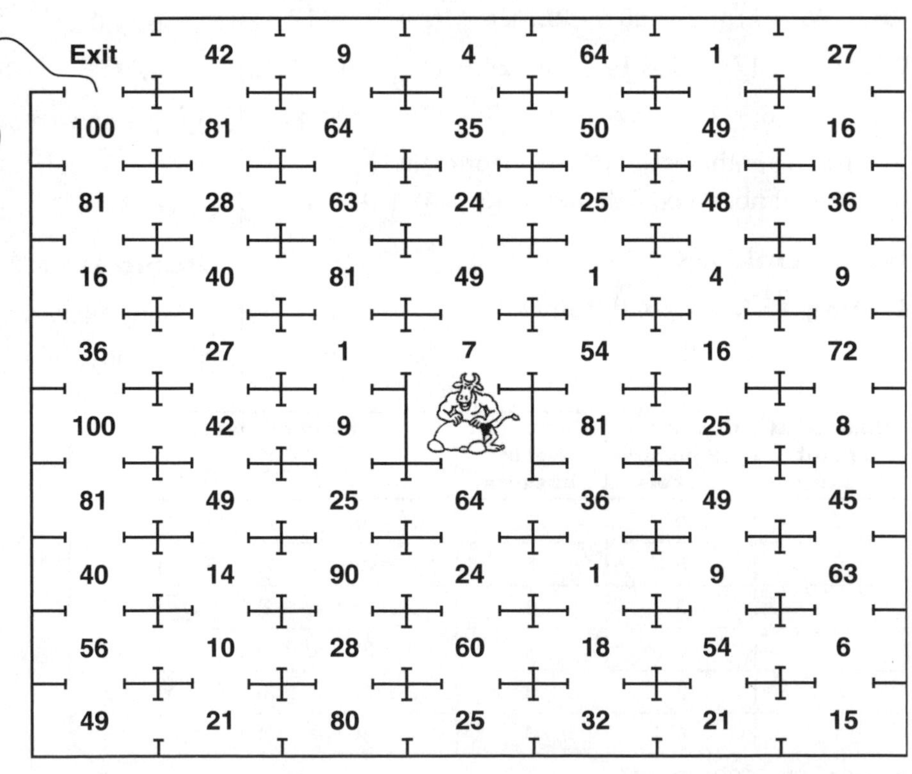

Copyright © Wright Group/McGraw-Hill

Name Date Time

Square and Rectangular Arrays

Follow these steps:

1. Use centimeter cubes to build arrays for each fact.
2. Record the arrays on the grids.
3. Name the shapes of the arrays.
4. Write the number models that match the arrays.

1. 3×3

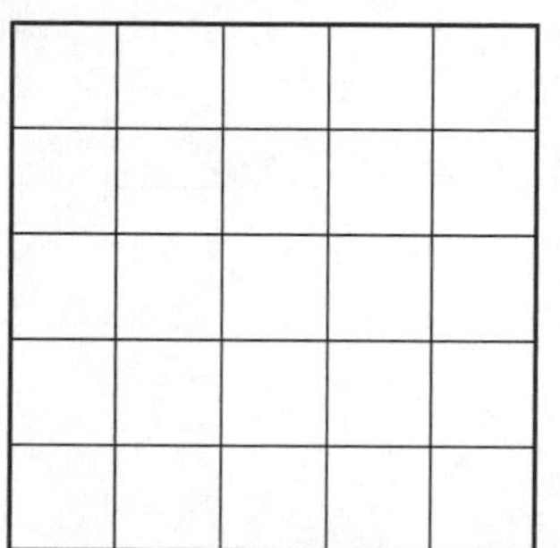

The shape is a ____________.

Number model: ____________

2. 3×4

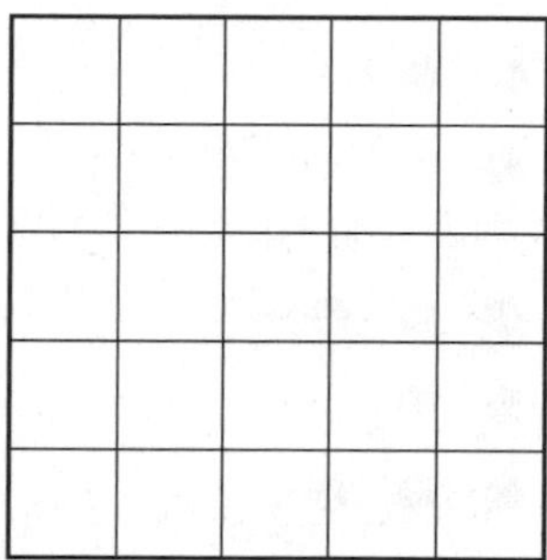

The shape is a ____________.

Number model: ____________

3. 4×5

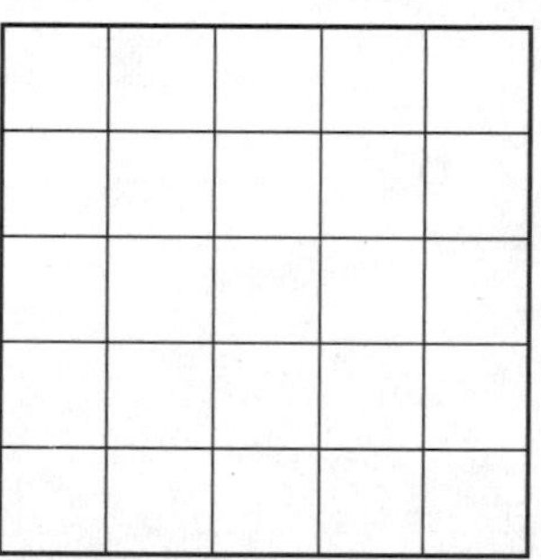

The shape is a ____________.

Number model: ____________

4. 4×4

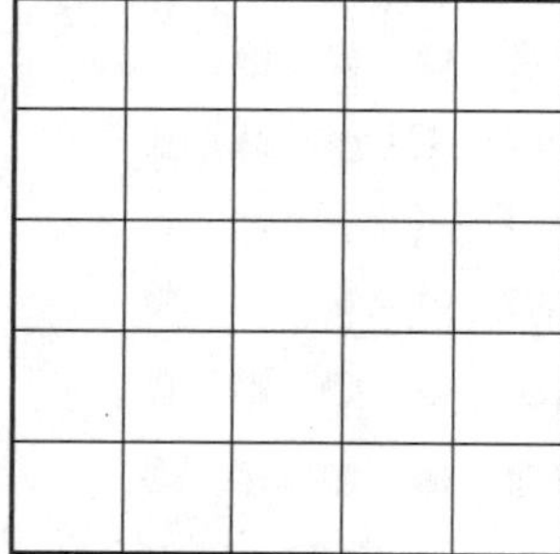

The shape is a ____________.

Number model: ____________

Compare the shapes and the number models for different arrays. What patterns do you see?

____

____

____

Copyright © Wright Group/McGraw-Hill

Name Date Time

Product Patterns

Find each product. Then look for patterns.

1. $1 \times 2 =$ ______

2. $2 \times 3 =$ ______

3. $3 \times 4 =$ ______

4. $4 \times 5 =$ ______

5. $5 \times 6 =$ ______

6. $6 \times 7 =$ ______

7. What happens when you subtract each product from the next larger product?

____

____

Read pages 198 and 199 in the *Student Reference Book* to learn more about patterns in multiplication.

Copyright © Wright Group/McGraw-Hill

Name Date Time

Factors and Products

Family Note Listen to your child explain what factors and products are before he or she writes the answers in the table. Then listen as your child tells you what he or she knows about multiplying by 1, multiplying by 0, and multiplying square numbers. Fact Triangles for the remaining multiplication/division facts are included with this Home Link.

Please return this Home Link to school tomorrow.

1. Explain to someone at home what factors and products are. Find the missing products and factors in the table.

Factor	Factor	Product
3	5	15
7		14
4	10	
8	8	
9		45
864	1	864
10		100
0	999	
	48	48
243		0

2. Write what you know about the products when you multiply by 1.

____

____

3. Write what you know about the products when you multiply by 0.

____

4. Write what you know about facts with square numbers.

____

Practice

Write these problems on the back of this page. Make a ballpark estimate for each. Solve. Show your work.

5. $7,201 + 6,988$

ballpark estimate ______________

6. $3,623 - 457$

ballpark estimate ______________

Unit

Copyright © Wright Group/McGraw-Hill

Name Date Time

LESSON 7·2

Turn-Around Facts

×, ÷	1	2	3	4	5	6	7	8	9	10
1		2	3	4	5	6	7	8	9	10
2	2		6	8	10	12	14	16	18	20
3	3	6		12	15	18	21	24	27	30
4	4	8	12		20	24	28	32	36	40
5	5	10	15	20		30	35	40	45	50
6	6	12	18	24	30		42	48	54	60
7	7	14	21	28	35	42		56	63	70
8	8	16	24	32	40	48	56		72	80
9	9	18	27	36	45	54	63	72		90
10	10	20	30	40	50	60	70	80	90	

Copyright © Wright Group/McGraw-Hill

Name Date Time

Multiplication Bingo (Easy Facts)

Family Note Today the class learned to play *Multiplication Bingo.* This game is a good way to practice the multiplication facts. Ask your child to show you how to play the game; then play a couple of games. When your child is ready to practice harder facts, use the cards and list of numbers on the next page. Encourage your child to keep a record of the facts he or she misses.

Keep this Home Link at home.

Materials
- ☐ number cards 1–6 and 10 (4 of each)
- ☐ 8 pennies or other counters for each player
- ☐ game mat for each player

Players 2 or 3

Directions

1. Write each of the following numbers in any order in one of the squares on a game mat: 1, 4, 6, 8, 9, 12, 15, 16, 18, 20, 24, 25, 30, 36, 50, 100.
2. Shuffle the number cards. Place the cards facedown on the table.
3. Take turns. When it is your turn, take the top 2 cards and call out the product of the 2 numbers. If the other players do not agree with your answer, check it using a calculator.
4. If your answer is correct and the product is a number on your grid, place a penny or a counter on that number.
5. If your answer is incorrect, you lose your turn.
6. The first player to get 4 counters in a row, column, or diagonal or 8 counters on the game mat calls out *Bingo!* and wins the game.

   If all the cards are used before someone wins, shuffle the cards again and keep playing.

Copyright © Wright Group/McGraw-Hill

Name Date Time

Multiplication Bingo (All Facts)

Follow the same rules as for *Multiplication Bingo,* with the following exceptions:

- Use a deck of number cards with 4 cards each for the numbers 2 through 9.
- Write each of the numbers in the list in one of the squares on the grid. Don't write the numbers in order.

List of numbers

24	35	48	63
27	36	49	64
28	42	54	72
32	45	56	81

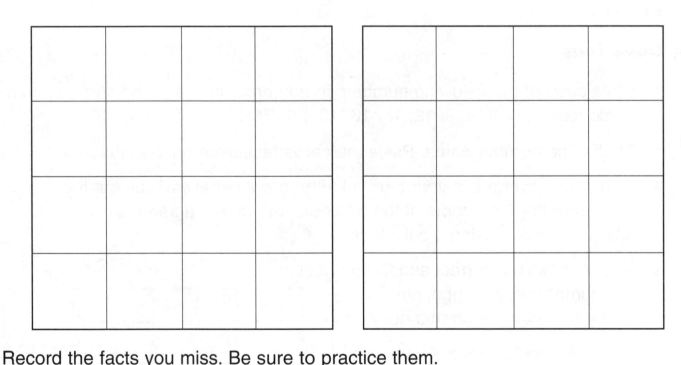

Record the facts you miss. Be sure to practice them.

Copyright © Wright Group/McGraw-Hill

Name Date Time

LESSON 7•3

Problems with Multiplication Diagrams

For each problem, fill in the diagram. Use a question mark to show the unknown part in the diagram. Write a number model and solve the problem.

1. Jo had 24 markers. Markers come in boxes of 8. How many boxes did she buy?

boxes	markers per box	markers in all

Number model: ______________ Answer: ______ boxes

---

2. Franklin was trying to figure out how many eggs his mom bought. She bought 4 cartons with one dozen eggs in each.

cartons	eggs per carton	eggs in all

Number model: ______________ Answer: ______ eggs

---

3. Ms. Cricket had 35 students. She needed one piece of chalk per student and had to buy 7 boxes of chalk. How many pieces of chalk were in each box?

boxes of chalk	pieces per box	total pieces

Number model: ______________ Answer: ______ pieces of chalk

Copyright © Wright Group/McGraw-Hill

Name Date Time

LESSON 7•3

Frames-and-Arrows Puzzles

Each puzzle has two rules. For each puzzle, color the arrow for one rule red and color the arrow for the other rule blue. For Problems 1 through 3, figure out where to place the rules to solve the problems. You may use your calculator.

1. ×9 ÷3

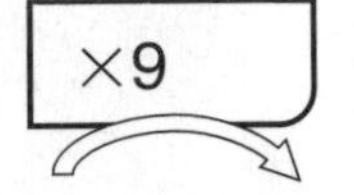
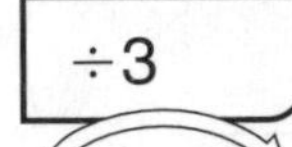
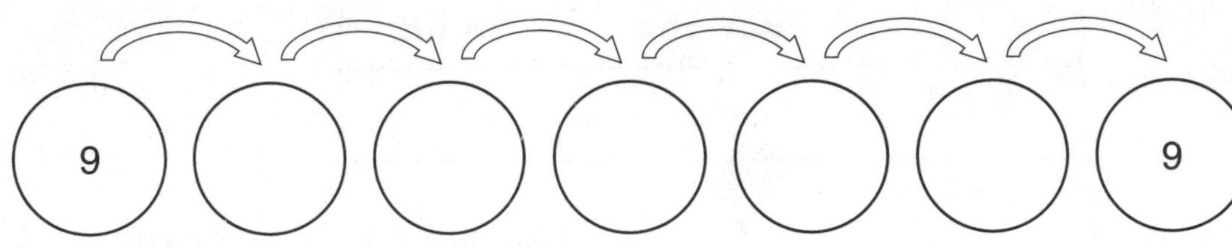

2. Find another way.

×9 ÷3

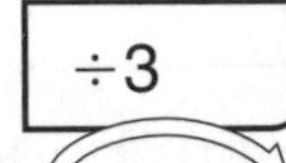
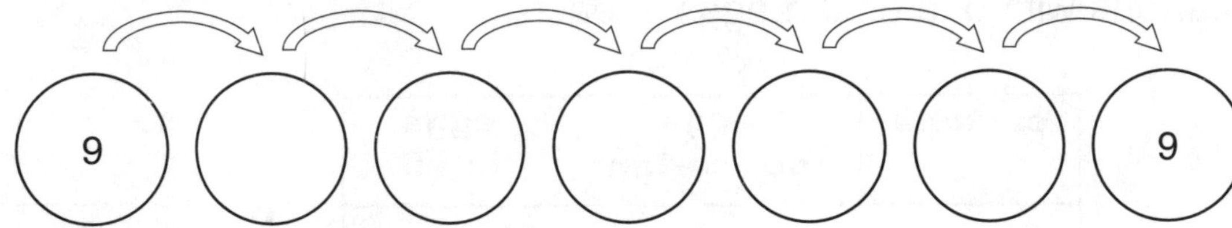

3. ×6 ÷4

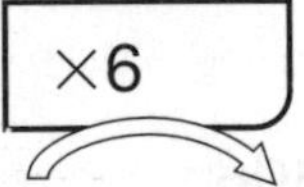
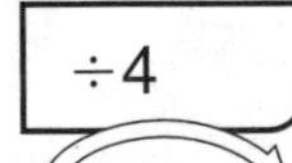
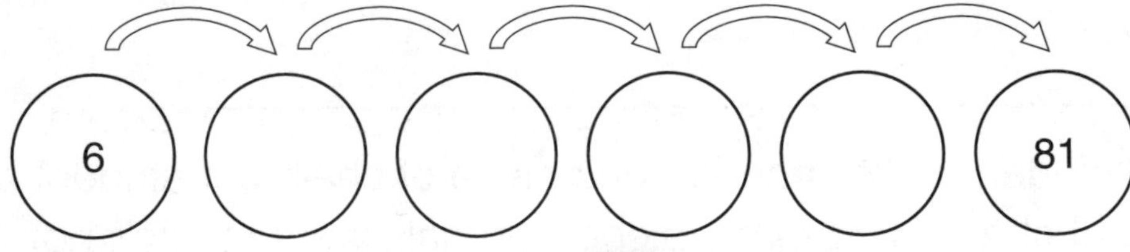

4. Make up a puzzle. Ask a partner to solve it.

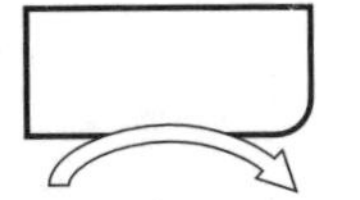
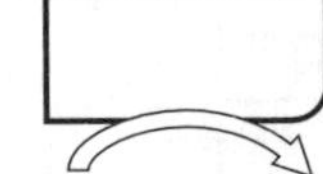
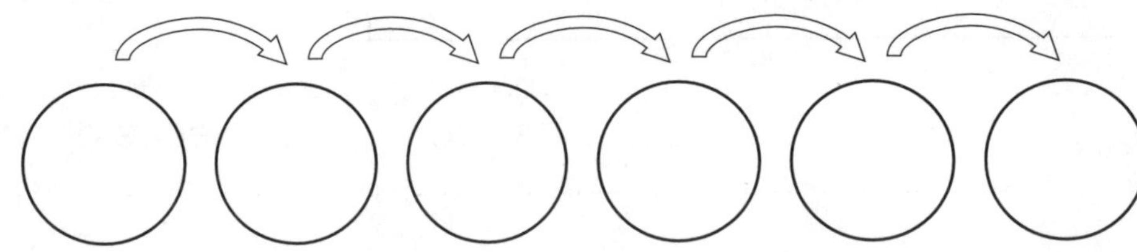

Copyright © Wright Group/McGraw-Hill

Name Date Time

Parentheses Puzzles

Family Note Observe as your child adds parentheses and explains what to do first in the number sentence puzzles in Problems 1 through 4. If needed, assist your child in writing a correct number model for the Try This problem. You might ask how many gifts Dalia would need to fill 8 bags and how many she would need to also take care of Denise.

Please return this Home Link to school tomorrow.

SRB 16–17

Show someone at home how to add parentheses to complete the number sentences below. Remember that the parentheses are used to show what you do first.

1 a. $17 - 10 + 3 = 10$ **1 b.** $17 - 10 + 3 = 4$

2 a. $26 - 7 \times 2 = 38$ **2 b.** $26 - 7 \times 2 = 12$

3 a. $24 - 17 - 6 = 1$ **3 b.** $24 - 17 - 6 = 13$

4 a. $3 \times 6 + 13 = 57$ **4 b.** $3 \times 6 + 13 = 31$

Make up other parentheses puzzles below.

5 a. ______________ **5 b.** ______________

6 a. ______________ **6 b.** ______________

Try This

7. Dalia made 8 party bags for her birthday party. Each bag contained 4 small gifts for her friends. When Denise said that she could come, Dalia had to make one more bag with 4 gifts. How many small gifts did Dalia need to fill her bags?

Walter wrote this number model: $8 \times (4 + 4) = 64$

Explain Walter's mistake.

____

____

____

Copyright © Wright Group/McGraw-Hill

Name Date Time

Dot Patterns with Number Models

The total dots in this dot array can be found by using patterns.

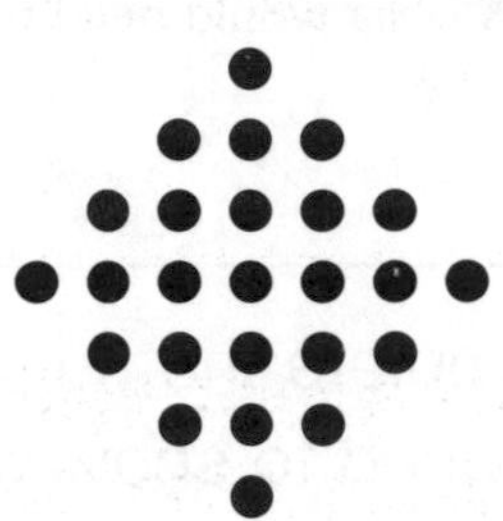

Here is one way to find the total:

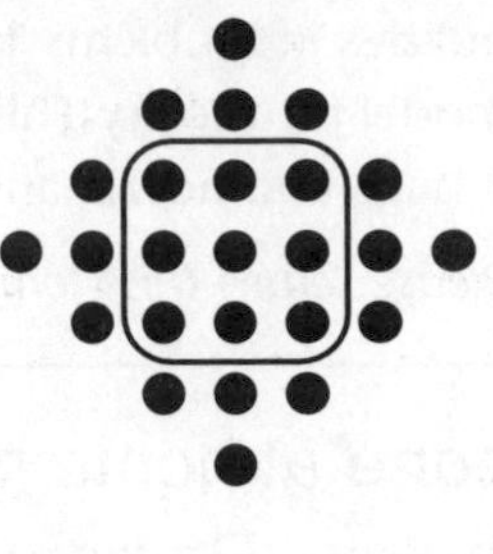

$9 + (4 \times 4)$

Find as many ways as you can to use patterns to find the total dots. Show each pattern on the dot array and write a number model to describe the pattern. Use parentheses in your number model if you can.

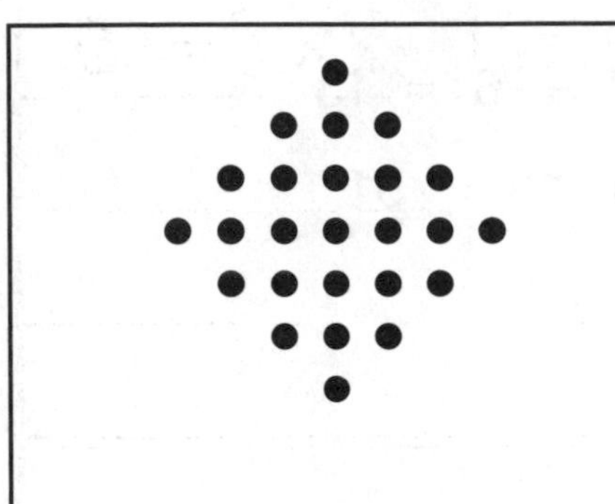 ________________	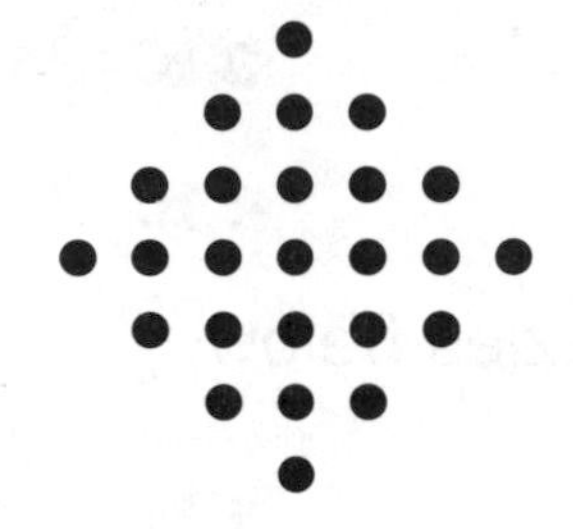 ________________	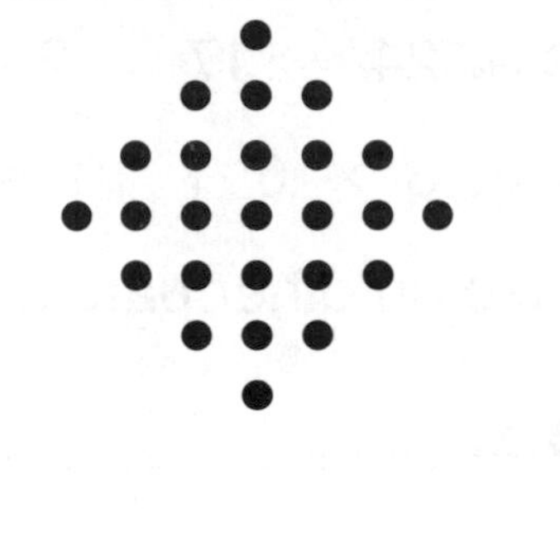 ________________

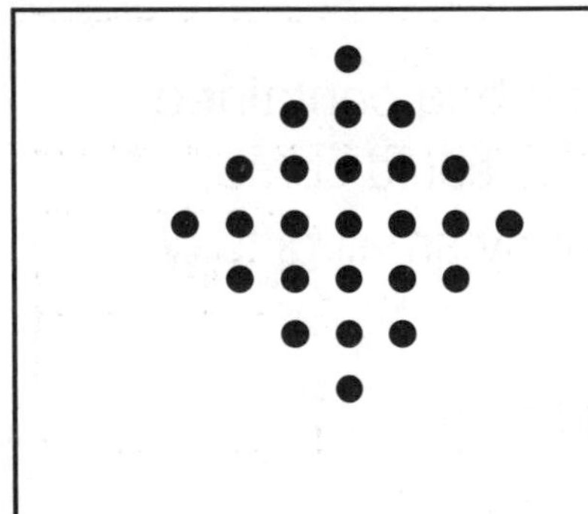 ________________	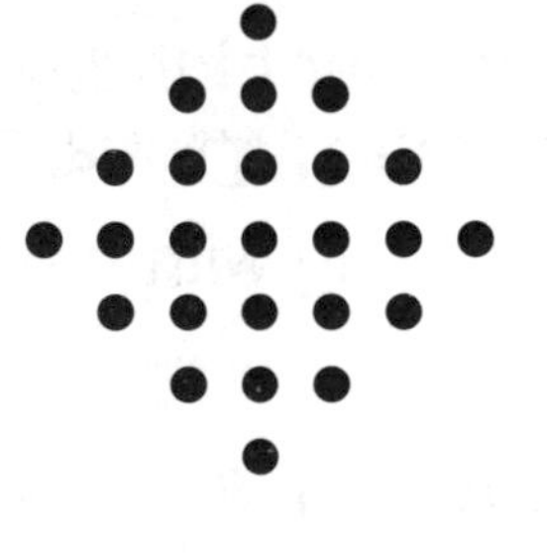 ________________	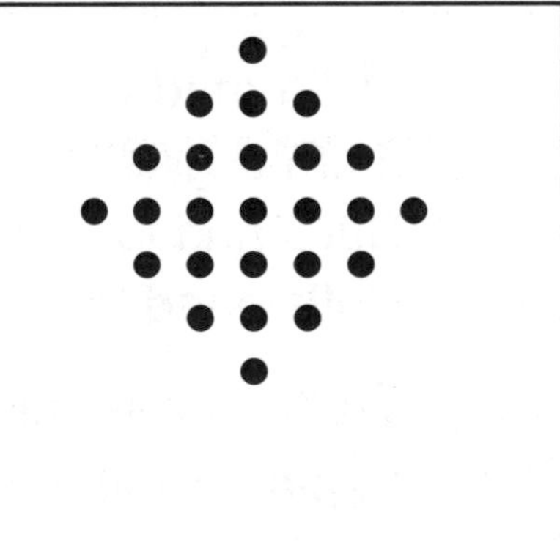 ________________

Copyright © Wright Group/McGraw-Hill

Name Date Time

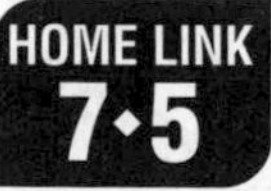

Basketball Math

Family Note We have been using points scored in basketball to illustrate the use of parentheses in number models. Work with your child to find various combinations of 3-point, 2-point, and 1-point baskets that add up to 15 points. Ask your child to explain what the parentheses in the number models tell you about how to find the answers.

Please return this Home Link to school tomorrow.

SRB 16 17

Tell someone at home how basketball players can shoot baskets worth 3 points, 2 points, and 1 point. Find different ways a player can score 15 points.

Scoring 15 Basketball Points

3 points	2 points	1 point	Number Models
3	2	2	$(3 \times 3) + (2 \times 2) + (2 \times 1) = 15$

Practice

Unit

Solve. Show your work.

1. $274 - 88$

2. $576 - 67$

3. $711 - 687$

Copyright © Wright Group/McGraw-Hill

Name Date Time

Equivalent Names

You need ten pennies.

1. Look at the first row on the table below. Using 10 pennies, you can make 3 groups of 3 pennies. A 3 is in the first column.

2. Because there is only 1 penny left, you cannot make any groups of 2 pennies. 0 is written in the Groups of 2 pennies column.

3. Because there is 1 penny left, you can make 1 group of 1 penny. 1 is written in the third column.

4. 10 pennies in all were used. 10 is written in the last column.

5. Complete the table. Find different ways to use 10 pennies in all for each row.

Groups of 3 pennies	Groups of 2 pennies	Groups of 1 penny	Total pennies
3	0	1	10
2			
1			
	3		
	2		
	1		
		2	
		1	

Copyright © Wright Group/McGraw-Hill

Name Date Time

Names for Digits

Write at least one number sentence for each digit. Follow these rules:

- You may use any operation ($+$, $-$, $\times$, and $\div$) as many times as you need to.
- You must use exactly four 3s each time. You must use only 3s.
- Use parentheses if you can.

You may use your calculator to help.

Digit	Number Sentence
0	Example: $(3 \times 3) - (3 \times 3) = 0$
1	
2	
3	
5	
6	
7	
8	
9	

Try This

How many ways can you make 4 using only 3s?

4	
4	

Copyright © Wright Group/McGraw-Hill

Name Date Time

HOME LINK 7•6

Extended Facts on Triangles

Family Note Today the class learned that if you know a basic multiplication fact, such as $4 \times 6 = 24$, you can get the answer to an extended multiplication fact like 40×6 or 4×600. The same approach works for extended division facts like $120 \div 3$ or $1{,}500 \div 5$. The extended Fact Triangles on this page work the same way as the basic Fact Triangles.

Please return this Home Link to school tomorrow.

Fill in the extended Fact Triangles. Write the fact families.

1.

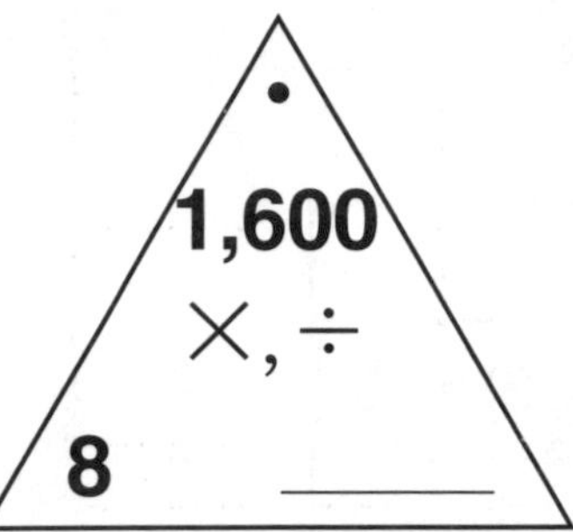

_____ × _____ = _____

_____ × _____ = _____

_____ ÷ _____ = _____

_____ ÷ _____ = _____

2.

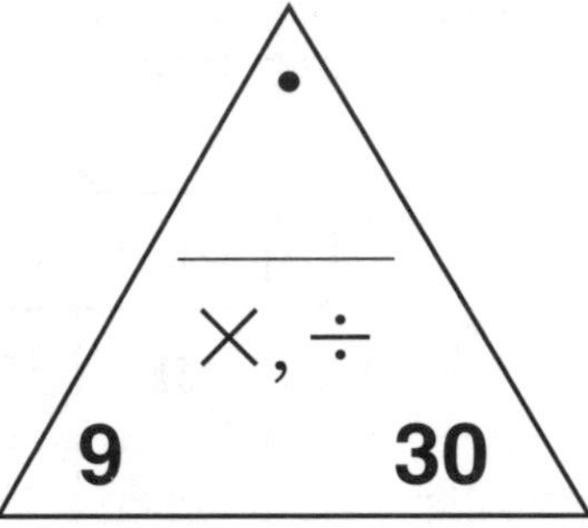

_____ × _____ = _____

_____ × _____ = _____

_____ ÷ _____ = _____

_____ ÷ _____ = _____

3.

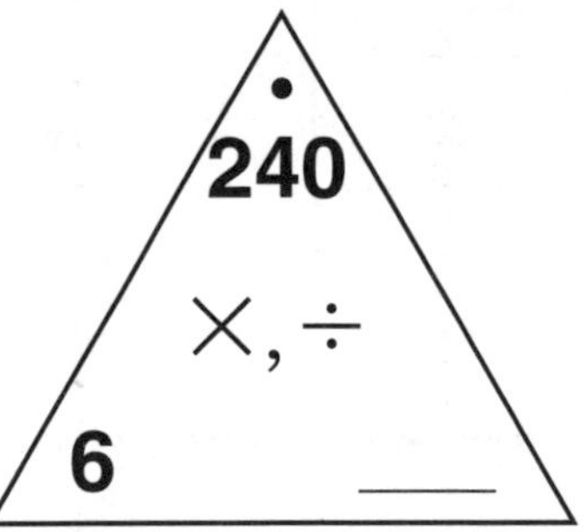

_____ × _____ = _____

_____ × _____ = _____

_____ ÷ _____ = _____

_____ ÷ _____ = _____

4. Write your own.

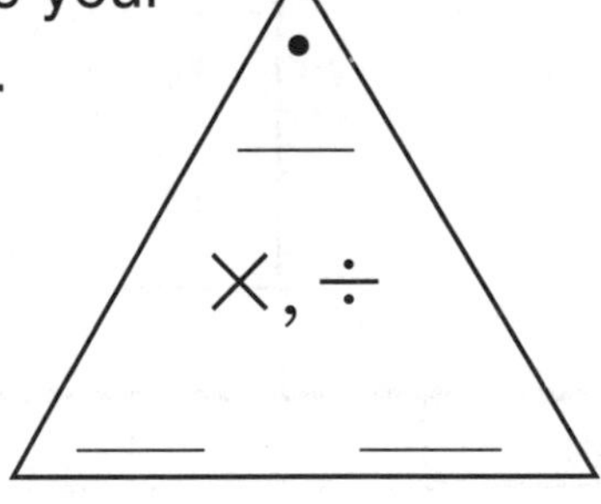

_____ × _____ = _____

_____ × _____ = _____

_____ ÷ _____ = _____

_____ ÷ _____ = _____

Copyright © Wright Group/McGraw-Hill

Name Date Time

LESSON 7·6

Multiples of 10s

Work with a partner.

One partner uses a calculator to skip-count by 1, 10, 100, and 1,000. Record the numbers in the correct place in the chart as they are displayed in the calculator. The other partner models each count with base-10 blocks. Use cube ▪, long |, and flat □ to record the count in the chart.

The first two numbers are done for you.

Count by 1s.				
one **1**	two 1s	three 1s	four 1s	five 1s
1 ▪	2 ▪▪			

Count by 10s.				
one **10**	two 10s	three 10s	four 10s	five 10s
10 |				

Count by 100s.				
one **100**	two 100s	three 100s	four 100s	five 100s

Try This

Using the patterns you see in the table above, complete the table below for 1,000s.

Count by 1000s.				
one **1,000**	two 1,000s	three 1,000s	four 1,000s	five 1,000s
1,000				

Copyright © Wright Group/McGraw-Hill

Name Date Time

HOME LINK 7•7

Estimation

Family Note Today we solved problems by making estimates. We emphasized that it is not always necessary to find the exact answer to a problem. For example, when you go to the store, you can estimate whether you have enough money to pay for the items you want to purchase. In most cases, it is not necessary to find the exact cost until you pay for your items.

Please return this Home Link to school tomorrow.

For each problem, first estimate whether the sum is greater than 500 or less than 500; then circle the correct comparison. Next give an exact result only to those problems with sums greater than 500.

a. 180 + 37 >500 <500 **Answer**	**b.** 1,358 + 392 >500 <500 **Answer**	**c.** 742 + 509 >500 <500 **Answer**
d. 118 + 292 >500 <500 **Answer**	**e.** 226 + 248 >500 <500 **Answer**	**f.** 377 + 168 >500 <500 **Answer**
g. 298 + 316 >500 <500 **Answer**	**h.** 195 + 188 >500 <500 **Answer**	**i.** 313 + 209 >500 <500 **Answer**

Copyright © Wright Group/McGraw-Hill

Name Date Time

LESSON 7•7 Rounding Numbers

Sometimes an exact answer to a problem is not needed. An answer that is close to the exact answer might be helpful enough. When we round a number, we find a number that is close to it but easier to use. Numbers ending in 0 are often easier to use. Here are some strategies for rounding a number.

1. Shade in the multiples of 10 on the number grid on *Math Masters*, page 21.

Put your finger on 27. When we round 27, it will go up or down to the nearest multiple of ten.

Is it fewer steps from 27 to 30 or from 27 to 20? ________________

Use your number grid to round these numbers. (Hint: When a number is exactly half-way between, we usually round to the higher number.)

2. 42 ______ **3.** 79 ______ **4.** 63 ______ **5.** 55 ______

Here is another way to think of rounding numbers.

Round 27. What would be multiples of 10 that are close to 27? ________________

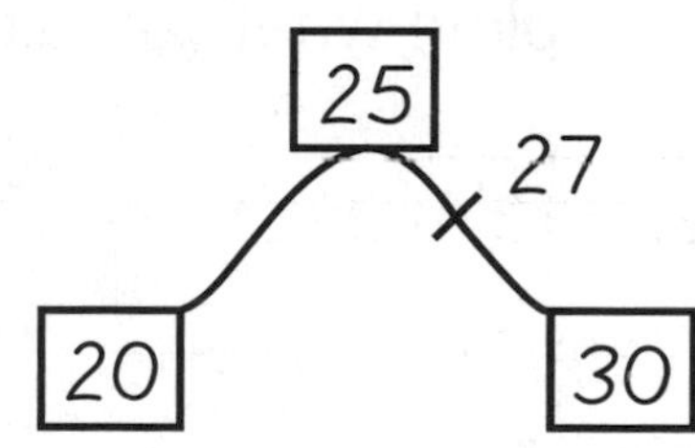

What number would be at the top of the hill? ______

Would 27 be heading toward 20 or toward 30? ______

6. Draw a picture to show how you would round 82.

Try This

7. Draw a picture or explain how you would round 4.7 to the nearest whole number.

Copyright © Wright Group/McGraw-Hill

Name Date Time

LESSON 7·7

Estimating Paper Consumption

On average, the total weight of all the paper used in the United States each day is about $1\frac{1}{2}$ pounds per person.

1. About how many pounds of paper per person are used in 1 week? Explain what you did.

About ______ pounds

______

______

______

______

______

2. About how many pounds of paper per person are used in one year? Explain what you did.

About ______ pounds

______

______

3. A 40-foot pine tree will produce about 12,000 sheets of paper. 100 sheets of paper weigh about 1 pound. About how many trees does it take to produce the amount of paper the average person uses in 1 year? Explain your thinking.

About ______ trees

______

______

Copyright © Wright Group/McGraw-Hill

Name Date Time

HOME LINK 7·8

A Multiplication Puzzle

Family Note Practice finding products like 4 × 70, 900 × 5, and 30 × 50 with your child before he or she works the two puzzles.

Please return this Home Link to school tomorrow.

Work with someone at home.

1. Find each product below (for Problems 5a through 5i).
2. Record each product in the box labeled with the letter of the problem. For example, write the product for Problem **a** in Box **a**.
3. Add the numbers in each row. Write the sum next to the row.
4. Add these sums and write the answer in the Total box.
5. The number in the Total box should equal 3 × 3,000.

a. 30 × 40
b. 20 × 70
c. 20 × 20
d. 10 × 80
e. 40 × 50
f. 20 × 10
g. 4 × 500
h. 10 × 10 × 10
i. 10,000 × 0

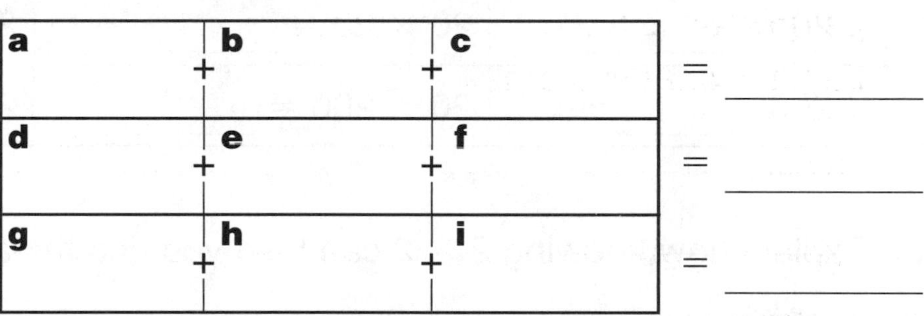

Total

Try This

6. Make a puzzle so the number in the Total box is 500.

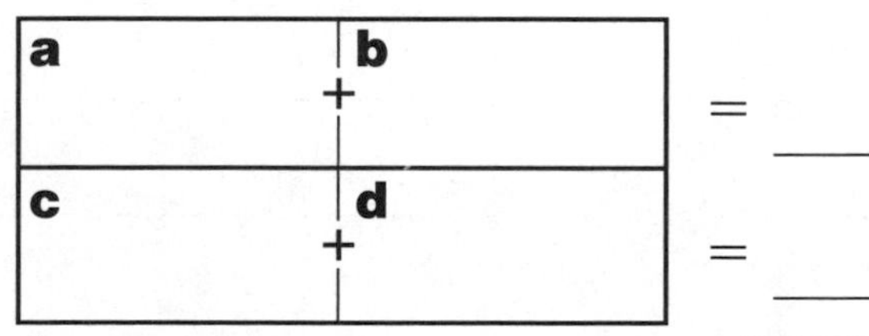

Total

a. ______ **b.** ______

c. ______ **d.** ______

Copyright © Wright Group/McGraw-Hill

Name Date Time

LESSON 7•8

Patterns in Extended Facts

1. Use base-10 blocks to help you solve the problems in the first 2 columns. Use the patterns from the first row and column to help you solve the other problems in the table.

2 × 1 = ______	20 × 1 = ______	200 × 1 = ______
2 × 10 = ______	20 × 10 = ______	200 × 10 = ______
2 × 100 = ______	20 × 100 = ______	200 × 100 = ______

2. Use what you learned in Problem 1 to help you solve the problems in the table below.

2 × 2 = ______	20 × 2 = ______	200 × 2 = ______
2 × 20 = ______	20 × 20 = ______	200 × 20 = ______
2 × 200 = ______	20 × 200 = ______	200 × 200 = ______

3. Explain how knowing 2 × 2 can help you find the answer to 20 × 20.

____

____

____

Copyright © Wright Group/McGraw-Hill

Name Date Time

Multidigit Multiplication

Solve the following problem:

An artist made a square mosaic with 99 rows of tiles and 99 tiles in each row. How many tiles were used?

Do not use your calculator. Show your work. Explain what you did.

Copyright © Wright Group/McGraw-Hill

Name Date Time

LESSON 7•9 Similar Pattern-Block Shapes

Exploration A:

Share the work with other members of your group for Problems 1 through 3. Work together on Problems 4 and 5.

1. Try to make a square out of square pattern blocks. The square should be larger than a single pattern block. Use as few squares as you can. Record the result on a sheet of paper by tracing around the pattern blocks or by using a template.

2. Make a larger triangle out of triangle pattern blocks. Again, use as few triangles as you can. Record the result by tracing around the blocks or by using a template.

3. Do the same thing with each of the following pattern blocks:

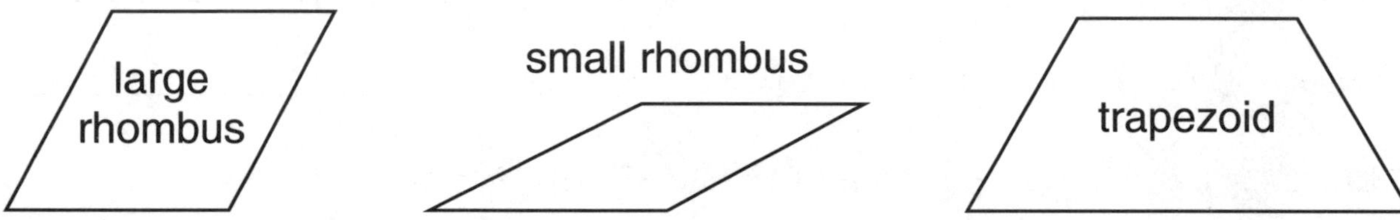

Hint: Use four trapezoid pattern blocks to make the larger trapezoid.

4. Can you make a larger hexagon out of hexagon pattern blocks? ______

5. Make a larger hexagon by combining hexagon pattern blocks with pattern blocks of another shape. Record the result by tracing around the blocks or by using a template on the back of your paper.

Follow-Up

6. How many pattern blocks did you use to make larger squares, triangles, rhombuses, and trapezoids? ______

7. How many pattern blocks would you need to make the next larger square? The next larger triangle? The next larger rhombus? Try to make them. ______

Copyright © Wright Group/McGraw-Hill

Name Date Time

Seven Sheep versus One Cow

Exploration B:

A farmer is switching from raising cows to raising sheep. She estimates that 7 sheep eat about as much as 1 cow.

Work as a group to answer the three questions below. Find the answers without using a calculator.

1. If a farmer has 10 well-fed cows in the pasture, how many sheep can she replace them with? ____________

2. How many sheep can she replace 50 cows with? ____________

3. A neighbor wants to sell the farmer 67 sheep. About how many of her cows will these sheep replace? ____________

On the back of this page, or on a separate sheet of paper, write a group report telling what your group did to find the answers.

Try This

4. Make up a problem about 7 sheep eating as much as 1 cow.

____

____

____

____

Use calculators, if you wish, to solve the problem.
Write it in your group report.

Copyright © Wright Group/McGraw-Hill

Name Date Time

Straw Triangles

Exploration C:

1. Try to build 5 triangles out of 9 straws, without bending the straws. Draw a picture of your solution below.

Try This

2. Take the 9 straws apart. Then try to build 7 triangles out of 9 straws. Show your solution to your teacher. Then do your best to draw a picture of it below.

Hint: The solution is a 3-dimensional figure.

Copyright © Wright Group/McGraw-Hill

Name Date Time

Mystery Numbers

Family Note Help your child find each missing number by using all the clues. Then help your child create more clues for two other mystery numbers.

Please return this Home Link to school tomorrow.

Find each missing number. Here are your clues.

Greater Than	Less Than	More Clues	Mystery Number
20	101	a 3-digit number	
197	200	any odd number	
67	80	has a zero in the ones place	
40	50	has the same digit in the tens place and the ones place	
917	1,072	has the same digit in the ones, tens, and hundreds places; has 4 digits	
996	1,015	a 3-digit even number	

Make up mystery-number puzzles. Write some clues and ask someone to find the numbers.

Greater Than	Less Than	More Clues	Mystery Number

Copyright © Wright Group/McGraw-Hill

Name Date Time

LESSON 7·9 Next-Larger Shapes

You will need *Math Masters,* page 228 and the shapes you made during Exploration A.

Follow these steps:

1. In the chart below, write the number of pattern blocks you used to make each of the different-size shapes in Exploration A.
2. Build the two next-larger squares, triangles, rhombuses, and trapezoids.
3. Record the number of pattern blocks you used for each shape in the chart.

Number of Pattern Blocks in Shapes

	smallest	next larger	next larger	next larger
square	1	4		
triangle	1			
large rhombus	1			
small rhombus	1			
trapezoid	1			

What patterns do you see in each series of shapes?

____

____

____

Copyright © Wright Group/McGraw-Hill

Name Date Time

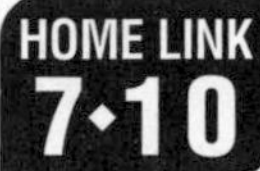

Unit 8: Family Letter

Fractions

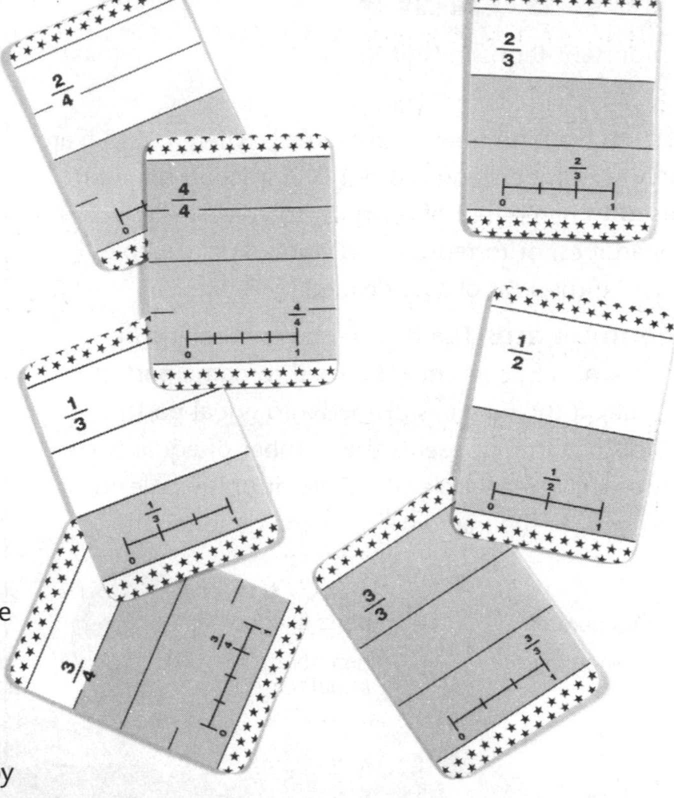

Unit 8 has two primary objectives:

- to review the uses of fractions and fraction notation
- to help children develop a solid understanding of equivalent fractions, or fractions that have the same value

The second objective is especially important, because understanding equivalent fractions will help children compare fractions and, later, calculate with fractions.

Children will build their understanding of equivalent fractions by working with Fraction Cards and name-collection boxes. Fraction Cards are shaded to show a variety of fractions.

Name-collection boxes contain equivalent names for the same number. For example, a $\frac{1}{2}$ name-collection box can contain fractions such as $\frac{2}{4}$, $\frac{3}{6}$, and $\frac{4}{8}$ and the decimal 0.50.

Children will also generate lists of equivalent fractions by folding circles and rectangles into different numbers of equal parts.

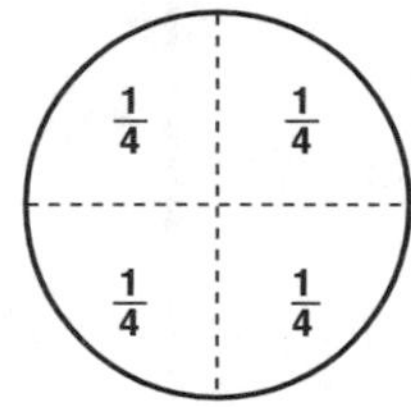

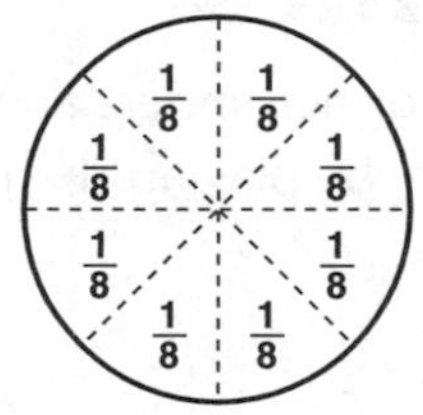

$\frac{1}{2}$

$\frac{1}{4} + \frac{1}{4}$ $\frac{3}{6}$

$1 - \frac{1}{2}$ $\frac{5}{10}$

$1 \div 2$ $\frac{3}{4} - \frac{1}{4}$

Throughout this unit, children will make up and solve number stories involving fractions in everyday contexts. They will solve number stories about collections of real-world objects such as crayons, books, and cookies.

Finally, children will begin to name quantities greater than 1 with fractions such as $\frac{3}{2}$ and $\frac{5}{4}$ and with mixed numbers such as $2\frac{1}{3}$.

Please keep this Family Letter for reference as your child works through Unit 8.

Copyright © Wright Group/McGraw-Hill

Unit 8: Family Letter *cont.*

Vocabulary

Important terms in Unit 8:

fraction A number in the form $\frac{a}{b}$ where *a* and *b* are whole numbers and *b* is not 0. A fraction may be used to name part of a whole, to compare two quantities, or to represent division. For example, $\frac{2}{3}$ can be thought of as 2 divided by 3.

denominator The number below the line in a fraction. A fraction may be used to name part of a whole. If the whole is divided into equal parts, the denominator represents the number of equal parts into which the whole (the ONE or unit whole) is divided. In the fraction $\frac{a}{b}$, *b* is the denominator.

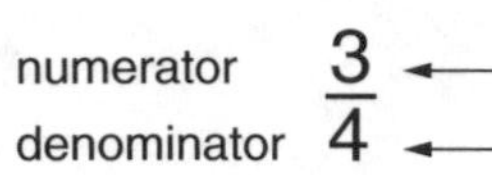

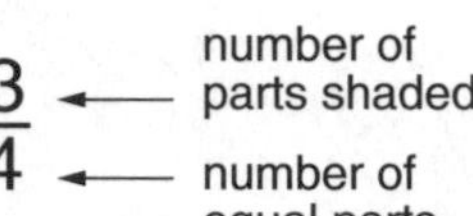

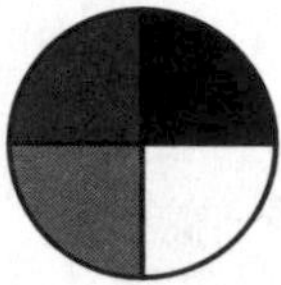

numerator The number above the line in a fraction. A fraction may be used to name part of a whole. If the whole (the ONE or unit whole) is divided into equal parts, the numerator represents the number of equal parts being considered. In the fraction $\frac{a}{b}$, *a* is the numerator.

equivalent fractions Fractions with different denominators that name the same number. For example, $\frac{1}{2}$ and $\frac{4}{8}$ are equivalent fractions.

mixed number A number that is written using both a whole number and a fraction. For example, $2\frac{1}{4}$ is a mixed number equal to $2 + \frac{1}{4}$.

Building Skills through Games

In Unit 8, your child will practice multiplication skills, build his or her understanding of fractions, and practice skills related to chance and probability by playing the following games. For detailed instructions, see the *Student Reference Book.*

Baseball Multiplication

Players use multiplication facts to score runs. Team members take turns pitching by rolling two dice to get two factors. Then players on the batting team take turns multiplying the two factors and saying the product.

Equivalent Fractions Game

Players take turns turning over Fraction Cards and try to find matching cards that show equivalent fractions.

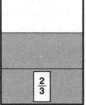

Fraction Top-It

Players turn over two Fraction Cards and compare the shaded parts of the cards. The player with the larger fraction keeps all the cards. The player with more cards at the end wins!

The Block-Drawing Game

Without letting the other players see the blocks, a Director puts five blocks in a paper bag and tells the players how many blocks are in the bag. A player takes a block out of the bag. The Director records the color of the block for all players to see. The player replaces the block. At any time, a player may say *Stop!* and guess how many blocks of each color are in the bag.

Copyright © Wright Group/McGraw-Hill

Do-Anytime Activities

To work with your child on the concepts taught in this unit and in previous units, try these interesting and rewarding activities:

1. Help your child find fractions in the everyday world—in advertisements, on measuring tools, in recipes, and so on.
2. Count together by a 1-digit number. For example, start at 0 and count by 7s.
3. Dictate 5-, 6-, and 7-digit numbers for your child to write, such as *thirteen thousand, two hundred forty-seven* (13,247) and *three million, two hundred twenty-nine thousand, eight hundred fifty-six* (3,229,856). Also, write 5-, 6-, and 7- digit numbers for your child to read to you.
4. Practice extended multiplication and division facts such as $3 \times 7 =$ __, $30 \times 7 =$ __, and $300 \times 7 =$ __, and $18 \div 6 =$ __, $180 \div 6 =$ __, and $1{,}800 \div 6 =$ __.

Copyright © Wright Group/McGraw-Hill

Unit 8: Family Letter *cont.*

As You Help Your Child with Homework

As your child brings home assignments, you may want to go over the instructions together, clarifying them as necessary. The answers listed below will guide you through this unit's Home Links.

Home Link 8•1

1. 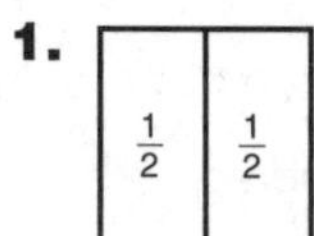

2. 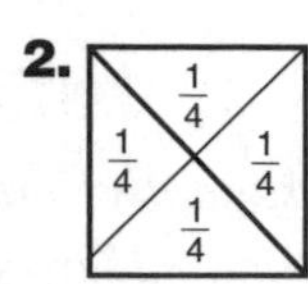

3. 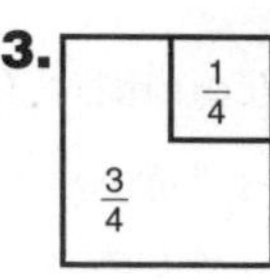

4. $\frac{5}{7}$ **5.** $\frac{2}{7}$

6. 187 **7.** 587 **8.** 192

Home Link 8•2

1. 0 **2.** 3 **3.** 6

4. 4

5. 198, 198, 198

Home Link 8•3

1. 7

2. 3

3. $\frac{1}{4}$, or $\frac{10}{40}$

4. $\frac{1}{5}$, or $\frac{10}{50}$

5. ○○○○○○(○○○○○○○○○)

6. ⊗⊗⊗⊗⊗⊗⊗⊗⊗○○○

Home Link 8•4

1. 9 pieces of fruit, $\frac{4}{9}$, $\frac{2}{9}$, $\frac{3}{9}$, $\frac{0}{9}$

2. $\frac{1}{3}$, $\frac{2}{3}$, $\frac{1}{4}$, $\frac{2}{4}$, $\frac{3}{4}$ **3.** 46

4. 1,269 **5.** 210 **6.** 999

Home Link 8•5

4. $\frac{2}{4}$; $\frac{1}{2}$ **5.** $\frac{3}{6}$; $\frac{1}{2}$ **6.** $\frac{4}{8}$; $\frac{1}{2}$

8. 4 cats **9.** $\frac{4}{16}$

10. 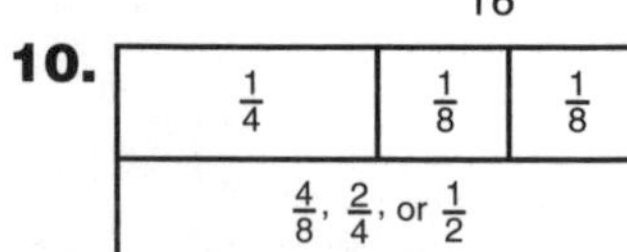

11.

$\frac{2}{6}$ or $\frac{1}{3}$	$\frac{1}{6}$	$\frac{1}{6}$
	$\frac{2}{6}$ or $\frac{1}{3}$	

Home Link 8•6

1. 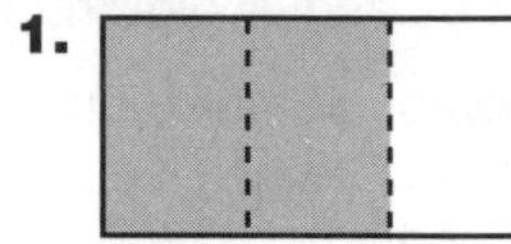 **2.** 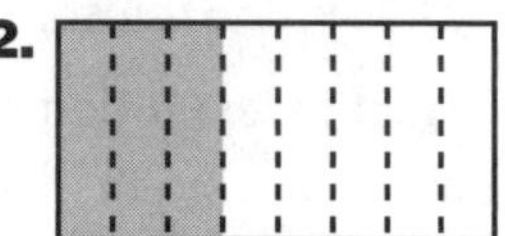

3. 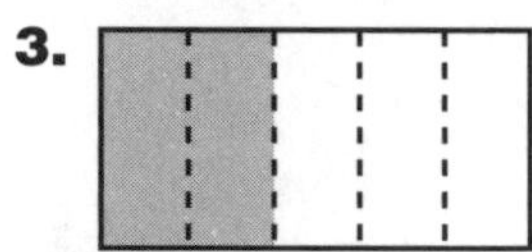 **4.** 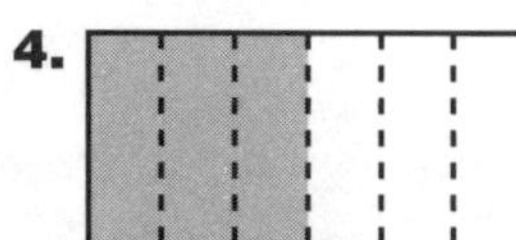

5. 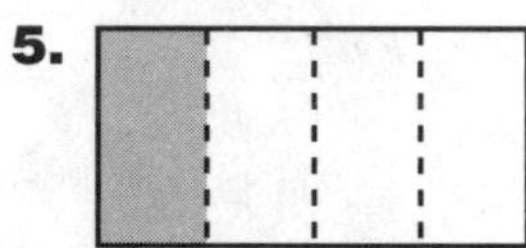 **6.** 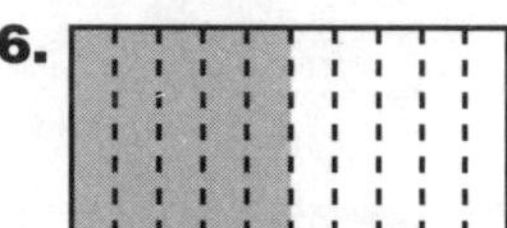

7. 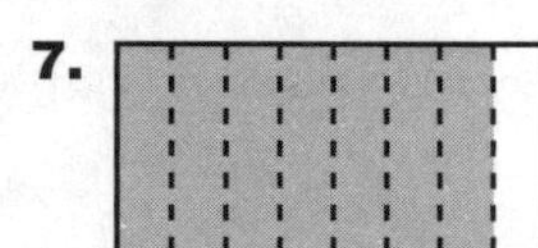 **8.** 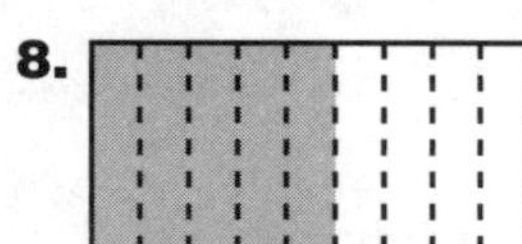

9. $\frac{2}{3}$, $\frac{7}{8}$, $\frac{5}{9}$ **10.** $\frac{3}{6}$, $\frac{5}{10}$ **11.** $>$

12. $<$ **13.** $>$ **14.** $=$ **15.** 56

16. 9 **17.** 3 **18.** 72

Home Link 8•7

1. 6; $\frac{6}{4}$; $1\frac{2}{4}$ or $1\frac{1}{2}$ **2.** 9; $\frac{9}{5}$; $1\frac{4}{5}$ **3.** 7; $\frac{7}{3}$; $2\frac{1}{3}$

4. $\frac{1}{12}$ **5.** $\frac{28}{12}$; $2\frac{4}{12}$ or $2\frac{1}{3}$ **6.** 13

7. 46 **8.** 124 **9.** 230

Home Link 8•8

1. 8 eggs **2.** $\frac{1}{4}$ of the lawn

3. 2 miles **4.** $1\frac{1}{4}$ trays

5. $\frac{1}{4}$ gallon **6.** 6,761

7. 2,908 **8.** 9,524

Copyright © Wright Group/McGraw-Hill

Name Date Time

Fractions All Around

Family Note Help your child understand the idea of the ONE as well as fractions of objects and sets. Help your child look for objects and pictures that have fractions or decimals printed on them.

Please return this Home Link to school tomorrow.

Each square flag below represents the ONE. Write the fractions that name each region inside each flag.

1. 

2. 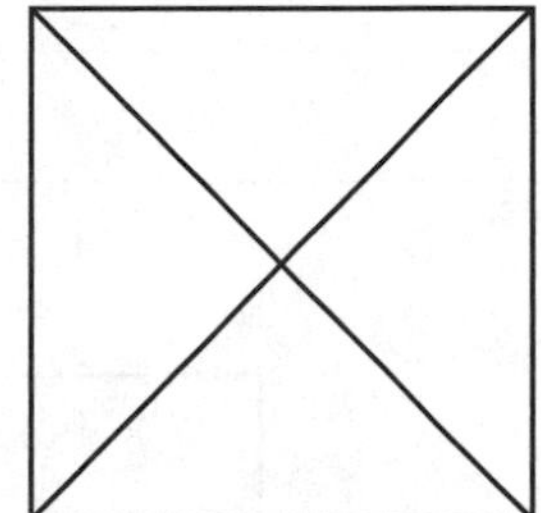

3. 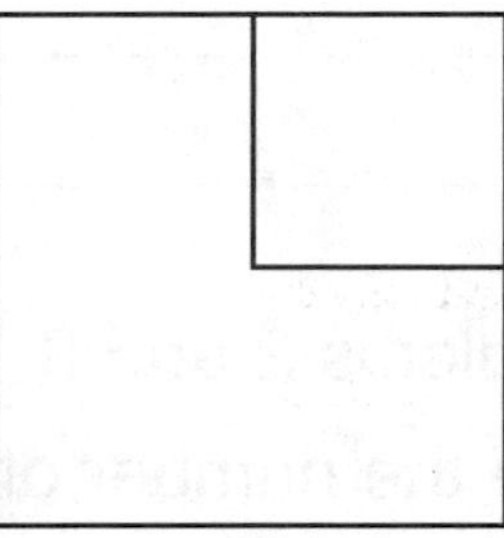

Write the fractions.

4. ______ of the buttons have 4 holes.

5. ______ of the buttons have 2 holes.

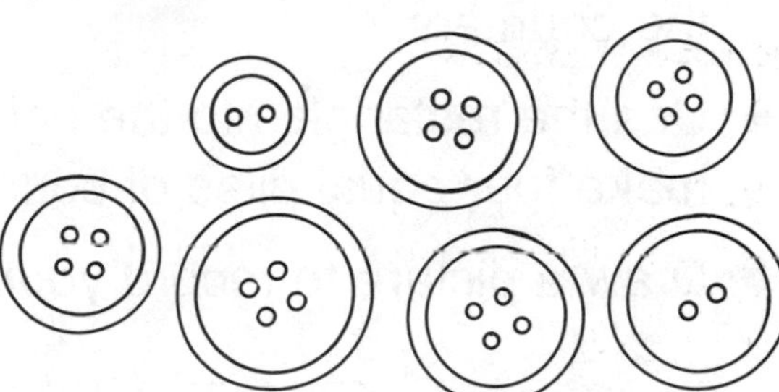

Look for items around your home that have fractions or decimals on them, such as recipes, measuring cups, wrenches, package labels, or pictures in newspapers. Ask permission to bring them to school to display in our Fractions Museum.

Unit

Solve. Show your work.

6. $275 - 88$

7. $684 - 97$

8. $429 - 237$

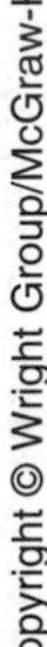
Copyright © Wright Group/McGraw-Hill

Name Date Time

Exploring Fractions

These show $\frac{1}{4}$.	These do **NOT** show $\frac{1}{4}$.
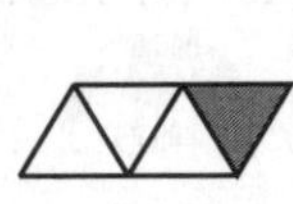 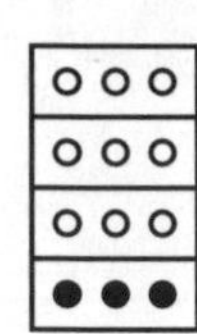 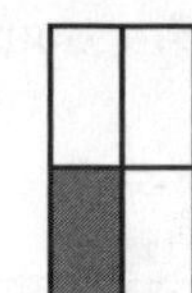 	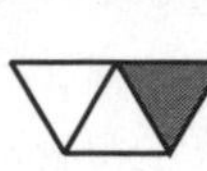 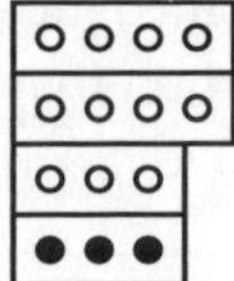 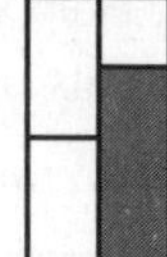 

1. Explain how you can tell whether something shows $\frac{1}{4}$.

____

____

For Problems 2 and 3—

- Take the number of counters.
- Figure out how to show $\frac{1}{4}$ of the counters.
- Use the rectangles to the right to make four equal piles of counters.
- Draw a picture to record your answer.

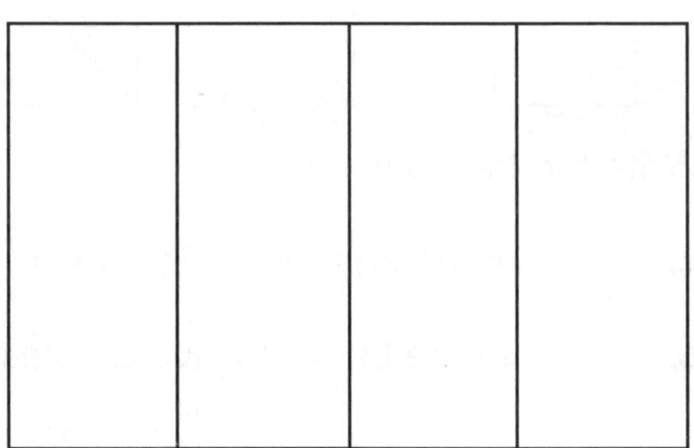

2. Take 8 counters. Show $\frac{1}{4}$ of the counters.

3. Take 20 counters. Show $\frac{1}{4}$ of 20 counters.

4. Divide the figure below into four equal parts.

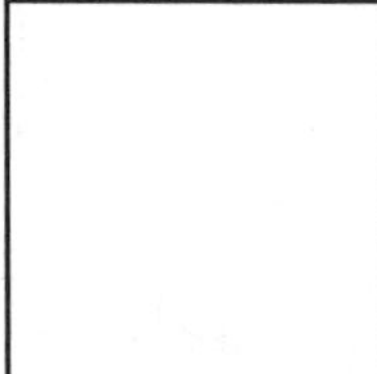

5. Divide the figure below into four equal parts another way.

Is $\frac{1}{4}$ in Problem 4 larger or $\frac{1}{4}$ in Problem 5 larger? Explain your answer on the back of your paper.

Copyright © Wright Group/McGraw-Hill

Name Date Time

Fraction Puzzles

Use centimeter cubes to help you solve the puzzles.

1. The 1st graders are building a little house with centimeter cubes. The drawing shows $\frac{2}{3}$ of the floor of their house. Use centimeter cubes to build the whole floor of the house. Then finish the picture.

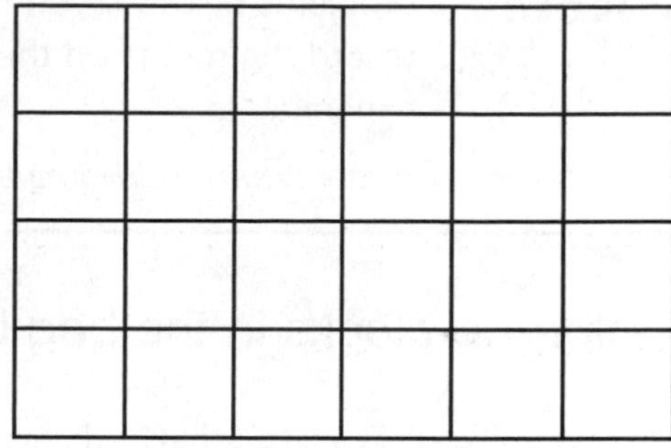

2. This drawing shows $\frac{7}{10}$ of a line segment. Use centimeter cubes to figure out how long the line segment is. Figure out how much longer the line segment should be to make it whole. Use a ruler to draw the rest of the whole line segment.

____

3. Make up a puzzle. Ask a partner to solve it.

This drawing shows $\frac{\square}{\square}$ of a ____________________.

Draw the whole ____________________.

Copyright © Wright Group/McGraw-Hill

Name Date Time

HOME LINK 8•2

Drawing Blocks

Family Note Have your child explain how to decide how many red blocks to put into each bag in the problems below. If you have time, do the block-drawing experiments with your child and record the results on the back of this page. Ask your child to explain how to do the experiments.

Please return this Home Link to school tomorrow.

Color the blocks in the bag blue.

Answer each question about how many red blocks to put into the bag.

Example: If I wanted to take out a blue block twice as often as a red block, I would put in 1 red block.

1. If I wanted to be sure to take out a blue block, I would put in ____ red block(s).

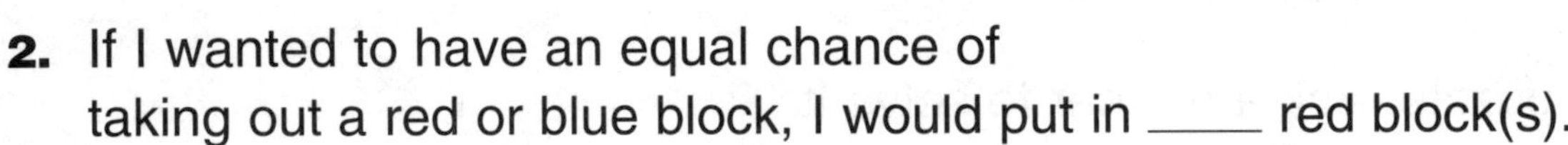

2. If I wanted to have an equal chance of taking out a red or blue block, I would put in ____ red block(s).

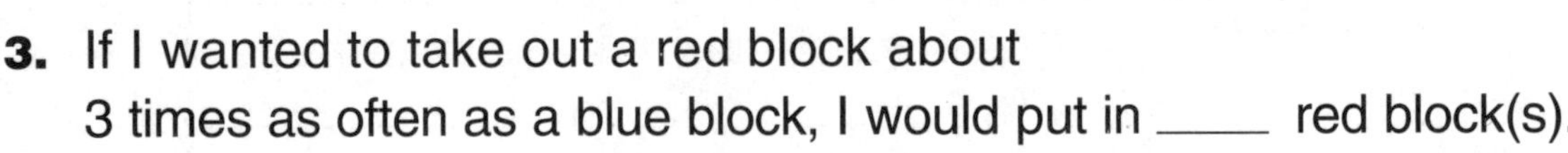

3. If I wanted to take out a red block about 3 times as often as a blue block, I would put in ____ red block(s).

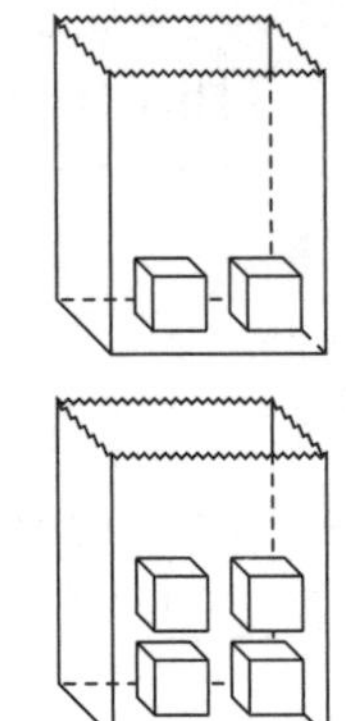

4. If I wanted to take out a red block about $\frac{1}{2}$ of the time, I would put in ______ red block(s).

Practice

Unit

Solve. Show your work.

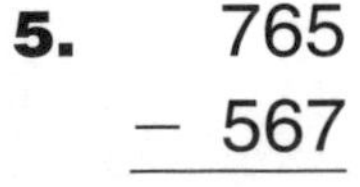

5. $765 - 567$

6. $987 - 789$

7. $432 - 234$

Copyright © Wright Group/McGraw-Hill

Name Date Time

Dice Data

Is it more likely that you will roll a 4 if you roll 1 die or that you will roll a sum of 4 if you roll 2 dice? ______________________

Check your prediction.

ONE DIE  Roll 1 die 20 times and keep a tally of the results.

1	2	3	4	5	6

(You should have 20 tally marks in the chart when you are done.)

- ◆ What fraction of the time did you roll a 4? $\frac{\square}{20}$
- ◆ What fraction of the time did you roll an even number? $\frac{\square}{20}$

If you roll 2 dice, do you think the sum is less likely, more likely, or equally likely to be even? ______________________
Check your prediction.

TWO DICE   Roll 2 dice 20 times and keep a tally of the results.

2	3	4	5	6	7	8	9	10	11	12

(You should have 20 tally marks in the chart when you are done.)

- ◆ What fraction of the time did you roll a sum of 4? $\frac{\square}{20}$
- ◆ What fraction of the time did you roll a sum of an even number? $\frac{\square}{20}$

Describe how rolling 1 die is the same as and different from rolling 2 dice. Think about which results are the same and which results are different. Write your answers on the back of this page.

Copyright © Wright Group/McGraw-Hill

Name Date Time

LESSON 8•3

Taking Apart and Putting Together

Exploration B

Materials ☐ *Math Masters,* p. 243 (2 squares)

☐ scissors

☐ glue or tape

☐ paper

There are two squares on *Math Masters,* page 243. Your task is to cut each square into pieces, and then to put all the pieces from both squares together to make one large square. DON'T START YET!

- Plan what you will do before you cut. It is possible to solve the puzzle by cutting each square into 2 pieces. You can also solve the puzzle by cutting each square into more than 2 pieces.
- Cut only on the dashed lines.
- Use all of the pieces.
- Don't leave any empty spaces between the pieces.
- Don't overlap any pieces.
- Glue or tape your finished square onto a full sheet of paper.
- Now cut out the two squares on *Math Masters,* page 243 and solve the puzzle.

Copyright © Wright Group/McGraw-Hill

Name Date Time

LESSON 8·3

Taking Apart *continued*

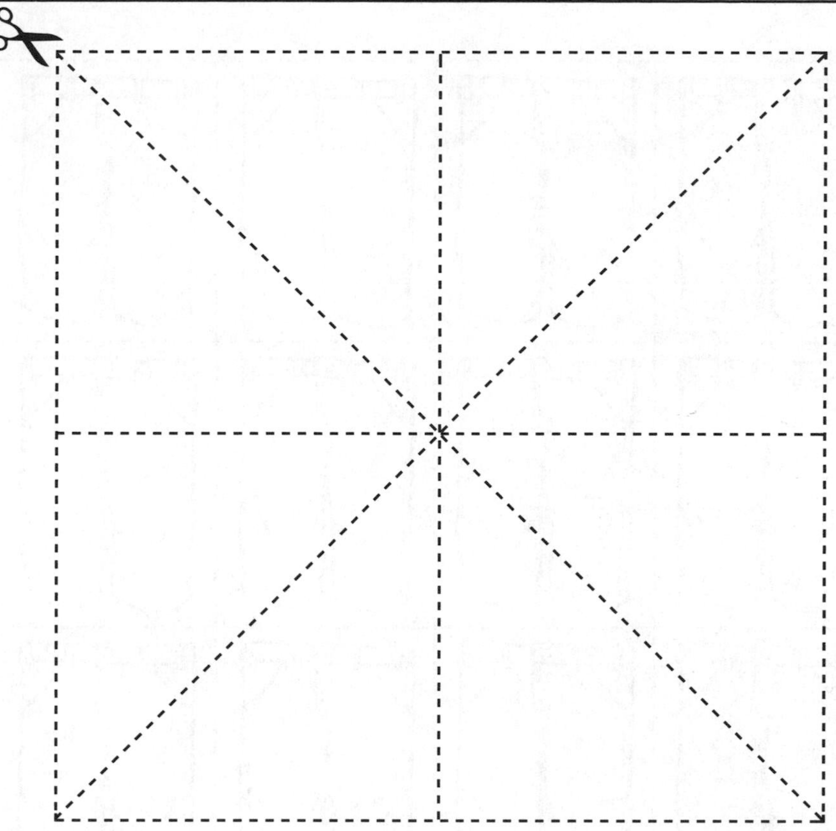

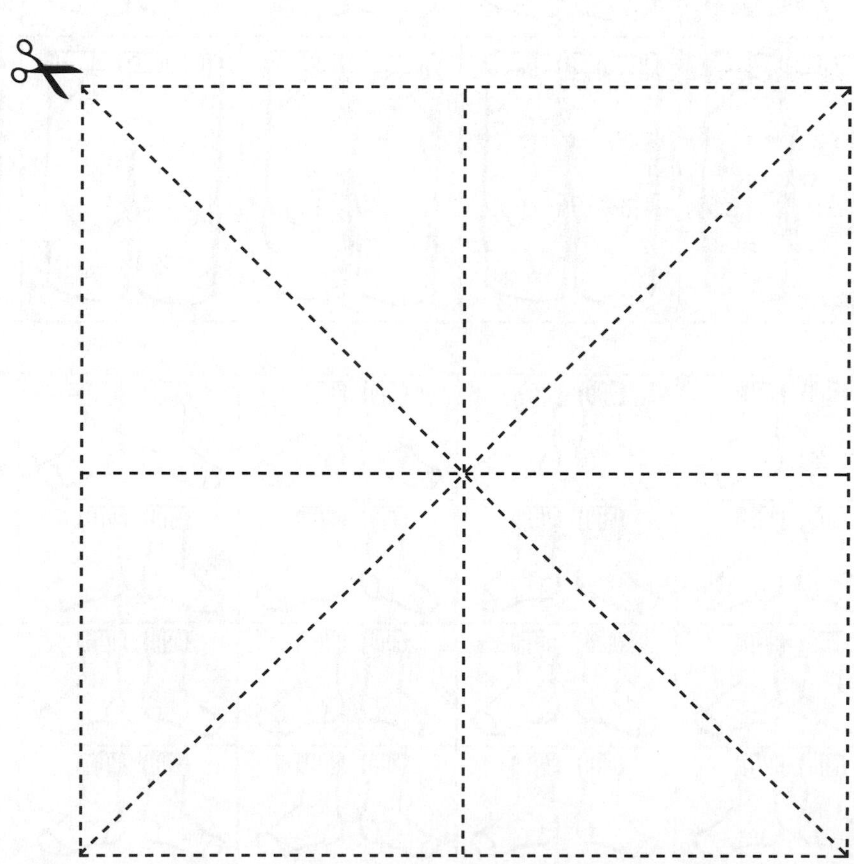

Copyright © Wright Group/McGraw-Hill

Name Date Time

LESSON 8•3

Pants and Socks Cutouts

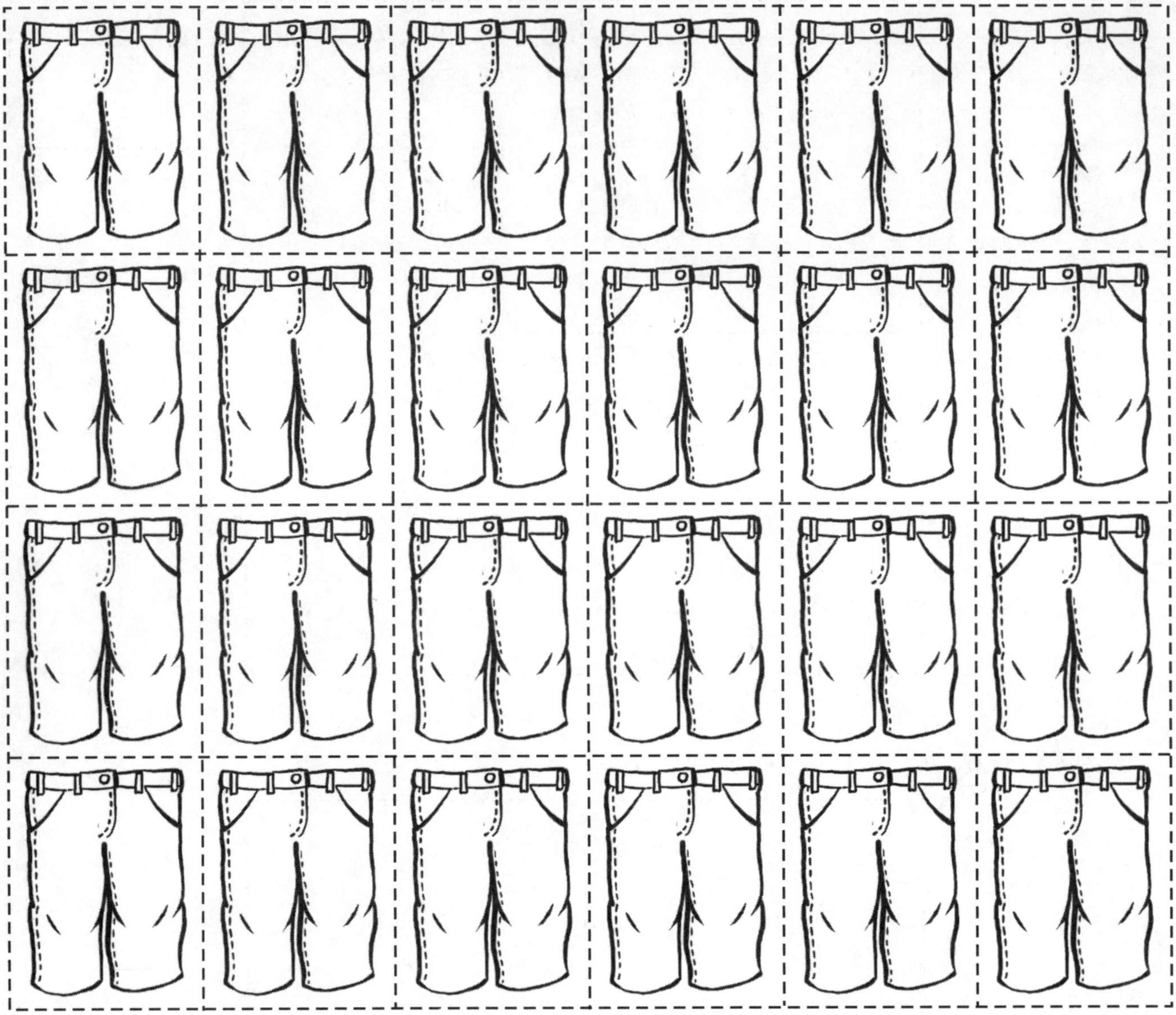

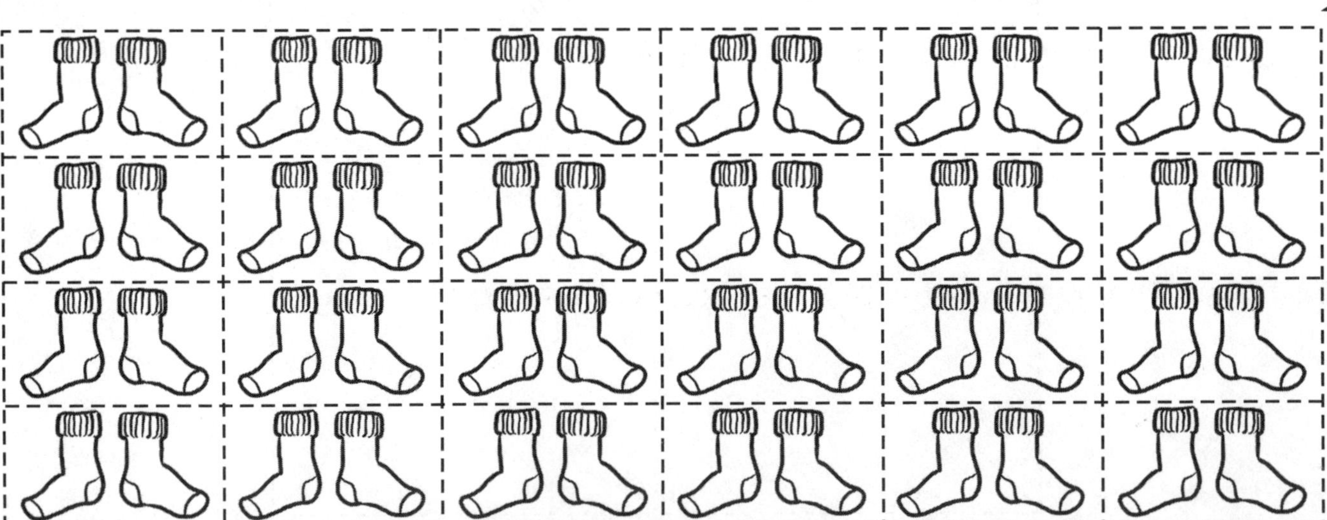

Copyright © Wright Group/McGraw-Hill

Name Date Time

Fraction Number Stories

Family Note Your child may benefit from modeling the number stories with pennies or counters. Help your child think about the problems as stories about equal shares or equal groups.
Please return this Home Link to school tomorrow.

Solve each problem. Tell someone at home how you did it.
Draw a picture on the back if it will help.

1. Lucy was playing a card game with 2 friends.
They were playing with a deck of 21 cards.
Lucy dealt $\frac{1}{3}$ of the deck to each person.
How many cards did Lucy get? _____ cards

2. Jonathan bought 12 pencils. He gave $\frac{1}{2}$ of them to his brother and $\frac{1}{4}$ of them to his friend Mike.
How many pencils did he give to Mike? _____ pencils

3. Gerard was reading a book with 40 pages.
He read 10 pages in an hour.
What fraction of the book did he read in an hour? __________

4. Melissa was reading a book with 50 pages.
She read 10 pages in an hour.
What fraction of the book did she read in an hour? __________

Follow the instructions below.

5. Draw 15 small circles. Circle $\frac{3}{5}$ of them.

6. Draw 12 small circles. Put an X through $\frac{3}{4}$ of them.

Copyright © Wright Group/McGraw-Hill

Name Date Time

Pattern-Block Puzzles

You will need your Pattern-Block Template and pattern blocks.

1. Cover the hexagon with triangle blocks. Use your template to trace the shapes on the hexagon.

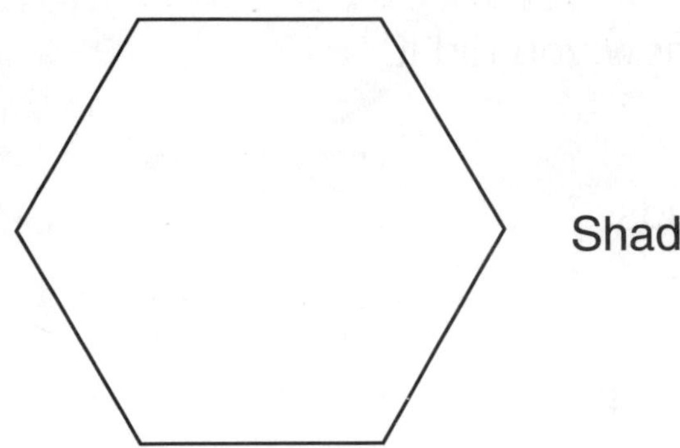

Shade 1 △.

Shaded part = $\frac{1}{\square}$

Part not shaded = $\frac{\square}{\square}$

2. Cover the hexagon with blue rhombus blocks. Use your template to trace the shapes on the hexagon.

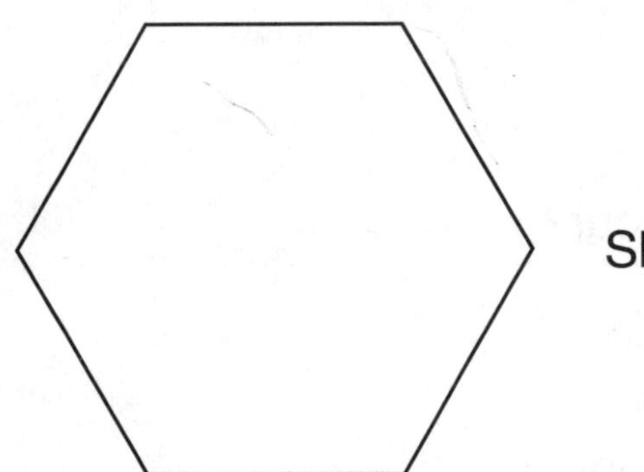

Shade 1 ◇.

Shaded part = $\frac{1}{\square}$

Part not shaded = $\frac{\square}{\square}$

3. Cover the polygon with triangle and blue rhombus blocks. Use your template to trace the shapes on the polygon.

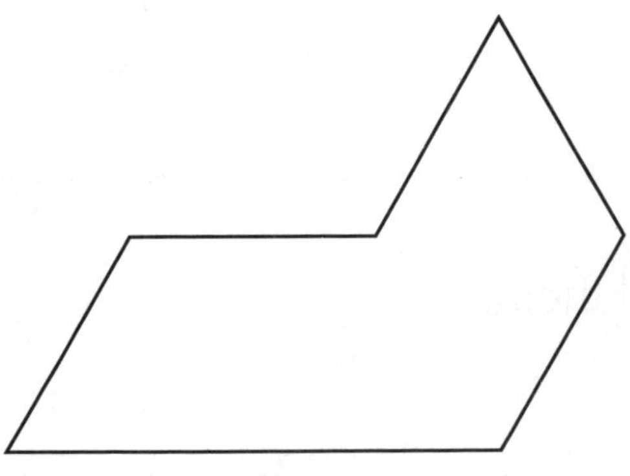

Shade 1 △.

Shaded part = $\frac{1}{\square}$

Part not shaded = $\frac{\square}{\square}$

Copyright © Wright Group/McGraw-Hill

Name Date Time

LESSON 8•4

Fraction Strips

Cut on the dashed lines.

1 Whole

0 1

Halves

Fourths

Eighths

Thirds

Sixths

Copyright © Wright Group/McGraw-Hill

Name Date Time

HOME LINK 8•4

Fraction Puzzles

Family Note We have been working with fractions of regions and sets. Ask your child to explain how he or she knows which fractions to write in Problem 1. Today we began to think of fractions on a number line. For Problem 2, help your child count the number of intervals from 0 to 1 in order to figure out which fraction each small mark indicates.

Please return this Home Link to school tomorrow.

SRB 22 24 26

1. How many pieces of fruit are shown? ____________

_____ of the fruit are bananas.

_____ of the fruit are pears.

_____ of the fruit are apples.

What fraction of the fruit are oranges? _____

2. Fill in the missing numbers on each number line.

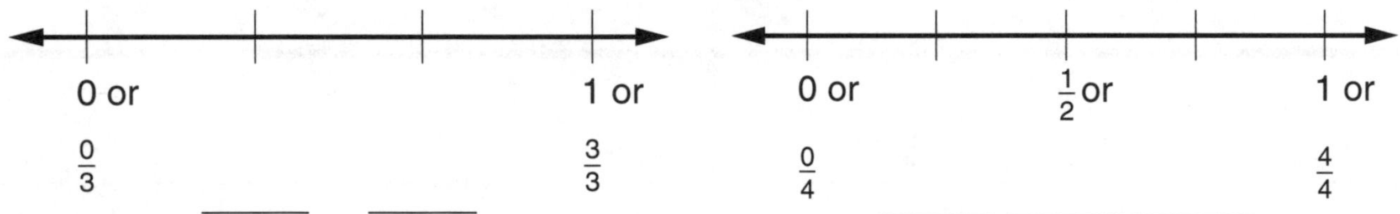

0 or $\frac{0}{3}$ _____ _____ 1 or $\frac{3}{3}$

0 or $\frac{0}{4}$ _____ $\frac{1}{2}$ or _____ _____ 1 or $\frac{4}{4}$

Practice

Write these problems on the back of this page. Solve and show your work.

3. $444 - 398 =$ _____

4. $777 + 492 =$ _________

5. ______ $= 888 - 678$

6. $324 =$ ______ $- 675$

Continue to look for items and pictures that have fractions or decimals on them. Ask for permission to bring them to school for the Fractions Museum.

Copyright © Wright Group/McGraw-Hill

Name Date Time

LESSON 8•4 Comparing Rulers & Number Lines

1. Look at your ruler and the Class Number Line.

   How is a ruler like a number line?

   ____

   ____

2. Look at the small lines between 0 and 1 on the inch ruler. What do these small lines mean?

   ____

   ____

3. Give examples of numbers that come between 0 and 1.

   ____

4. Look at the magnified inches on *Math Masters,* page 250.

   Fill in the blanks under each ruler with the correct fractions.

   How did you know which fractions to write?

   ____

   ____

   ____

   ____

   ____

Copyright © Wright Group/McGraw-Hill

Name Date Time

LESSON 8·4

Comparing Rulers & Number Lines *cont.*

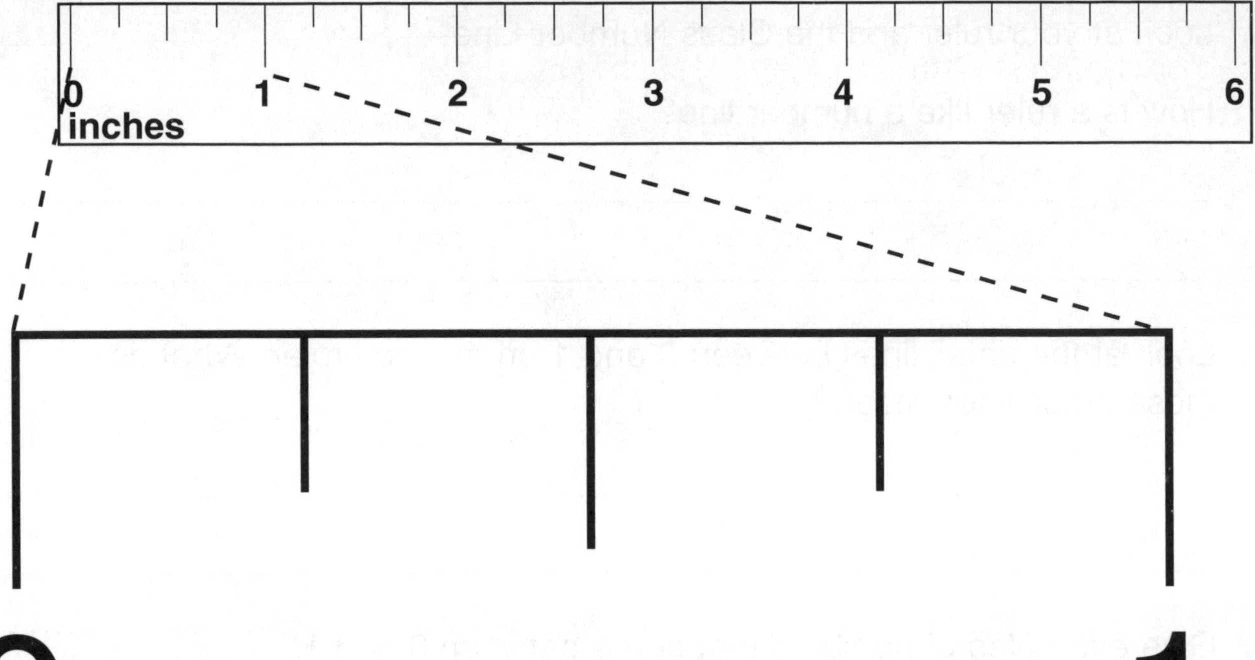

0 ____ ____ ____ 1

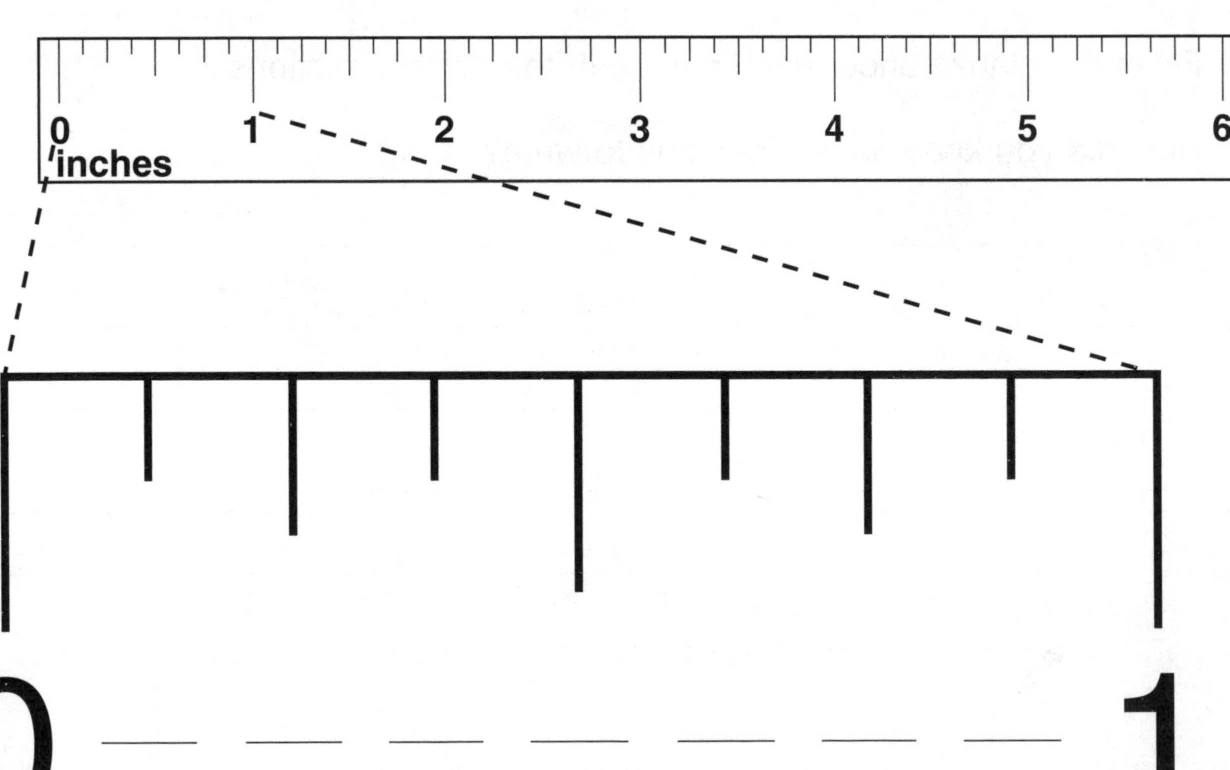

0 ____ ____ ____ ____ ____ ____ ____ 1

Copyright © Wright Group/McGraw-Hill

Name Date Time

Solving Fraction-Strip Problems

Use a set of fraction strips from *Math Masters,* page 247 to solve the problems on this page.

You may want to fold each strip to different lengths to model the problems below.

For each problem, record the answer by tracing the number line for the separate fraction-strip pieces with a different color on the blank fraction-strip number line. Label each piece that you trace.

Example: Without using eighths, which 2 different fraction-strip pieces could you use to make a fraction strip that is as long as $\frac{6}{8}$?

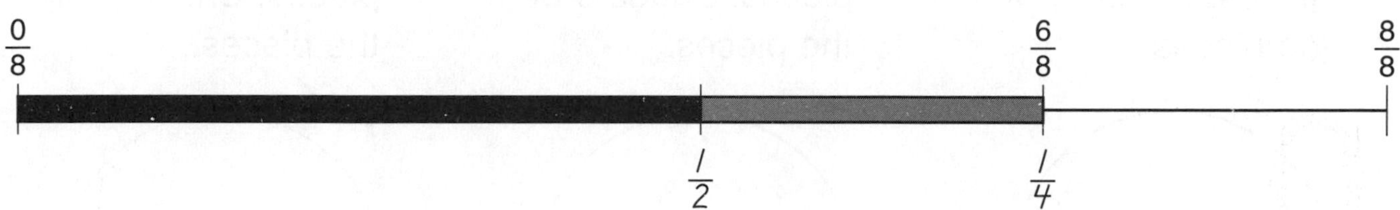

1. Without using fourths, which 2 different fraction-strip pieces could you use to make a fraction strip that is as long as $\frac{3}{4}$? __________

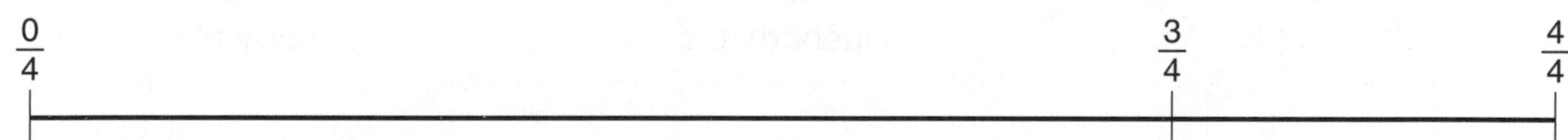

2. Without using thirds, which 2 different fraction-strip pieces could you use to make a fraction strip that is as long as $\frac{2}{3}$? __________

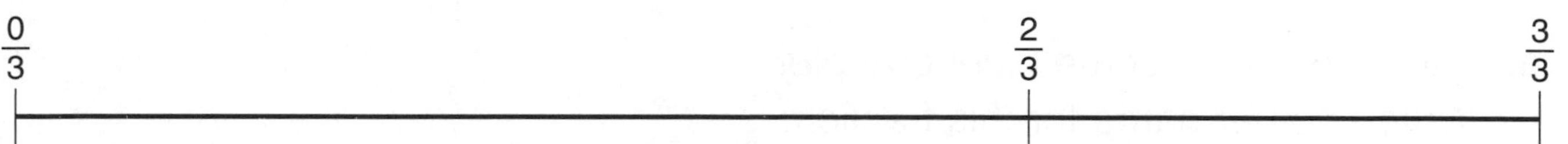

3. Without using sixths, which 2 different fraction-strip pieces could you use to make a fraction strip that is as long as $\frac{5}{6}$? __________

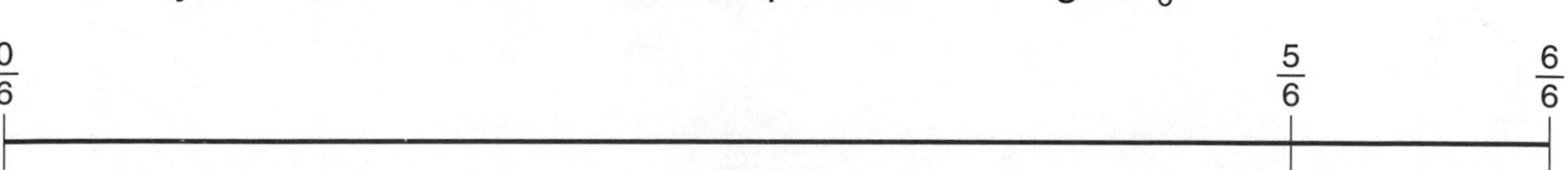

4. On the back of this page, make up a fraction-strip problem.

Copyright © Wright Group/McGraw-Hill

Name Date Time

Equivalent Fractions

Family Note The class continues fraction work by finding equivalent names for fractions. Different fractions that name the same amount are called equivalent fractions. The fractions that complete Problems 4–6 are equivalent. If needed, help your child name the fractional parts in these problems. Ask your child to explain the fraction name she or he chooses in Problem 9—a fraction that is equivalent to $\frac{1}{4}$ and describes the fraction of cats circled.

Please return this Home Link to school tomorrow.

The pictures show three kinds of pie. Use a straightedge to do the following:

1. Divide the peach pie into 4 equal pieces. Shade 2 of the pieces.

2. Divide the blueberry pie into 6 equal pieces. Shade 3 of the pieces.

3. Divide the cherry pie into 8 equal pieces. Shade 4 of the pieces.

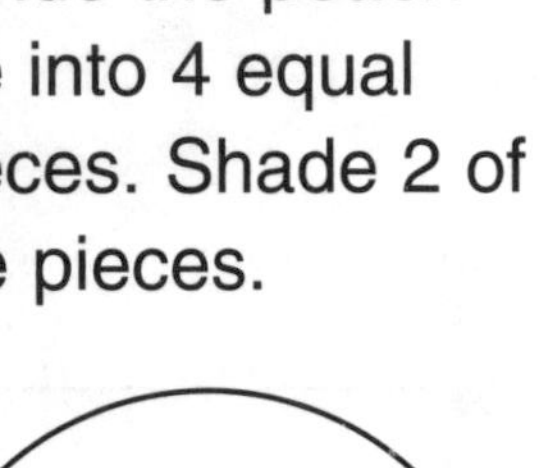

peach pie

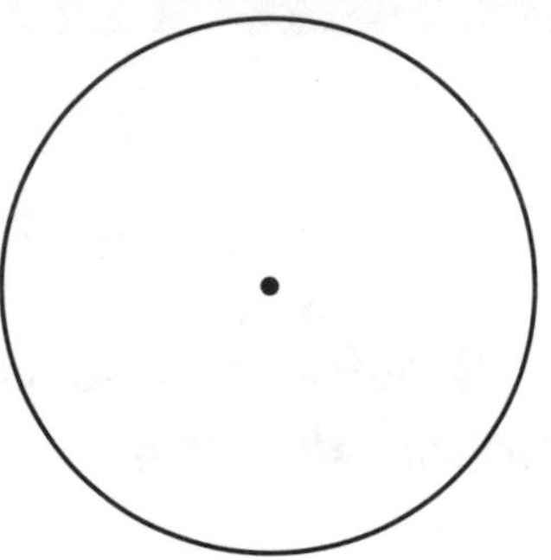

blueberry pie

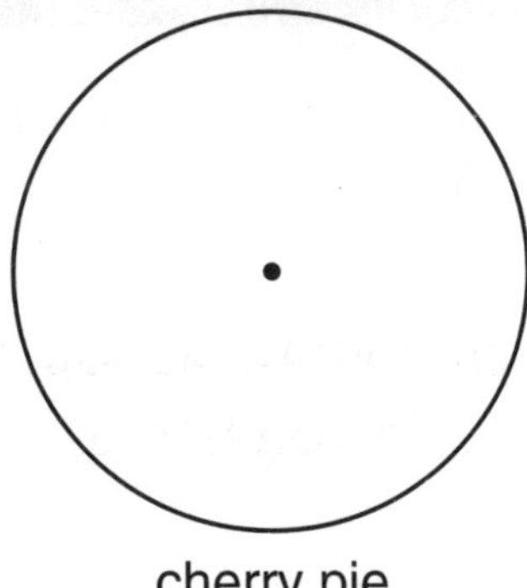

cherry pie

What fraction of each pie did you shade?

4. I shaded _____ of the peach pie.
Write another name for this fraction: _____

5. I shaded _____ of the blueberry pie.
Write another name for this fraction: _____

6. I shaded _____ of the cherry pie.
Write another name for this fraction: _____

Copyright © Wright Group/McGraw-Hill

Name Date Time

Equivalent Fractions *continued*

7. Circle $\frac{1}{4}$ of the cats.

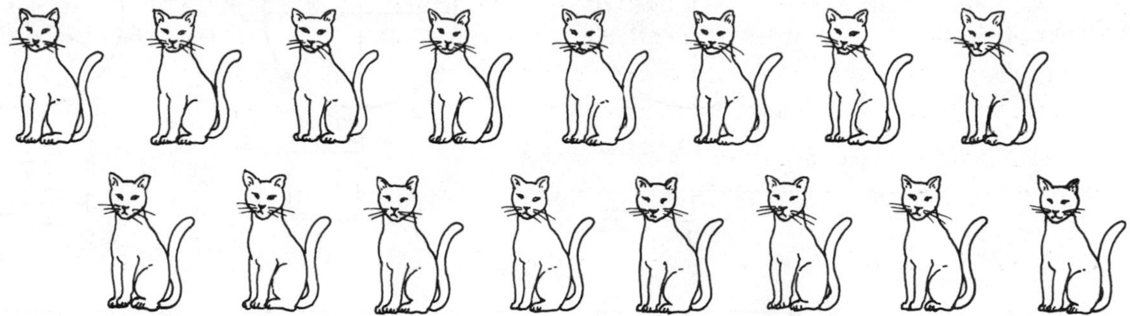

8. How many cats did you circle? __________

9. Write a fraction that describes the group of cats you circled and that is equivalent to $\frac{1}{4}$. __________

Each whole rectangle below is ONE. Write a fraction inside each part.

10.

$\frac{1}{4}$

11.

$\frac{1}{6}$

Copyright © Wright Group/McGraw-Hill

Name Date Time

LESSON 8•5 Equivalent Fractions in Shapes

1. Shade $\frac{1}{2}$ of each circle. Complete the fractions.

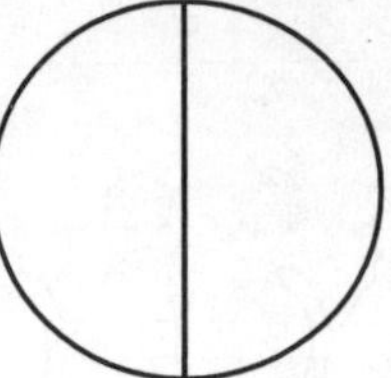

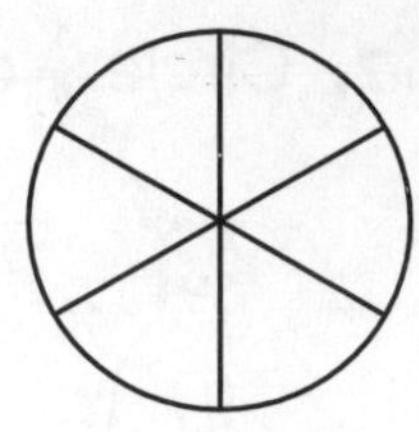

$\frac{1}{2}$

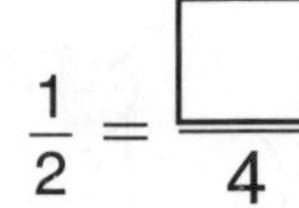

$\frac{1}{2} = \frac{\square}{4}$

$\frac{1}{2} = \frac{\square}{6}$

2. Shade $\frac{1}{3}$ of each rectangle. Complete the fractions.

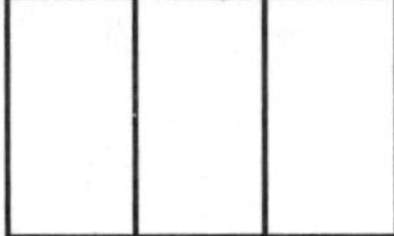

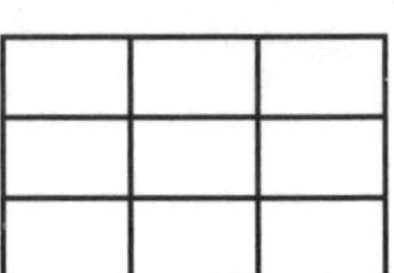

$\frac{1}{3}$

$\frac{1}{3} = \frac{\square}{6}$

$\frac{1}{3} = \frac{\square}{9}$

3. Make up your own:

Shade $\frac{\square}{\square}$ of each square. Write the fractions.

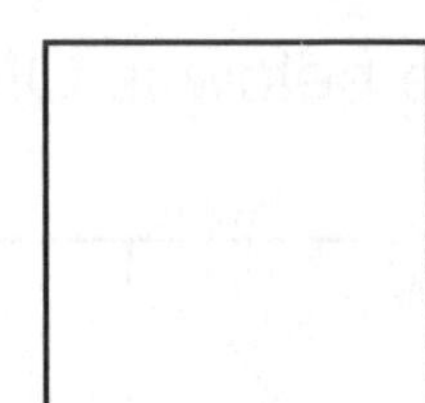

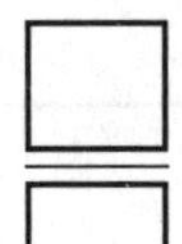

$\frac{\square}{\square} = \frac{\square}{\square}$

$\frac{\square}{\square} = \frac{\square}{\square}$

Copyright © Wright Group/McGraw-Hill

Name Date Time

LESSON 8•5 Rules for Equivalent Fractions

1. Look at *Math Journal 2,* page 194. Record the fractions equivalent to $\frac{1}{2}$ below. As you record them, put them in an order that will help you find a pattern.

$\frac{1}{2}$	

2. Use your pattern to write a rule for finding equivalent fractions. Write your rule on the lines below.

____

____

Try your rule to see whether it works. List 3 other fractions equivalent to $\frac{1}{2}$ using your rule. (Use pictures or counters to check your fractions.)

_____ _____ _____

3. Use your rule to find 2 fractions equivalent to $\frac{1}{3}$. _____ _____
Check your answers with the Fraction Cards.

Try This

4. Use your rule to find equivalent fractions for the fractions in the table below. Show any work that you do on the back of this page.

Fraction	Equivalent Fractions
$\frac{1}{8}$	
$\frac{5}{8}$	
$\frac{2}{9}$	

Copyright © Wright Group/McGraw-Hill

Name Date Time

HOME LINK 8·6

Comparing Fractions to $\frac{1}{2}$

Family Note Your child's class is comparing fractions to determine whether they are larger, smaller, or equal to $\frac{1}{2}$. Ask your child to explain how to tell which category a fraction fits into. For more on this topic, see *Student Reference Book* pages 13, 31, and 32.

Please return this Home Link to school tomorrow.

Shade each rectangle to match the fraction below it. **Example:** $\frac{2}{4}$

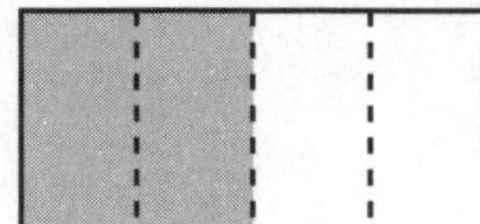

1. 

$\frac{2}{3}$

2. 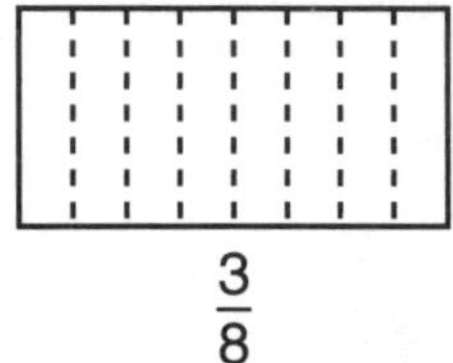

$\frac{3}{8}$

3. 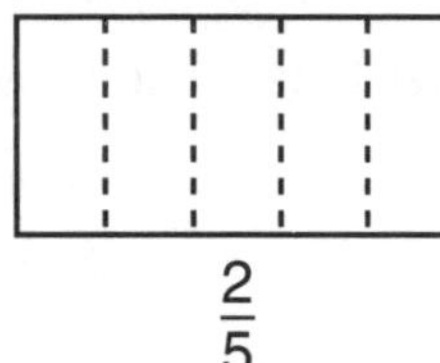

$\frac{2}{5}$

4. 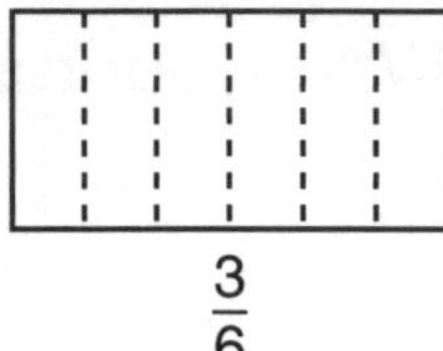

$\frac{3}{6}$

5. 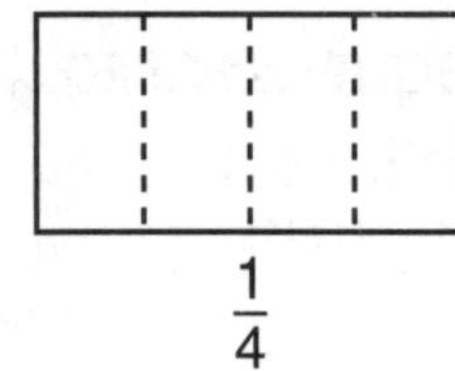

$\frac{1}{4}$

6. 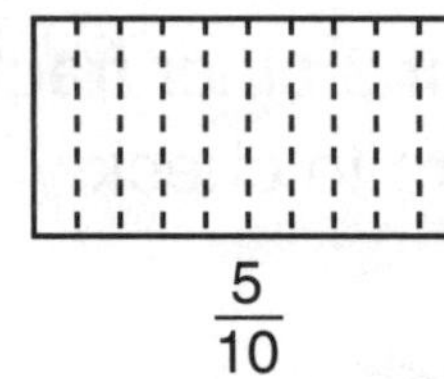

$\frac{5}{10}$

7. 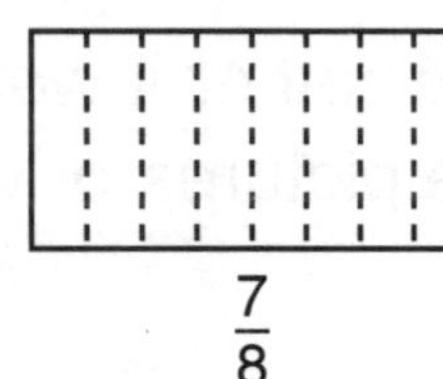

$\frac{7}{8}$

8. 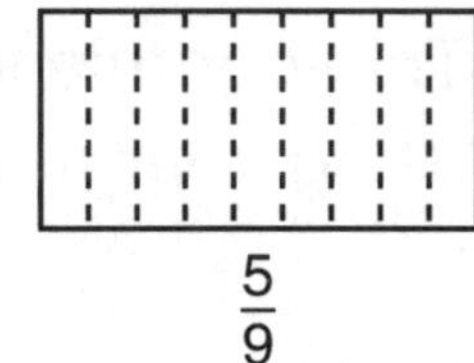

$\frac{5}{9}$

9. List the fractions above that are greater than $\frac{1}{2}$. __________

10. List the fractions above that are equal to $\frac{1}{2}$. __________

Insert $<$, $>$, or $=$ in each problem below. Draw pictures to help you.

11. $\frac{6}{8}$ ______ $\frac{1}{2}$ **12.** $\frac{2}{9}$ ______ $\frac{1}{2}$

13. $\frac{10}{12}$ ______ $\frac{1}{2}$ **14.** $\frac{6}{12}$ ______ $\frac{1}{2}$

$<$ means *is less than*
$>$ means *is greater than*
$=$ means *is equal to*

Practice

Solve.

15. $7 \times 8 =$ __________ **16.** $54 = 6 \times$ __________

17. $8 \times$ __________ $= 24$ **18.** $9 \times 8 =$ __________

Copyright © Wright Group/McGraw-Hill

Name Date Time

Exploring Fraction Patterns

For each problem, record your work on the grid below.

1. Use a straightedge to divide the square into halves. Label each $\frac{1}{2}$ on your drawing.

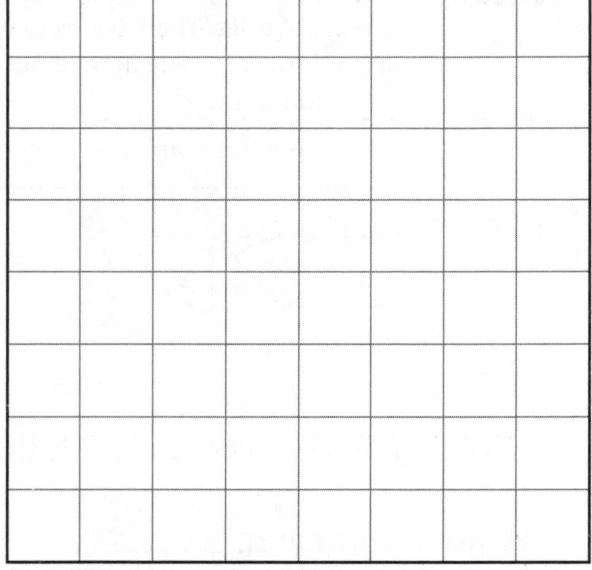

This is the WHOLE or ONE.

2. Use a straightedge to divide one of your halves into 2 equal parts.

   What fraction of the WHOLE is each new section worth? ______

   Write the fraction equivalent to $\frac{1}{2}$. ______

3. Use a straightedge to divide one of your smallest sections into 2 equal parts.

   What fraction of the WHOLE is each new section worth? ______

   Write the fraction equivalent to $\frac{1}{2}$. ______

4. If you were to divide your smallest section into 2 equal parts, what fraction of the WHOLE would each new section be worth?

   ______ Write the fraction equivalent to $\frac{1}{2}$. ______

5. On the back of your paper, list at least three patterns you notice in the fractions you have made on the grid and the fractions you have written on this paper.

Copyright © Wright Group/McGraw-Hill

Name Date Time

HOME LINK 8•7

Fractions and Mixed Numbers

Family Note Today the class began looking at fractions greater than 1 and mixed numbers. We have been working with region or area models (shaded areas) for these numbers. Problem 5 asks about fractions of a set. The *whole* is a dozen eggs, so each egg is $\frac{1}{12}$ of the whole. Have your child explain how he or she figured out what the fraction and mixed number should be for the egg-carton drawings.

Please return this Home Link to school tomorrow.

1.

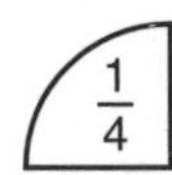

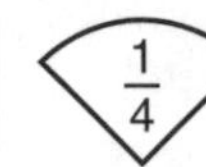

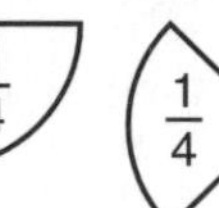

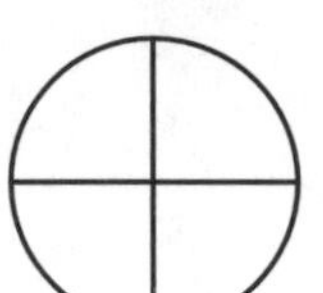

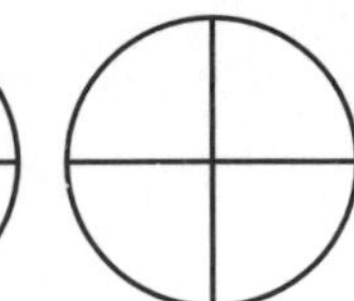

How many fourths? ______ fourths

Color 6 fourths.

Write the fraction: ______

Write the mixed number: ______

2.

How many fifths? ______ fifths

Color 9 fifths.

Write the fraction: ______

Write the mixed number: ______

3.

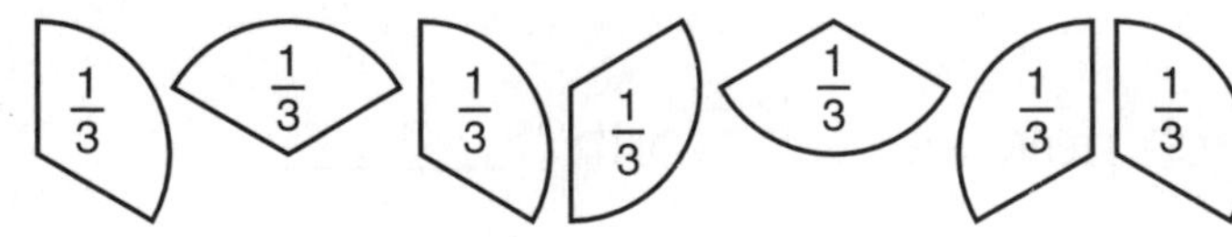

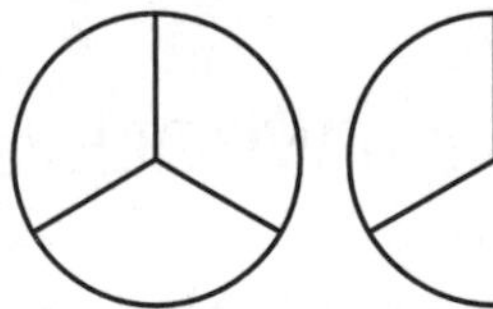

How many thirds? ______ thirds

Color 7 thirds.

Write the fraction: ______

Write the mixed number: ______

Copyright © Wright Group/McGraw-Hill

Name Date Time

HOME LINK 8•7

Fractions and Mixed Numbers *cont.*

Try This

4.

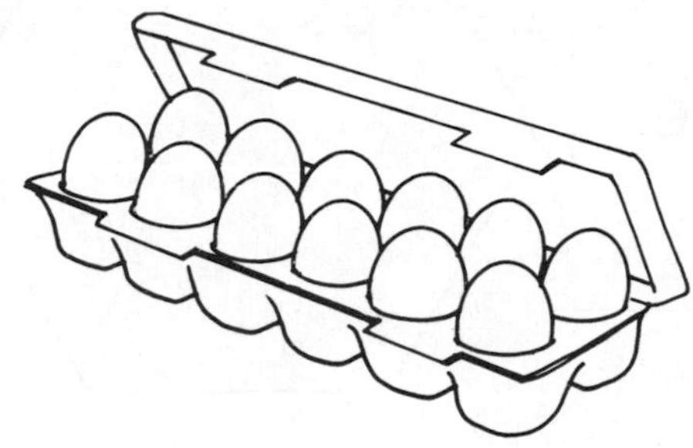

What fraction of the WHOLE carton is each egg? $\frac{\square}{12}$

5.

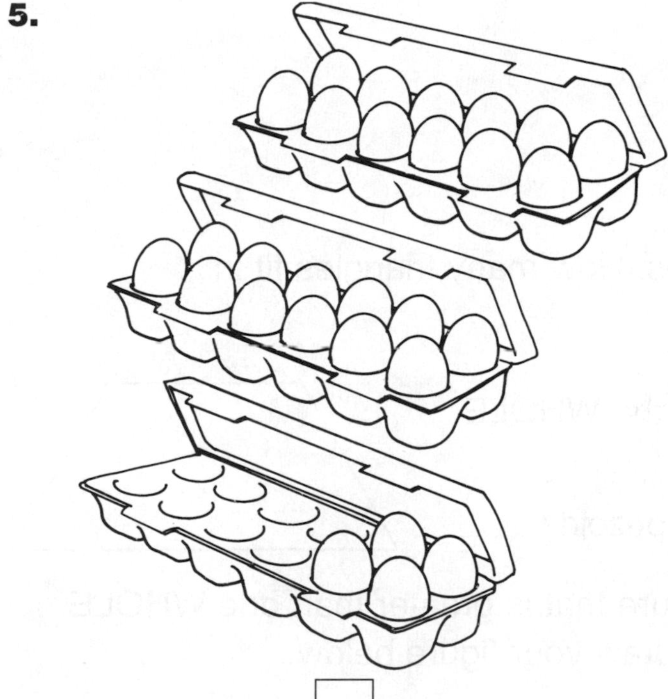

Write the fraction: $\frac{\square}{12}$

Write the fraction as a mixed number: $\square \frac{\square}{12}$

Practice

Write these problems on the back of this page. Solve and show your work.

6. $301 - 288$

7. $27 + 19$

8. $600 - 476$

9. $131 + 99$

Copyright © Wright Group/McGraw-Hill

Name Date Time

Comparing Figures

Use only triangles, rhombuses, trapezoids, and hexagons from your pattern blocks to solve the problems below.

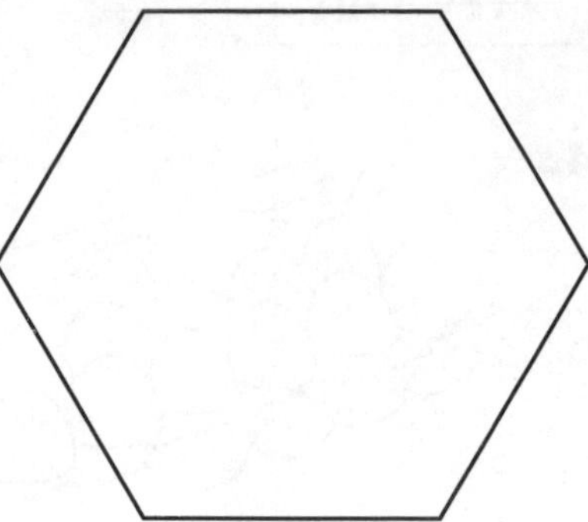

1. One hexagon is the WHOLE. Cover the WHOLE with triangles.

   How many triangles fit in the whole hexagon? ______

   Use your pattern blocks to build a figure that is greater than one WHOLE. Use your Pattern-Block Template to draw your figure below.

   Cover your new drawing with triangles. How many triangles fit in your figure? ____________________

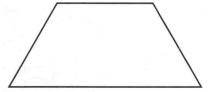

2. One trapezoid is the WHOLE. Cover the WHOLE with triangles.

   How many triangles fit in the whole trapezoid? ______

   Use your pattern blocks to build a figure that is greater than one WHOLE. Use your Pattern-Block Template to draw your figure below.

   Cover your new drawing with triangles. How many triangles is your figure worth? ____________________

Copyright © Wright Group/McGraw-Hill

Name Date Time

LESSON 8•7

Fractions on a Number Line

1. Identify at least 3 fractions that are between 80 and 81. On a half-sheet of paper, record your fractions as mixed numbers and as fractions. Then place them on the number line below.

80 ←——————————————————→ 81

2. Identify at least 3 fractions that are between 2 and 5. On a half-sheet of paper, record your fractions as mixed numbers and as fractions. Then place them on the number line below.

2 ←——————————————————→ 5

Copyright © Wright Group/McGraw-Hill

Name Date Time

Fraction Number Stories

Family Note In class we have been solving many kinds of fraction number stories. If some of these Home Link problems seem difficult, encourage your child to model them with pennies or draw pictures to help solve them.

Please return this Home Link to school tomorrow.

SRB 22–24

Solve these fraction stories. Use pennies, counters, or pictures to help.

1. Elizabeth bought a dozen eggs. She dropped her bag on the way home, and $\frac{2}{3}$ of the eggs broke. How many eggs broke? _____ eggs

2. Katie mowed $\frac{3}{4}$ of the lawn before lunch. What fraction of the lawn did she have to finish after lunch? _____ of the lawn

3. Donnie lives 1 mile from school. One day he walked $\frac{1}{2}$ of the way to school when he remembered he had to return home to get a book. When he finally made it to school, how far did he walk in all? _____ miles

4. Sheridan made 4 trays of cookies. She took 2 trays to school for her classmates. She took $\frac{3}{4}$ of a tray of cookies to her teacher. How many trays of cookies did Sheridan have left? _____ trays

5. Jackson needed 2 pints of milk for his recipe. If he had one gallon of milk in the refrigerator, how much did he use? (*Hint:* 1 gallon = 4 quarts, and 1 quart = 2 pints) _____ gallon

Practice

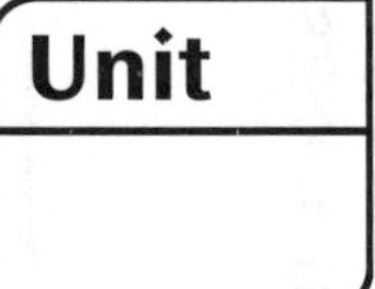

Write these problems on the back of this page. Solve and show your work.

6. 2,083 + 4,678 = __________

7. 6,714 − 3,806 = __________

8. 4,762 + 4,762 = __________

Copyright © Wright Group/McGraw-Hill

Name Date Time

HOME LINK 8•9

Unit 9: Family Letter

Multiplication and Division

In Unit 9, children will develop a variety of strategies for multiplying whole numbers. They will begin by using mental math (computation done by counting fingers, drawing pictures, making diagrams, and computing in one's head). Later in this unit, children will be introduced to two specific algorithms, or methods, for multiplication: the partial-products algorithm and the lattice method.

Partial-Products Algorithm

The partial-products algorithm is a variation of the traditional multiplication algorithm that most adults learned as children. Note that the multiplication is done from left to right and emphasizes place value in the numbers being multiplied.

		28	
		× 4	
Multiply 4 × 20.	→	80	First, calculate 4 [20s].
Multiply 4 × 8.	→	+ 32	Then calculate 4 [8s].
Add the two partial products.	→	112	Finally, add the two partial products.

It is important that when children verbalize this method, they understand and say *4 [20s],* not *4 × 2.* In doing so, they gain a better understanding of the magnitude of numbers along with better number sense.

		379	
		× 4	
Multiply 4 × 300.	→	1,200	First, calculate 4 [300s].
Multiply 4 × 70.	→	280	Second, calculate 4 [70s].
Multiply 4 × 9.	→	+ 36	Then calculate 4 [9s].
Add the three partial products.	→	1,516	Finally, add the three partial products.

Check that when your child is verbalizing this strategy, he or she says *4 [300s],* not *4 × 3;* and *4 [70s],* not *4 × 7.* Using this strategy will also help to reinforce your child's facility with the basic multiplication facts and their extensions.

Copyright © Wright Group/McGraw-Hill

Lattice Method

Third Grade Everyday Mathematics introduces the lattice method of multiplication for several reasons: This algorithm is historically interesting; it provides practice with multiplication facts and addition of 1-digit numbers; and it is fun. Also, some children find it easier to use than other methods of multiplication.

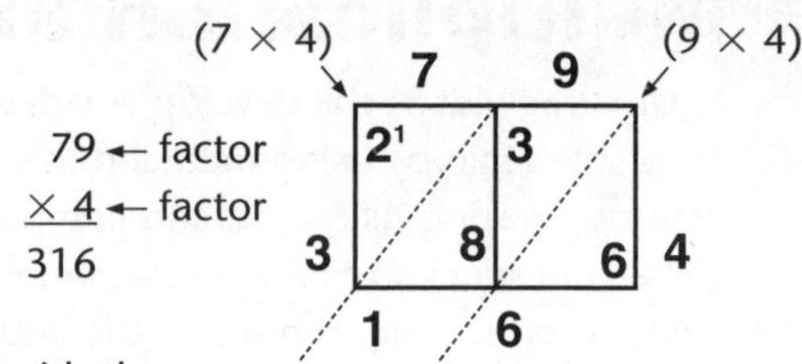

Step 1 Write the factors on the outside of the lattice. Line up one factor with the column(s); the other with the row(s).

Step 2 Multiply each digit in one factor by each digit in the other factor.

Step 3 Write each product in one small box; ones place digits in the bottom-right half; tens place digits in the upper-left half. When the product is a single-digit answer, write a zero in the upper-left half.

Step 4 Beginning on the right, add the numbers inside the lattice along each diagonal. If the sum on a diagonal exceeds 9, add the excess 10s in the next diagonal to the left.

The lattice method and the partial-products algorithm help prepare children for a division algorithm they will learn in fourth grade. Children will choose the algorithms that work best for them.

Also in this unit, children will…

- Write and solve multiplication and division number stories involving multiples of 10, 100, and 1,000.
- Solve division number stories and interpret the remainders.
- Increase their understanding of positive and negative numbers.

Vocabulary

Important terms in Unit 9:

algorithm A step-by-step set of instructions for doing something such as carrying out computation or solving a problem.

degree Celsius (°C) A unit for measuring temperature on the Celsius scale. 0°Celsius is the freezing point of water. 100°Celsius is the boiling point of water.

degree Fahrenheit (°F) A unit for measuring temperature on the Fahrenheit scale. 32°F is the freezing point of water. 212°F is the boiling point of water.

negative number A number less than or below zero; a number to the left of zero on a horizontal number line. The symbol − may be used to write a negative number. For example, negative 5 is usually written as −5.

positive number A number that is greater than zero; a number to the right of zero on a horizontal number line. A positive number may be written using the + symbol but it is usually written without it. For example, +10 = 10.

factor of a counting number *n* A counting number whose product with some other counting number equals *n*. For example, 2 and 3 are factors of 6 because 2 × 3 = 6. But 4 is not a factor of 6 because 4 × 1.5 = 6 and 1.5 is not a counting number.

Copyright © Wright Group/McGraw-Hill

Do-Anytime Activities

To work with your child on the concepts taught in this unit and in previous units, try these interesting and rewarding activities:

1. As the class proceeds through the unit, give your child multiplication problems related to the lessons covered, such as 9×23, 3×345, 20×65, and 43×56.
2. Continue to work on multiplication and division facts by using Fact Triangles and fact families, or by playing games.
3. Play *Baseball Multiplication, Factor Bingo,* and other games described in the *Student Reference Book.*
4. Write decimals for your child to read, such as 0.82 (eighty-two hundredths); 0.7 (seven tenths); 0.348 (three hundred forty-eight thousandths); and so on. Ask your child to identify digits in various places—the tenths place, hundredths place, thousandths place. Look for decimals in newspapers and on food containers.
5. Practice extended multiplication and division facts such as $3 \times 7 = ?$, $3 \times 70 =$ __, $3 \times 700 =$ __; $18 \div 6 =$ __, $180 \div 6 =$ __, and $1{,}800 \div 6 =$ __.

As You Help Your Child with Homework

As your child brings home assignments, you may want to go over the instructions together, clarifying them as necessary. The answers listed below will guide you through this unit's Home Links.

Home Link 9•1

1. 31 **2.** 25 **3.** 22

4. 13 or 18 **5.** 12 or 24 **6.** 56; 560; 5,600

7. 20; 200; 20,000

Home Link 9•2

1. a. 56; 56 **b.** 560; 560 **c.** 7
d. 70 **e.** 8 **f.** 8

2. a. 63; 63 **b.** 630; 630 **c.** 7
d. 70 **e.** 9 **f.** 9

3. a. 40; 40 **b.** 400; 400 **c.** 50
d. 50 **e.** 8 **f.** 80

Home Link 9•3

1. 7 raccoons **2.** 500 lb **3.** 100 arctic foxes

4. 600 lb **5.** 400 lb **6.** 60 beluga whales

Home Link 9•4

1. 93 **2.** 375 **3.** 765

4. 258 **5.** 1,134

Home Link 9•5

1. yes; estimate; $\$0.80 \times 7 = \$5.60$

2. \$12.72; calculate; $\$2.12 \times 6 = \$12.72$

3. \$0.90; Sample answer: calculate; 10 cards is \$6.00 times 2. Compare that with \$1.29 times 10. Then subtract to find the difference.

Home Link 9•6

1 row: yes; 18 chairs
2 rows: yes; 9 chairs
3 rows: yes; 6 chairs
4 rows: no
5 rows: no
6 rows: yes; 3 chairs
7 rows: no
8 rows: no
9 rows: yes; 2 chairs
10 rows: no
18 rows: yes; 1 chair

1; 18; 2; 9; 3; 6

Copyright © Wright Group/McGraw-Hill

Unit 9: Family Letter *cont.*

Home Link 9•7

1. a. 1 b. 9 c. 1 d. $0.25
 e. $19.25 f. $77.00 ÷ 4 = $19.25
2. 42
3. 192
4. 315

Home Link 9•8

1. 8 tables
2. 7 cartons
3. 10 packs
4. 116
5. 425
6. 768

Home Link 9•9

1. 92
2. 415
3. 822
4. 7,248

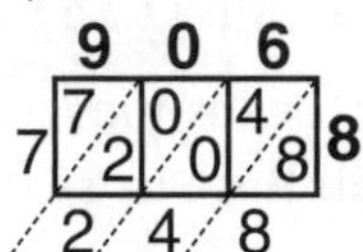

Home Link 9•10

1. 171

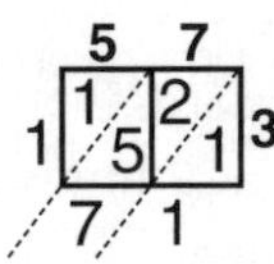

2. 364

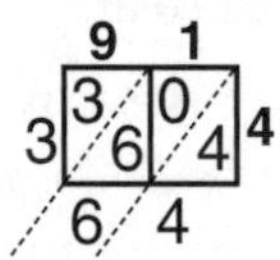

3. 1,632

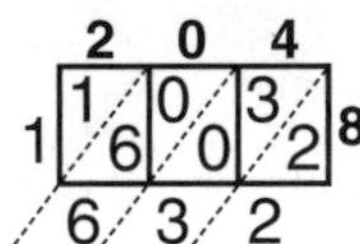

4. 4,320

Home Link 9•11

1. 760

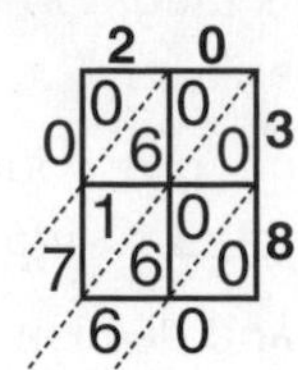

2. 850

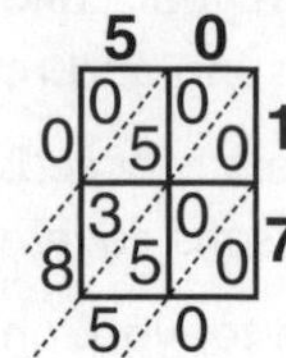

3. 5,580

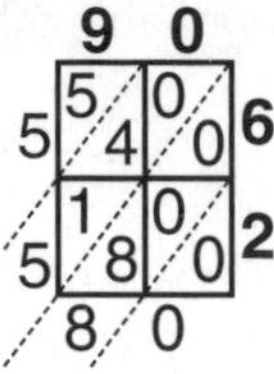

4. 1,120
5. 2,100

Home Link 9•12

1. 735

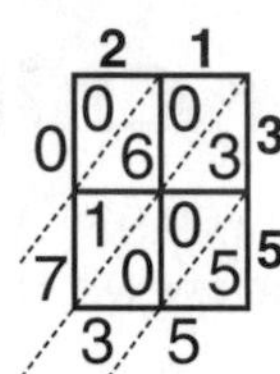

2. 731

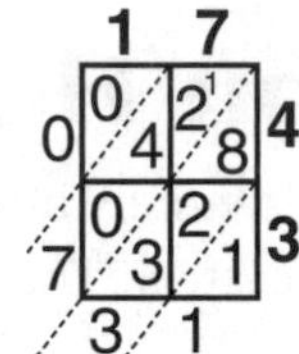

3. 3,596

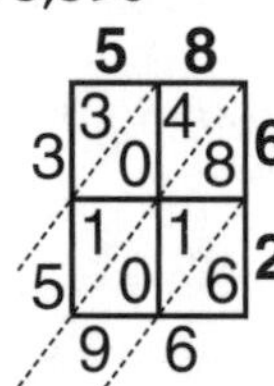

4. 2,695
5. 3,003

Home Link 9•13

1. −40°F; −40°C
2. 220°F; 104°C
3. 10°C
4. 18° colder
5. yes; no; It would be about 86°F outside.
6. yes; no; Water freezes at 0°C, so it would be cold enough to ice-skate.

Copyright © Wright Group/McGraw-Hill

Name Date Time

Who Am I?

Family Note The problems in this Home Link involve children solving whole-number riddles. Your child will use place-value concepts, number sense, and computation skills to solve the riddles. To provide practice with basic and extended facts, multiplication fact practice is added at the bottom of this Home Link.

Please return this Home Link to school tomorrow.

In each riddle, I am a different whole number. Use the clues to find out who I am.

1. **Clue 1:** I am greater than 30 and less than 40.
Clue 2: The sum of my digits is less than 5.

Who am I? __________

2. **Clue 1:** I am greater than 15 and less than 40.
Clue 2: If you double me, I become a number that ends in 0.
Clue 3: $\frac{1}{5}$ of me is equal to 5.

Who am I? __________

3. **Clue 1:** I am less than 100.
Clue 2: The sum of my digits is 4.
Clue 3: Half of me is an odd number.

Who am I? __________

4. **Clue 1:** If you multiply me by 2, I become a number greater than 20 and less than 40.
Clue 2: If you multiply me by 6, I end in 8.
Clue 3: If you multiply me by 4, I end in 2.

Who am I? __________

5. **Clue 1:** Double my tens digit to get my ones digit.
Clue 2: Double me and I am less than 50.

Who am I? __________

Practice

Solve.

6. $8 \times 7 =$ __________
$80 \times 7 =$ __________
$800 \times 7 =$ __________

7. $5 \times 4 =$ __________
$5 \times 40 =$ __________
$50 \times 400 =$ __________

Copyright © Wright Group/McGraw-Hill

Name Date Time

LESSON 9•1

Extending Multiplication Fact Patterns

Fill in the missing numbers.

1. $1 \times 10 =$ ______ $1 \times 100 =$ ______

$2 \times 10 =$ ______ $2 \times 100 =$ ______

$3 \times 10 =$ ______ $3 \times 100 =$ ______

$4 \times 10 =$ ______ $4 \times 100 =$ ______

$5 \times 10 =$ ______ $5 \times 100 =$ ______

2. $6 \times 100 =$ ______ $6 \times 1{,}000 =$ ______

$7 \times 100 =$ ______ $7 \times 1{,}000 =$ ______

$8 \times 100 =$ ______ $8 \times 1{,}000 =$ ______

$9 \times 100 =$ ______ $9 \times 1{,}000 =$ ______

3. 1 [10] = ______ 1 [100] = ______

2 [10s] = ______ 2 [100s] = ______

7 [10s] = ______ 7 [100s] = ______

5 [10s] = ______ 5 [100s] = ______

8 [10s] = ______ 8 [100s] = ______

4. Explain how you can use the patterns above to find the answer to 8 [1,000s].

____

____

____

____

Try This

5. $10 \times 100 =$ ______ 10 [100s] = ______

$10 \times 1{,}000 =$ ______ 10 [1,000s] = ______

Copyright © Wright Group/McGraw-Hill

Name Date Time

Multiplication Facts and Extensions

Family Note Help your child practice multiplication facts and their extensions. Observe as your child creates fact extensions, demonstrating further understanding of multiplication.

Please return this Home Link to school tomorrow.

Solve each problem.

1. **a.** 8 [7s] = ______, or 8 × 7 = ______

b. 8 [70s] = ______, or 8 × 70 = ______

c. How many 8s in 56? ______ **d.** How many 8s in 560? ______

e. How many 7s in 56? ______ **f.** How many 70s in 560? ______

2. **a.** 9 [7s] = ______, or 9 × 7 = ______

b. 9 [70s] = ______, or 9 × 70 = ______

c. How many 9s in 63? ______ **d.** How many 9s in 630? ______

e. How many 7s in 63? ______ **f.** How many 70s in 630? ______

3. **a.** 8 [5s] = ______, or 8 × 5 = ______

b. 8 [50s] = ______, or 8 × 50 = ______

c. How many 8s in 400? ______ **d.** How many 80s in 4,000? ______

e. How many 50s in 400? ______ **f.** How many 50s in 4,000? ______

4. Write a multiplication fact you are trying to learn.
Then use your fact to write some fact extensions like those above.

____

____

____

____

Copyright © Wright Group/McGraw-Hill

Name Date Time

LESSON 9•2

Using Multiplication/Division Diagrams

For each number story, complete the multiplication/division diagram, write a number model, and answer the question.

1. Tiffany keeps her button collection in a case with 10 shelves. On each shelf there are 16 buttons. How many buttons are in Tiffany's collection?

Number model: ____________________

Answer: ____________________ (unit)

number of shelves	buttons per shelf	buttons in all

2. Rashida walks her neighbor's dog every day. She gets paid $20.00 every week. If Rashida saves her money for 30 weeks, how much money would she have?

Number model: ____________________

Answer: ____________________ (unit)

number of weeks	dollars per week	dollars in all

3. The third grade class helped plant 4 tulip gardens at school. 50 tulip bulbs fit into each garden. How many tulip bulbs were planted?

Number model: ____________________

Answer: ____________________ (unit)

number of gardens	bulbs per garden	bulbs in all

Try This

4. There were 2,000 books collected in the book drive. Each class received 200 books. How many classes received books?

Number model: ____________________

number of classes	books per class	books in all

Answer: ____________________ (unit)

Copyright © Wright Group/McGraw-Hill

Name Date Time

Allowance Plans

Sara is discussing a raise in allowance with her parents. They ask her to choose one of three plans.

Plan A Each week, Sara would get 1¢ on Monday, double Monday's amount on Tuesday, double Tuesday's amount on Wednesday, and so on. Her allowance would keep on doubling each day through Sunday. Then she would start with 1¢ again on Monday.

Plan B Sara would get 32¢ on Sunday, Monday, Wednesday, and Friday of each week. She would get nothing on Tuesday, Thursday, and Saturday.

Plan C Sara would get 16¢ on each day of each week.

Which plan should Sara choose to get the most money? ______________________

Show your work on the back of this page. Explain how you found your answer. Use number sentences in your explanation.

____

____

____

____

____

Try This

For the plan you chose, how much money would Sara earn in a year?

____

____

Copyright © Wright Group/McGraw-Hill

Name Date Time

LESSON 9•3

Array Multiplication

Exploration A:

Work in a group of three or four.

Materials
- ☐ array grid (*Math Masters,* pp. 273 and 274, cut out and glued together)
- ☐ base-10 blocks (cubes and longs)
- ☐ red and blue crayons or coloring pencils
- ☐ *Math Journal 2,* p. 211

1. Cover a 4-by-28 array of squares on the array grid using as few base-10 blocks as you can.
- ◆ Start at the lower-left corner.
- ◆ First, use as many longs as you can. Then, cover the rest of the squares in your array with cubes.

2. Draw a picture of your array for Problem 1 on journal page 211.
- ◆ Color the squares you covered with longs red.
- ◆ Color the squares you covered with cubes blue.

3. Record the result next to the picture.

4. Now repeat Steps 1 through 3 to find the total number of squares in a 3-by-26 array. Record your work for Problem 2 on the journal page.

5. Finally, do the same for a 6-by-32 array. Record your work for Problem 3 on the journal page.

Copyright © Wright Group/McGraw-Hill

Name Date Time

Array Grid

GLUE OR TAPE EDGE OF PAGE 274 HERE

Start here.

Copyright © Wright Group/McGraw-Hill

Name Date Time

Array Grid *continued*

Copyright © Wright Group/McGraw-Hill

Name Date Time

LESSON 9·3

Geoboard Areas

Exploration B:

Work alone or with a partner.

Materials ☐ geoboard and rubber bands, or Geoboard Dot Paper (*Math Masters,* p. 415)

☐ *Math Journal 2,* p. 212

1 square unit

1. On the geoboard or geoboard dot paper, make a rectangle whose area is 12 square units.

   Record the lengths of the longer and shorter sides in the table on journal page 212.

2. Make a different rectangle having the same area. Record the lengths of the sides in the table.
3. Repeat Steps 1 and 2 to make two different rectangles whose areas are 6 square units each. Record the lengths of the sides in the table.
4. Repeat Steps 1 and 2 to make two different rectangles (or a square and a rectangle) whose areas are 16 square units each. Record the lengths of the sides in the table.
5. Try to make a rectangle or square whose area is an odd number of square units. Record the results in your table.
6. Continue with other areas if there is time.
7. Complete journal page 212.

Copyright © Wright Group/McGraw-Hill

Name Date Time

LESSON 9·3

Fractions of Fractions of Regions

Exploration C: Work in a group of three or four.

Materials ☐ *Math Masters,* p. 277 ☐ crayons; scissors; glue or tape

You can learn a lot about fractions by folding rectangles. Each rectangle on *Math Masters,* page 277 is ONE. The marks on some rectangles show where to fold these rectangles into thirds, fifths, or sixths.

1. What is $\frac{1}{2}$ of $\frac{1}{4}$? To find out, do the following:

- Cut out rectangle **A** on *Math Masters,* page 277. Fold it into 4 equal parts. Each part is $\frac{1}{4}$ of the rectangle.
- Keep the rectangle folded. Now fold the folded rectangle in half. Each part is $\frac{1}{2}$ of $\frac{1}{4}$ of the rectangle.
- Unfold. How many parts are there? Color one of the parts. The colored part is $\frac{1}{8}$ of the rectangle. Complete the number model on the rectangle.

2. Repeat the same steps for rectangles **C** through **H** on *Math Masters,* page 277. Share the work among members of your group.

Follow-Up

Write a group report about your findings. Attach some rectangles on your report to illustrate your thinking. Answer these questions in your report:

3. Is $\frac{1}{2}$ of $\frac{1}{4}$ the same fractional part of the rectangle as $\frac{1}{4}$ of $\frac{1}{2}$?

Is $\frac{1}{2}$ of $\frac{1}{3}$ the same as $\frac{1}{3}$ of $\frac{1}{2}$?

4. Look at the number models in the rectangles. Can you make up a rule to help you complete the number models without folding rectangles?

5. Predict $\frac{1}{8}$ of $\frac{1}{2}$ of a rectangle. Predict $\frac{1}{2}$ of $\frac{1}{6}$. Check your predictions by folding rectangles I and J.

Copyright © Wright Group/McGraw-Hill

Name Date Time

LESSON 9·3 Fractions of Fractions of Regions *cont.*

A

$\frac{1}{2}$ of $\frac{1}{4}$ = ______

B

$\frac{1}{4}$ of $\frac{1}{2}$ = ______

C

$\frac{1}{2}$ of $\frac{1}{3}$ = ______

D

$\frac{1}{3}$ of $\frac{1}{2}$ = ______

E

$\frac{1}{2}$ of $\frac{1}{5}$ = ______

F

$\frac{1}{3}$ of $\frac{1}{5}$ = ______

G

$\frac{1}{4}$ of $\frac{1}{3}$ = ______

H

$\frac{1}{4}$ of $\frac{1}{5}$ = ______

I

$\frac{1}{8}$ of $\frac{1}{2}$ = ______

J

$\frac{1}{2}$ of $\frac{1}{6}$ = ______

Copyright © Wright Group/McGraw-Hill

Name Date Time

Multiplication Number Stories

Family Note Your child's class is beginning to solve multidigit multiplication and division problems. Although we have practiced multiplication and division with multiples of 10, we have been doing most of our calculating mentally. Encourage your child to explain a solution strategy for each of the problems below.

Please return this Home Link to school tomorrow.

SRB 250–253

1. How many 30-pound raccoons would weigh about as much as a 210-pound harp seal? ______

2. How much would an alligator weigh if it weighed 10 times as much as a 50-pound sea otter? ______

3. How many 20-pound arctic foxes would weigh about as much as a 2,000-pound beluga whale? ______

4. Each porcupine weighs 30 pounds. A black bear weighs as much as 20 porcupines. How much does the black bear weigh? ______

5. A bottle-nosed dolphin could weigh twice as much as a 200-pound common dolphin. How much could the bottle-nosed dolphin weigh? ______

Try This

6. How many 2,000-pound beluga whales would weigh as much as one 120,000-pound right whale? ______

Copyright © Wright Group/McGraw-Hill

Name _______________ Date _______________ Time _______________

LESSON 9·4

Array Multiplication 1

1. How many squares are in a 4-by-28 array? Make a picture of the array.

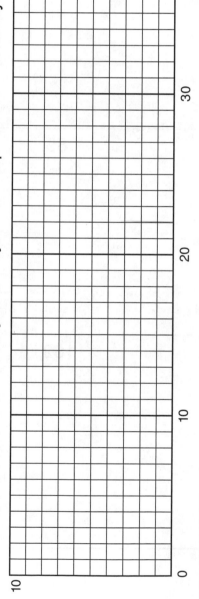

Total squares: _______

$4 \times 28 =$ _______

2. How many squares are in a 3-by-26 array? Make a picture of the array.

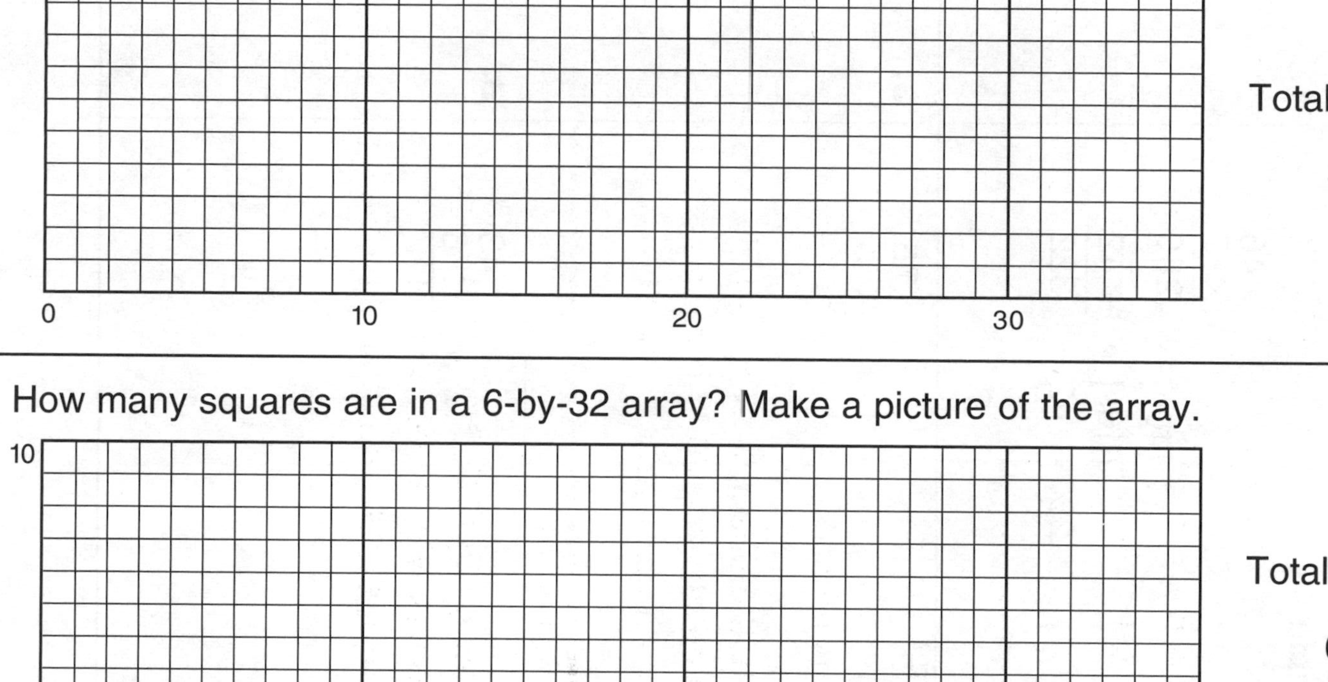

Total squares: _______

$3 \times 26 =$ _______

3. How many squares are in a 6-by-32 array? Make a picture of the array.

Total squares: _______

$6 \times 32 =$ _______

Copyright © Wright Group/McGraw-Hill

Name Date Time

The Partial-Products Algorithm

Family Note Today the class began working with our first formal procedure for multiplication—the partial-products algorithm. Encourage your child to explain this method to you.

Please return this Home Link to school tomorrow.

Use the partial-products algorithm to solve these problems:

Example

	46
	× 7
7 [40s]→	280
7 [6s]→	+ 42
280 + 42→	322

1. 31 × 3

2. 75 × 5

3. 85 × 9

4. 43 × 6

5. 162 × 7

Copyright © Wright Group/McGraw-Hill

Name Date Time

Base-10 Block Multiplication

1. Use longs and cubes to show 6 groups of 32.

Count the number of longs.
Count the number of cubes.
Record your counts here:

I have ______ ten(s), which is the same as ______.

I have ______ one(s), which is the same as ______.

Total: ______

Number model: $6 \times 32 =$ ______

2. Use longs and cubes to show 5 groups of 27.

Count the number of longs.
Count the number of cubes.
Record your counts here:

I have ______ ten(s), which is the same as ______.

I have ______ one(s), which is the same as ______.

Total: ______

Number model: $5 \times 27 =$ ______

3. Make up your own. Use longs and cubes to show ______ groups of ______.

Count the number of longs.
Count the number of cubes.
Record your counts here:

I have ______ ten(s), which is the same as ______.

I have ______ one(s), which is the same as ______.

Total: ______

Number model: ______ × ______ = ______

Copyright © Wright Group/McGraw-Hill

Name Date Time

LESSON 9•4

Number Patterns

1. Suppose you were asked to find the sum of all of the whole numbers from 1 through 10. These addends make a count-by-1s pattern. A number model for this problem could look like this:

1 + 2 + 3 + 4 + 5 + 6 + 7 + 8 + 9 + 10 = _____

There are several ways you can find the sum. Here is one way:

1 + 10 = _____

2 + 9 = _____

3 + 8 = _____

4 + 7 = _____

5 + 6 = _____

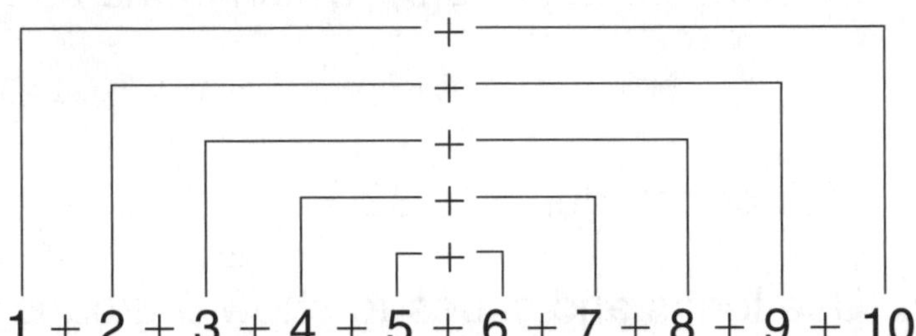

How many 11s in all? _____

The sum of the whole numbers from 1 through 10 is _____ × 11 = _____.

2. Use the same method to find the sum in this count-by-2s pattern:

2 + 4 + 6 + 8 + 10 + 12 + 14 + 16 + 18 + 20 = ______

2 + 20 = ______ 4 + 18 = ______ 6 + 16 = ______

8 + 14 = ______ 10 + 12 = ______

How many ______s in all? ______

So the sum of the even numbers 2 through 20 is ______ × ______ = ______.

3. Make up your own count-by-_____s pattern of addends. Then find the sum.

Copyright © Wright Group/McGraw-Hill

Name Date Time

Saving at the Stock-Up Sale

Family Note Today the class used mental math and the partial-products algorithm to solve shopping problems. Note that for some of the problems below, an estimate will answer the question. For others, an exact answer is needed. If your child is able to make the calculations mentally, encourage him or her to explain the solution strategy to you.

Please return this Home Link to school tomorrow.

SRB 250–253 191

Decide whether you will need to estimate or calculate an exact answer to solve each problem below. Then solve the problem and show what you did. Record the answer and write the number model (or models) you used.

1. Phil has $6.00. He wants to buy Creepy Creature erasers. They cost $1.05 each. If he buys more than 5, they are $0.79 each. Does he have enough money to buy 7 Creepy Creature erasers? ______

   ______

   Number model: ______

2. Mrs. Katz is buying cookies for a school party. The cookies cost $2.48 per dozen. If she buys more than 4 dozen, they cost $2.12 per dozen. How much are 6 dozen? ______

   ______

   Number model: ______

3. Baseball cards are on sale for $1.29 per card, or 5 cards for $6. Marty bought 10 cards. How much did he save with the special price? ______

   Explain how you found your answer.

   ______

   ______

   ______

   ______

Copyright © Wright Group/McGraw-Hill

Name Date Time

LESSON 9·5

Dollars and Dimes

Use the Stock-Up Sale posters on pages 216 and 217 in your *Student Reference Book.* Suppose that you have only dollars and dimes. Write the least amount of money you could use to buy each item.

Use dollars and dimes to help you.

Items to Be Purchased	Dollars and Dimes Needed
Example: 1 box of 12 Greeting Cards Price: $3.29	3 dollars 3 dimes Total: $ 3.30
1 roll of Gift-Wrapping Paper Price: ______	______ dollars ______ dimes Total: $______
1 roll of Transparent Tape Price: ______	______ dollars ______ dimes Total: $______
1 box of Tissues Price: ______	______ dollars ______ dimes Total: $______
1 Paperback Book Price: ______	______ dollars ______ dimes Total: $______

Copyright © Wright Group/McGraw-Hill

Name Date Time

10% Sales Tax at the Stock-Up Sale

You will need *Math Journal 2,* page 217 and your *Student Reference Book*. Figure out how much money Mason, Vic, and Andrea will each need if a 10% sales tax is added to their purchases.

- One way to figure the 10% sales tax is to find $\frac{1}{10}$ of the dollars and then $\frac{1}{10}$ of the cents. Then add the amounts.
- If $\frac{1}{10}$ of the cents amount is between pennies, round to the higher amount.

Example: 10% of $2.43

$\frac{1}{10}$ of $2.00 is $0.20; $\frac{1}{10}$ of $0.40 is $0.04. $\frac{1}{10}$ of $0.03 is less than a penny so round to the higher amount, or $0.01. $0.20 + $0.05 = $0.25. So 10% of $2.43 is $0.25.

1. How much will Mason need for 5 bars of soap with 10% sales tax?

____

2. How much will Vic need for 5 toothbrushes at the sale price with 10% sales tax?

____

3. How much will Andrea need for 5 bottles of glue at the sale price with 10% sales tax?

____

Copyright © Wright Group/McGraw-Hill

Name Date Time

HOME LINK 9•6 Arrays and Factors

Family Note Discuss with your child all the ways to arrange 18 chairs in equal rows. Then help your child use this information to list the factors of 18 (pairs of numbers whose product is 18).

Please return this Home Link to school tomorrow.

SRB 64–67

Work with someone at home.

The third-grade class is putting on a play. Children have invited 18 people. Gilda and Harvey are in charge of arranging the 18 chairs. They want to arrange them in rows with the same number of chairs in each row, with no chairs left over.

Yes or no: Can they arrange the chairs in ...	**If yes, how many chairs in each row?**
1 row? ______	______ chairs
2 rows? ______	______ chairs
3 rows? ______	______ chairs
4 rows? ______	______ chairs
5 rows? ______	______ chairs
6 rows? ______	______ chairs
7 rows? ______	______ chairs
8 rows? ______	______ chairs
9 rows? ______	______ chairs
10 rows? ______	______ chairs
18 rows? ______	______ chairs

List all the factors of the number 18. (*Hint:* 18 has exactly 6 factors.)

______ ______ ______

______ ______ ______

How does knowing all the ways to arrange 18 chairs in equal rows help you find the factors of 18? Tell someone at home.

____

____

____

____

____

____

____

Copyright © Wright Group/McGraw-Hill

Name Date Time

Finding Factors

Materials ☐ 2 different-colored counters, 2 different-colored crayons
☐ *Finding Factors* gameboard (see below)

Players 2

Object of the Game To shade five products in a row, column, or diagonal

Directions

1. Player A places a counter on one of the factors in the Factor Strip at the bottom of the gameboard.
2. Player B places a second counter on one of the factors in the Factor Strip. (Two counters can cover the same factor.) Now that two factors are covered, Player B wins the square that is the product of the two factors. Player B shades this square with his or her color.
3. Player A moves either **one** of the counters to a new factor on the Factor Strip. If the product of the two covered factors has not been shaded, Player A shades this square with his or her color and wins the square.
4. Play continues until 5 squares in a row, column, or diagonal are shaded in the same color.

1	2	3	4	5	6
7	8	9	10	12	14
15	16	18	20	21	24
25	27	28	30	32	35
36	40	42	45	48	49
54	56	63	64	72	81

Factor Strip

1	2	3	4	5	6	7	8	9

Copyright © Wright Group/McGraw-Hill

Name Date Time

Sharing Money with Friends

Family Note In class we are thinking about division, but we have not yet introduced a procedure for division. We will work with formal division algorithms in *Fourth Grade Everyday Mathematics.* Encourage your child to solve the following problems in his or her own way and to explain the strategy to you. These problems provide an opportunity to develop a sense of what division means and how it works. Sometimes it helps to model problems with pennies, beans, or other counters that stand for bills and coins.

Please return this Home Link to school tomorrow.

SRB 73

1. $77 is shared equally by 4 friends.

a. How many $10 bills does each friend get? ______________

b. How many $1 bills does each friend get? ______________

c. How many $1 bills are left over? ______________

d. If the leftover money is shared equally, how many cents does each friend get? ______________

e. Each friend gets a total of $______________.

f. Number model: ______________________________

Practice

Use the partial-products method to solve these problems. Show your work.

2. $\begin{array}{r} 21 \\ \times\ 2 \\ \hline \end{array}$

3. $\begin{array}{r} 48 \\ \times\ 4 \\ \hline \end{array}$

4. $\begin{array}{r} 63 \\ \times\ 5 \\ \hline \end{array}$

Copyright © Wright Group/McGraw-Hill

Name Date Time

Equal Shares of Money

The price of admission to the neighborhood magic show is $1.25 per person. How many people could you take to the show if you had $25.00? ______
Show your work, and explain how you figured it out.

______
______
______
______
______
______

Try This

How many people could go to the show if you had $32.00? ______
Explain your answer.

______
______
______

Copyright © Wright Group/McGraw-Hill

Name Date Time

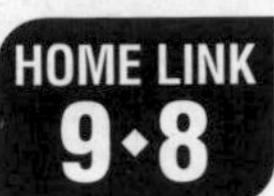

Equal Shares and Equal Parts

Family Note As the class continues to investigate division, we are looking at remainders and what they mean. The focus of this assignment is on figuring out what to do with the remainder, NOT on using a division algorithm. Encourage your child to draw pictures, use a calculator, or use counters to solve the problems.

Please return this Home Link to school tomorrow.

SRB 73 74

Solve the problems below. Remember that you will have to decide what the remainder means in order to answer the questions. You may use your calculator, counters, or pictures to help you solve the problems.

1. There are 31 children in Dante's class. Each table in the classroom seats 4 children. How many tables are needed to seat all of the children?

____

2. Emily and Linnea help out on their uncle's chicken farm. One day the hens laid a total of 85 eggs. How many cartons of a dozen eggs could they fill?

____

3. Ms. Jerome is buying markers for a scout project. She needs 93 markers. If markers come in packs of 10, how many packs must she buy?

____

Practice

Solve each problem using the partial-products algorithm.
Use the back of this Home Link.

4. $29 \times 4 =$ ________ **5.** $85 \times 5 =$ ________ **6.** $96 \times 8 =$ ________

Copyright © Wright Group/McGraw-Hill

Name Date Time

Picturing Division

For each problem—

- Draw a picture.
- Answer the question.
- Explain what you did with what was left over.

1. There are 18 children in art class. If 4 children can sit at each table, how many tables do they need?

Picture:

Answer: They need ______ tables.

Explanation: ______________________________

____

2. Hot dogs come in packages of 8. If José is having a birthday party and needs 20 hot dogs, how many packages must he buy?

Picture:

Answer: He must buy ______ packages.

Explanation: ______________________________

____

____

Copyright © Wright Group/McGraw-Hill

Name Date Time

LESSON 9·8

Pizza with Remainders

The third-grade class is having a pizza party. The class expects 22 children, 1 teacher, and 2 parents. Each pizza will be divided into 8 equal slices.

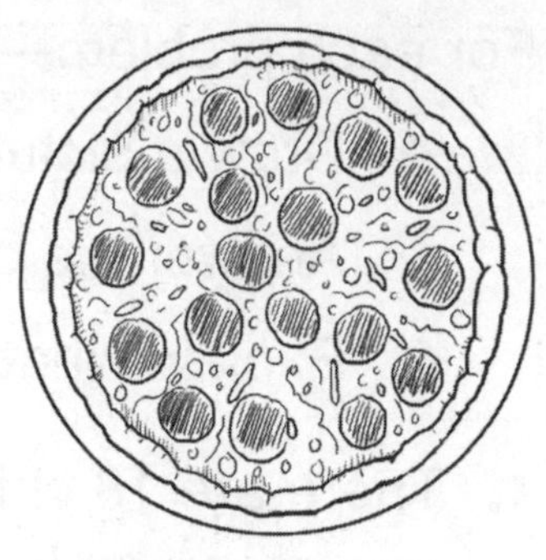

1. In all, how many people are coming to the party?

    ____

2. Suppose that each person who comes to the party will eat 1 slice of pizza.

    a. How many whole pizzas will the people eat? ______________

    b. How many additional slices will be needed? ______________

    c. What fractional part of a whole pizza is that? ______________

    d. Is that more or less than half of a whole pizza? ______________

    e. How many whole pizzas should the teacher order? ______________

3. Suppose instead that each person will eat 2 slices of pizza.

    a. How many slices of pizza will the people eat? ______________

    b. How many whole pizzas will the people eat? ______________

    c. How many additional slices will be needed? ______________

    d. What fractional part of a whole pizza is that? ______________

    e. How many whole pizzas should the teacher order? ______________

4. Lakeisha brought 2 granola bars to the party. She decided to share them equally with her 3 best friends. What fractional part of a granola bar did she and her friends get? ______________

Copyright © Wright Group/McGraw-Hill

Name Date Time

Multiplication Two Ways, Part 1

Family Note Observe as your child solves these problems. See if your child can use more than one method of multiplication, and find out which method your child prefers. Both methods are discussed in the *Student Reference Book* on pages 68–72 and in the Unit 9 Family Letter.

Please return this Home Link to school tomorrow.

Use the lattice method and the partial-products algorithm.

1. $2 \times 46 =$ ________

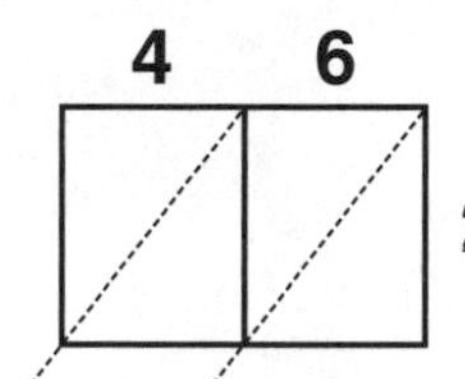

$$\begin{array}{r} 46 \\ \times\ 2 \\ \hline \end{array}$$

2. $5 \times 83 =$ ________

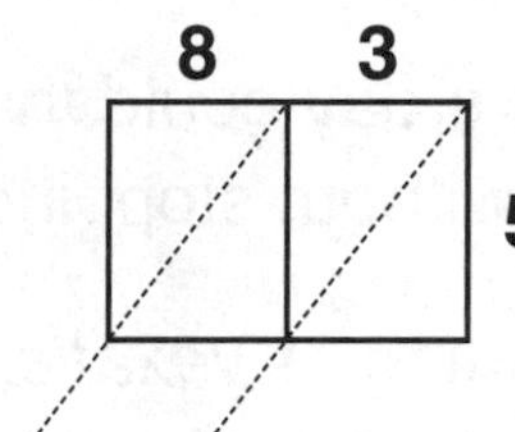

$$\begin{array}{r} 83 \\ \times\ 5 \\ \hline \end{array}$$

3. $3 \times 274 =$ ________

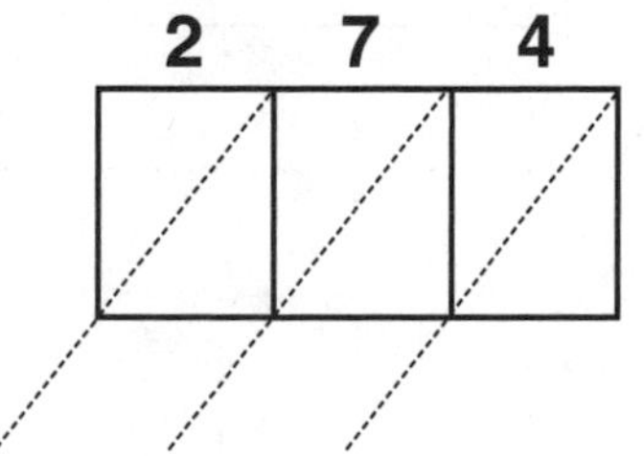

$$\begin{array}{r} 274 \\ \times\ \ 3 \\ \hline \end{array}$$

4. $8 \times 906 =$ ________

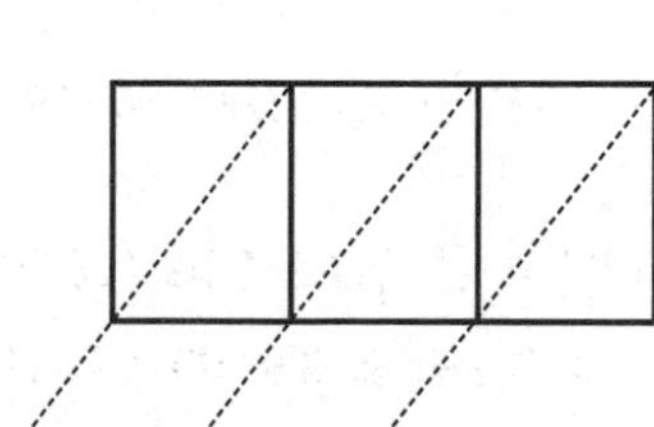

$$\begin{array}{r} 906 \\ \times\ \ 8 \\ \hline \end{array}$$

Copyright © Wright Group/McGraw-Hill

Name Date Time

LESSON 9•9

Mathematics in Music

The French composer Erik Satie lived from 1866 to 1925. He wrote a piece of music called *Vexations,* in which the same tune is played 840 times in a row without stopping. It takes about 30 seconds to play this tune once.

1. About how many minutes would it take to play all of *Vexations* without stopping? about _______ minutes

2. How many hours is that? _______ hours

3. Suppose someone played the whole piece 4 times without stopping. Could this be done in 1 day? _______________

4. How many times a day could the whole piece be played without stopping? _______________

5. Look up the meaning of *vexation* in a dictionary. Explain why you think Satie gave the piece of music that name.

____

____

____

____

____

Copyright © Wright Group/McGraw-Hill

Name Date Time

LESSON 9•10

Array Multiplication 2

Exploration D:

Work in a group of 2 to 4.

Materials ☐ array grid

☐ base-10 blocks (at least 3 flats and 24 longs)

☐ *Math Journal 2,* p. 229

☐ green and red crayons or coloring pencils

1. Cover a 20-by-13 array of squares on the array grid using as few base-10 blocks as possible.

- Start at the lower-left corner.
- Use flats first and then longs.

2. Make a picture of this array in Problem 1 on journal page 229.

- Color the squares covered by flats green.
- Color the squares covered by longs red.

3. Record the result next to the picture.

4. Cover an 18-by-30 array of squares on the array grid using as few base-10 blocks as possible.

- Start at the lower-left corner.
- Use flats first and then longs.

5. Make a picture of this array in Problem 2 on journal page 229.

- Color the squares covered by flats green.
- Color the squares covered by longs red.

6. Record the result next to the picture.

Copyright © Wright Group/McGraw-Hill

Name Date Time

LESSON 9•10

Array Multiplication 3

Exploration D: continued

Work in a group of 2 to 4.

Materials
- ☐ array grid
- ☐ base-10 blocks (at least 4 flats, 25 longs, and 28 cubes)
- ☐ *Math Journal 2,* p. 230
- ☐ green, red, and blue crayons or coloring pencils

1. Cover a 17-by-34 array of squares on the array grid using as few base-10 blocks as possible.
- Start at the lower-left corner.
- Use flats first, and then longs, and finally cubes.

2. Make a picture of this array in Problem 1 on journal page 230.
- Color the squares covered by flats green.
- Color the squares covered by longs red.
- Color the squares covered by cubes blue.

3. Record the result next to the picture.

4. Cover a 22-by-28 array of squares on the array grid using as few base-10 blocks as possible.
- Start at the lower-left corner.
- Use flats first, and then longs, and finally cubes.

5. Make a picture of this array in Problem 2 on journal page 230.
- Color the squares covered by flats green.
- Color the squares covered by longs red.
- Color the squares covered by cubes blue.

6. Record the result next to the picture.

Copyright © Wright Group/McGraw-Hill

Name Date Time

LESSON 9•10

Equilateral Triangles

Exploration E:

Materials
- ☐ *Math Masters,* pp. 298 and 299
- ☐ triangle pattern blocks
- ☐ Pattern-Block Template
- ☐ blank paper (optional)

Problem

How many triangle pattern blocks will fit inside each of the triangles on *Math Masters,* page 299?

All of the triangles on *Math Masters,* page 299 are equilateral triangles. The sides of each triangle are all the same length. The smallest triangle is 1 inch on each side. The sides of each of the other triangles are also drawn to the whole inch.

Work with a partner or a small group. Follow the steps below. Share ideas about ways to find solutions and complete the table.

1. How many 1-inch triangles fit inside the 2-inch triangle? You may use pattern blocks to find out. Record your answer in the table on *Math Masters,* page 298.
2. How many 1-inch triangles fit inside the 3-inch triangle? Record your answer in the table. *Hint: A part of the 3-inch triangle is a 2-inch triangle.*
3. Look for a pattern. Predict how many 1-inch triangles will fit inside the 4-inch triangle. Check your prediction with pattern blocks. Record and compare your answer to your prediction. Repeat for the 5-inch triangle.
4. Predict how many 1-inch triangles will fit in 6-inch through 10-inch triangles. Build or draw each triangle with pattern blocks or by tracing shapes from the Pattern-Block Template onto blank paper. Record and compare your predictions with your answers.
5. Look at the table with others in your group. Discuss the number pattern in the answers. Together decide on ways to describe the pattern. Write your description of the pattern below your table.

Copyright © Wright Group/McGraw-Hill

Name Date Time

LESSON 9•10

Equilateral Triangles *continued*

Exploration E: continued

Fill in the table.

Length of each side in inches	1	2	3	4	5	6	7	8	9	10
Number of 1-in. triangles inside	1									

Describe number patterns that you see in the table.

Copyright © Wright Group/McGraw-Hill

Name Date Time

Equilateral Triangles *continued*

Exploration E: continued

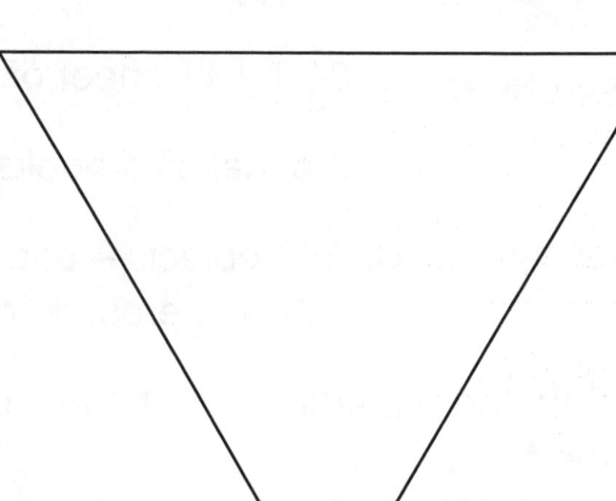

Copyright © Wright Group/McGraw-Hill

Name Date Time

Building Bridges

Exploration F:

Work alone or with a partner.

Materials

- ☐ $8\frac{1}{2}$-by-11 sheet of paper
- ☐ centimeter ruler; scissors
- ☐ 2 equal-size books
- ☐ paper for recording
- ☐ light objects—paper clips, rubber bands, straws, pencils, crayons, erasers, calculators, and so on

1. Fold the paper into fourths as shown. Cut along the folds.

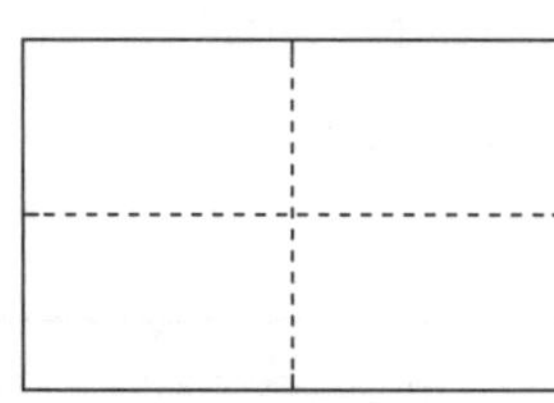

2. Make a bridge between two books with one of the rectangles as shown. This is Bridge #1. Check to see if this bridge will hold any of the light objects. Record what you find.

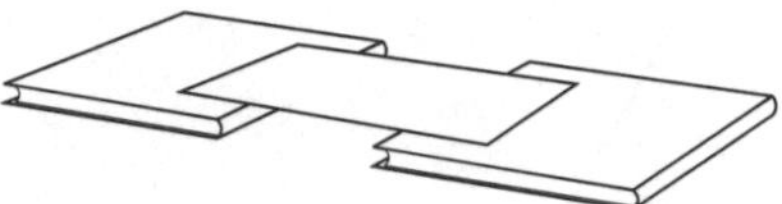

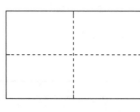

Bridge #1

3. Fold another rectangle into 8 or 9 equal-size fan-folds as shown. This will make the folds a little more than 1 cm apart. This is Bridge #2. Place it between the two books. Test the bridge by placing light objects, and then heavier objects, on it. Record the objects this bridge can hold.

Fan-folded Rectangle

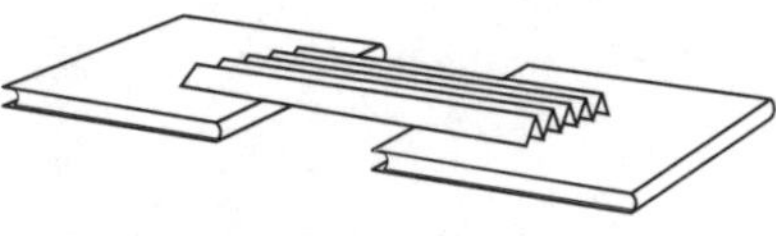

Bridge #2

4. Fold another rectangle into 12 to 14 equal-size folds (each a little more than $\frac{1}{2}$ centimeter apart). This is Bridge #3. Test what this bridge can hold. Record your results.

Practice

Compare your results with results of other members of the class. Discuss these questions. Record your thoughts on a piece of paper.

- Do the sizes of the folds affect how much the bridge holds?
- What shapes do you see in the fan-folded rectangles?
- Why are the fan-folded bridges able to hold up more than the unfolded bridge?

Copyright © Wright Group/McGraw-Hill

Name Date Time

Multiplication Two Ways, Part 2

Family Note The class continues to practice the partial-products algorithm and the lattice method. Encourage your child to try these problems both ways and to compare the answers to be sure they are correct.

Please return this Home Link to school tomorrow.

Show someone at home how to use both the lattice method and the partial-products algorithm.

1. $3 \times 57 =$ ________

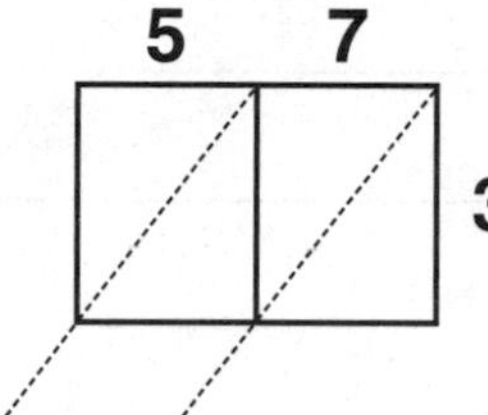

$$\begin{array}{r} 57 \\ \times\ 3 \\ \hline \end{array}$$

2. $4 \times 91 =$ ________

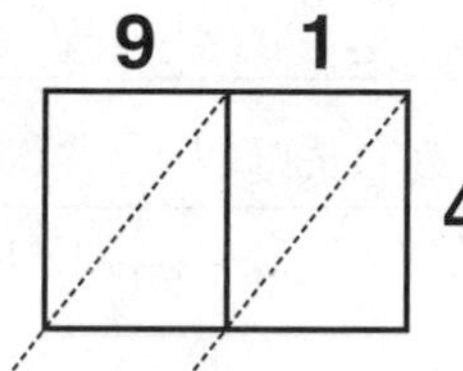

$$\begin{array}{r} 91 \\ \times\ 4 \\ \hline \end{array}$$

3. $8 \times 204 =$ ________

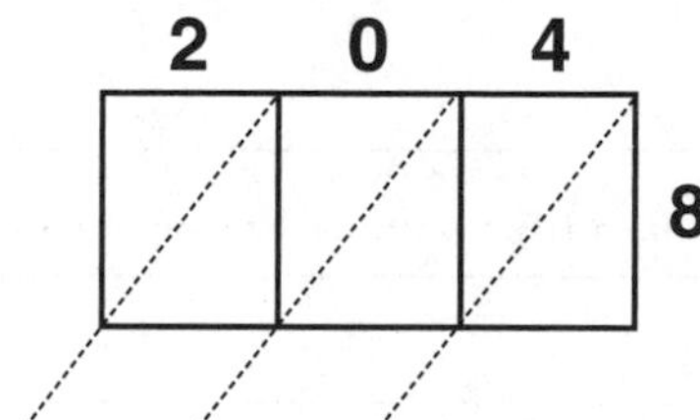

$$\begin{array}{r} 204 \\ \times\ 8 \\ \hline \end{array}$$

4. $9 \times 480 =$ ________

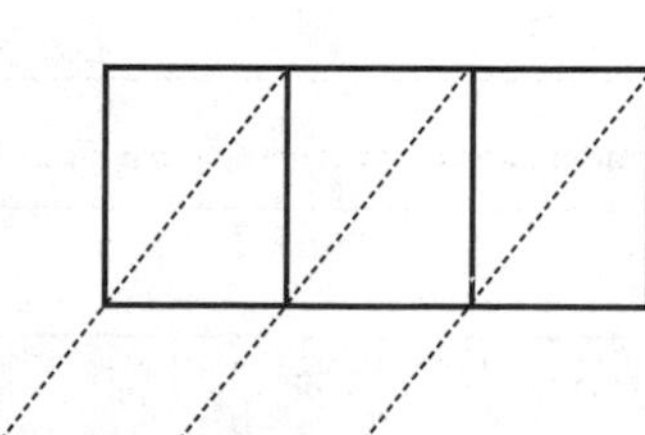

$$\begin{array}{r} 480 \\ \times\ 9 \\ \hline \end{array}$$

Copyright © Wright Group/McGraw-Hill

Name Date Time

Triangular Numbers

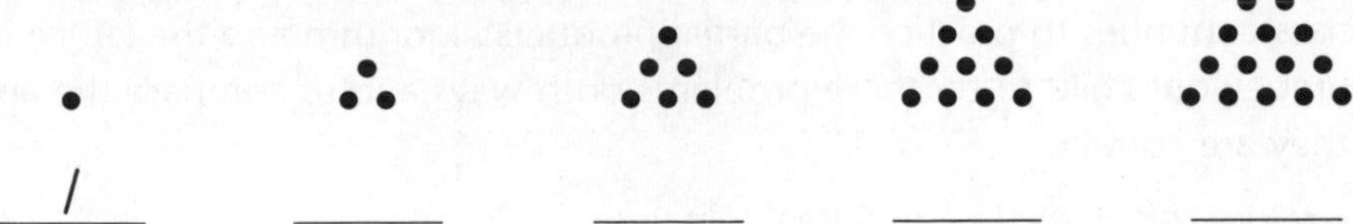

1. How many dots are in each of the triangular arrays? List the number of dots on the line below each triangular array. These are triangular numbers. What patterns do you see?

2. Show the tenth triangular number. How many dots are in the triangular array? Explain how you figured it out.

Copyright © Wright Group/McGraw-Hill

Name Date Time

LESSON 9•11 Array Multiplication 4

1. How many squares are in a 20-by-13 array?

Total squares = ______

$20 \times 13 =$ ______

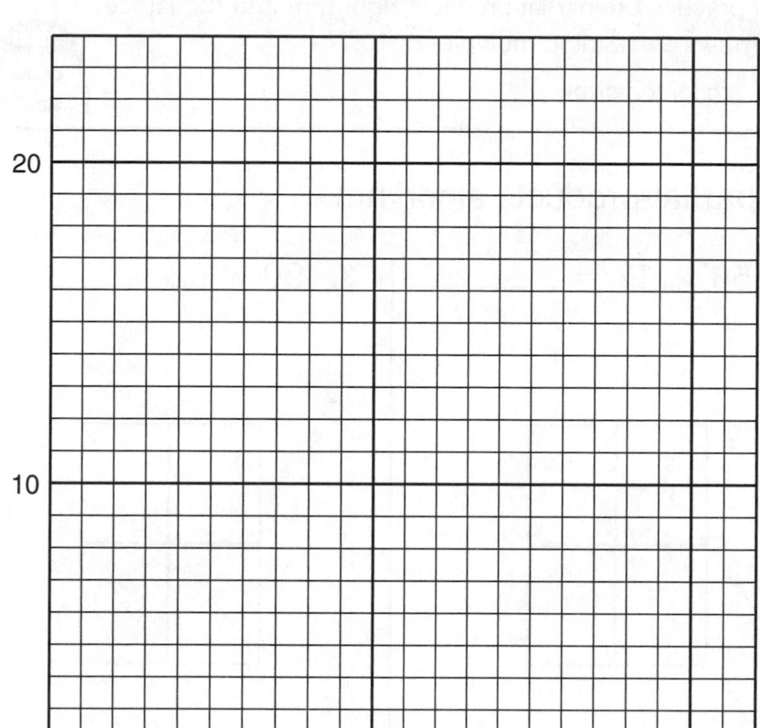

2. How many squares are in an 18-by-30 array?

Total squares = ______

$18 \times 30 =$ ______

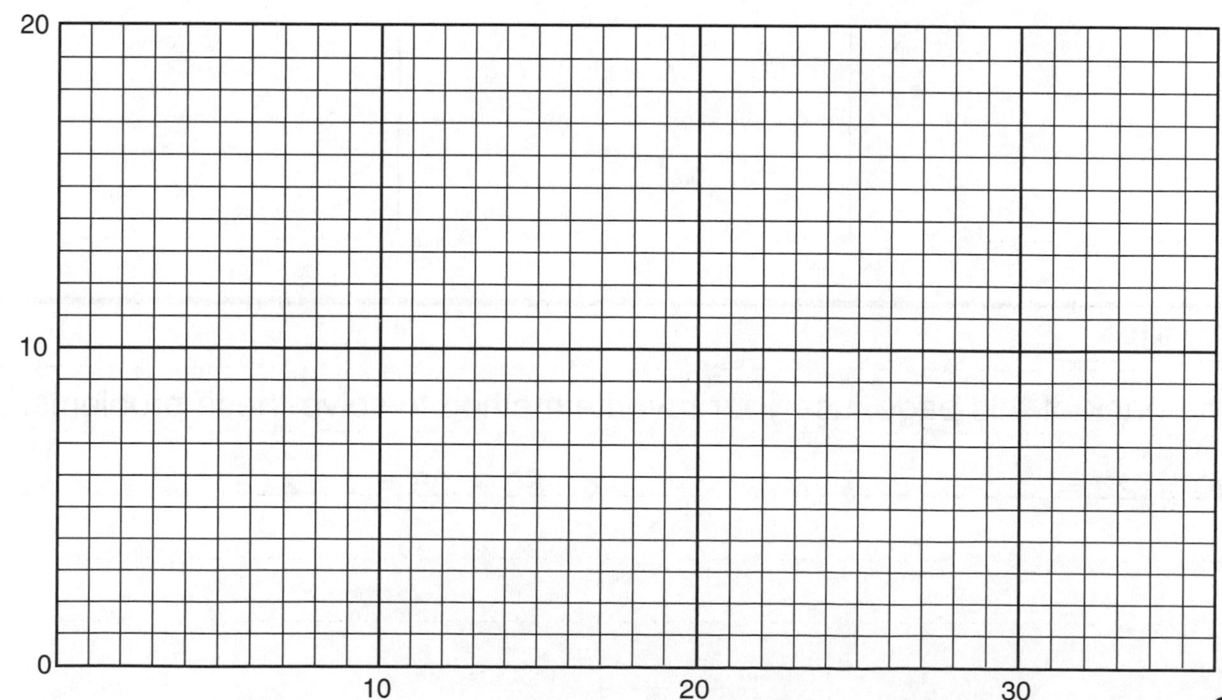

Copyright © Wright Group/McGraw-Hill

Name Date Time

2-Digit Multiplication: Two Ways

Family Note Your child's class continues to practice the partial-products algorithm and the lattice method, now with 2-digit numbers and 2-digit multiples of 10.

Please return this Home Link to school tomorrow.

Use the lattice method and the partial-products algorithm.

1. $20 \times 38 =$ ______

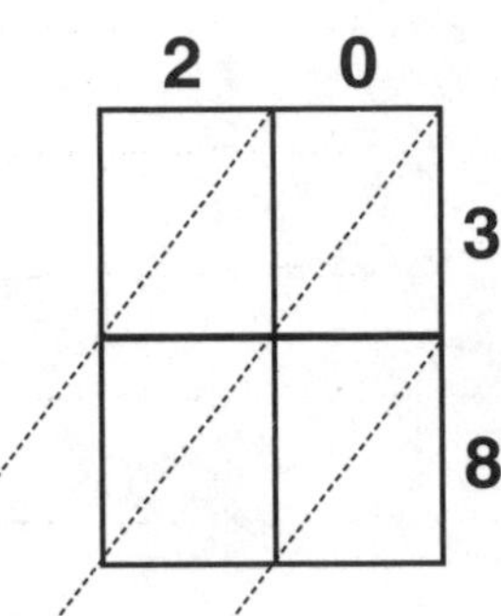

2. $50 \times 17 =$ ______

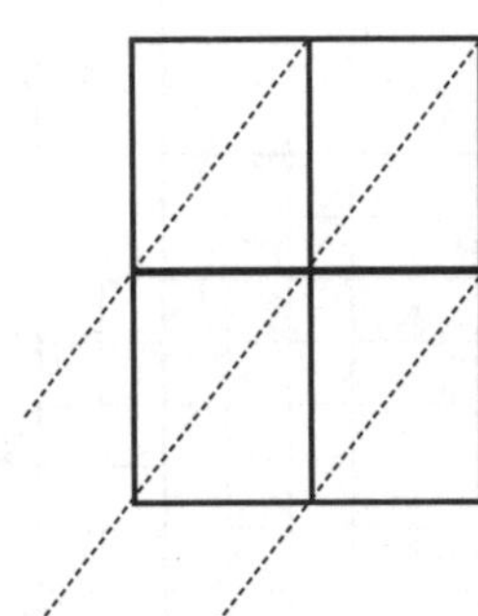

3. $90 \times 62 =$ ______

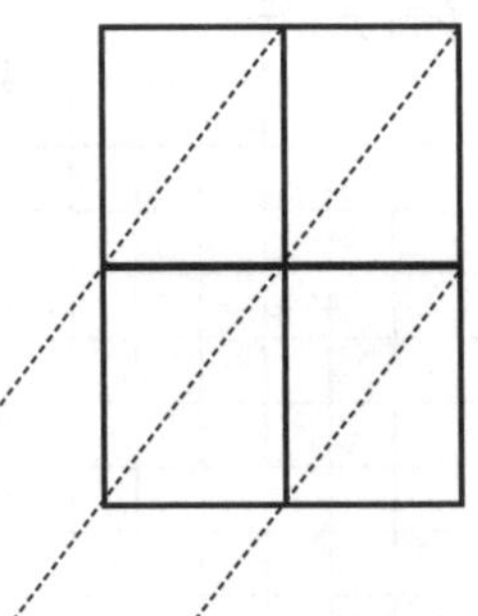

Practice

On the back of this page, use your favorite method to solve these problems.

4. $40 \times 28 =$ ______

5. $60 \times 35 =$ ______

Copyright © Wright Group/McGraw-Hill

Name Date Time

Copyright © Wright Group/McGraw-Hill

LESSON 9•11 An Error in Lattice Multiplication

There is a mistake in the following problem.
Circle the mistake, and describe it in words.

1.

	3	8	
0	0 / 6	1^2 / 6	2
9	2 / 7	7 / 2	9
	0	2	

Mistake: ______________________

Name Date Time

Copyright © Wright Group/McGraw-Hill

LESSON 9•11 An Error in Lattice Multiplication

There is a mistake in the following problem.
Circle the mistake, and describe it in words.

1.

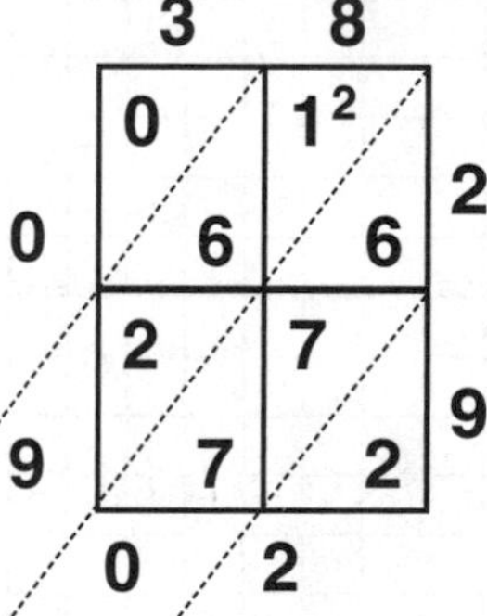

Mistake: ______________________

Name Date Time

LESSON 9•12

Array Multiplication 5

1. How many squares are in a 17-by-34 array? Total squares = ________

17 × 34 = ________

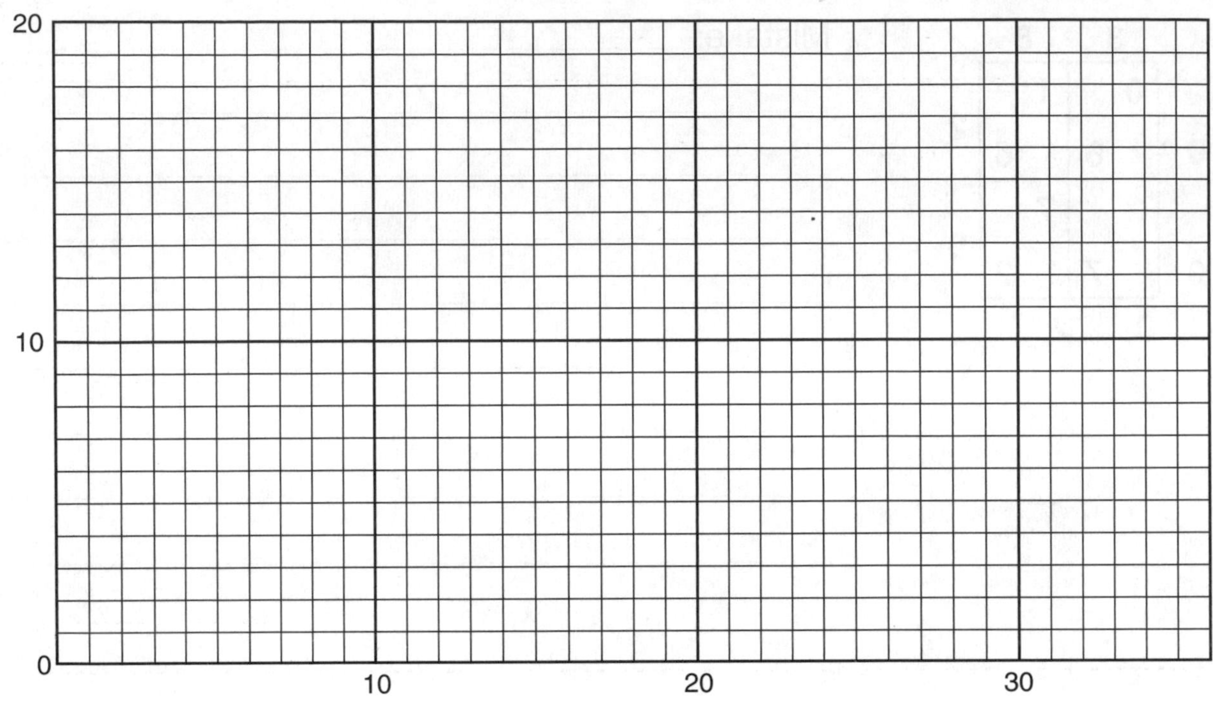

2. How many squares are in a 22-by-28 array? Total squares = ________

22 × 28 = ________

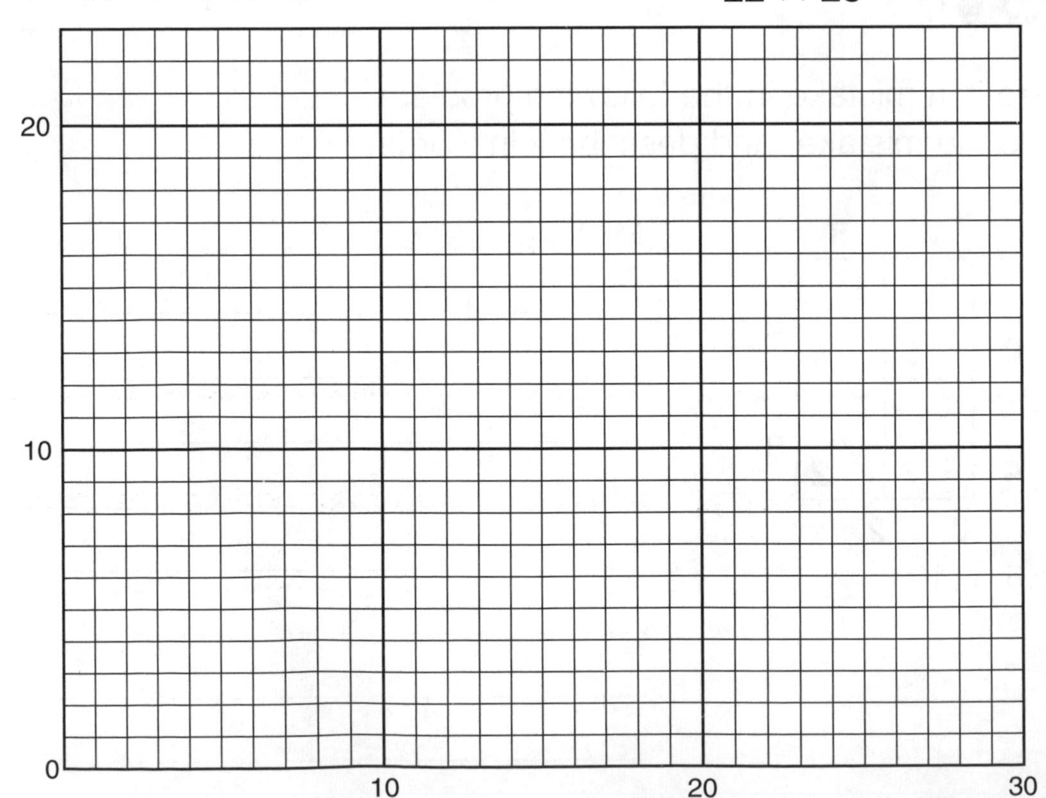

Copyright © Wright Group/McGraw-Hill

Name Date Time

2 Digits × 2 Digits

Family Note The class continues to practice the partial-products algorithm and the lattice method, now with any 2-digit numbers. Encourage your child to try these problems both ways and to compare the answers to be sure they are correct.

Please return this Home Link to school tomorrow.

SRB 68–72

Use the lattice method and the partial-products algorithm.

1. 21 × 35 = ________

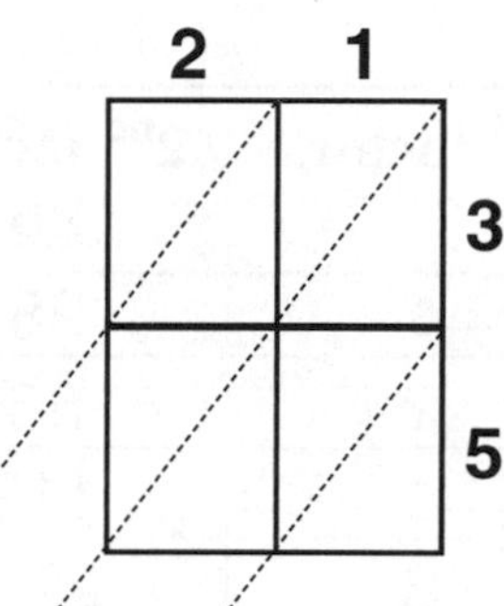

2. 17 × 43 = ________

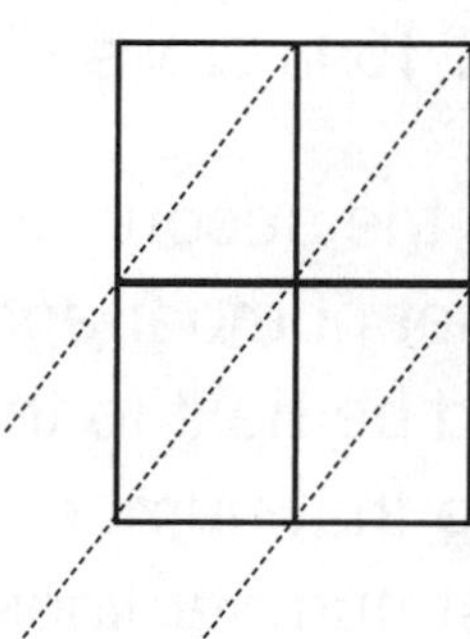

3. 58 × 62 = ________

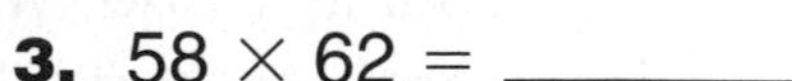

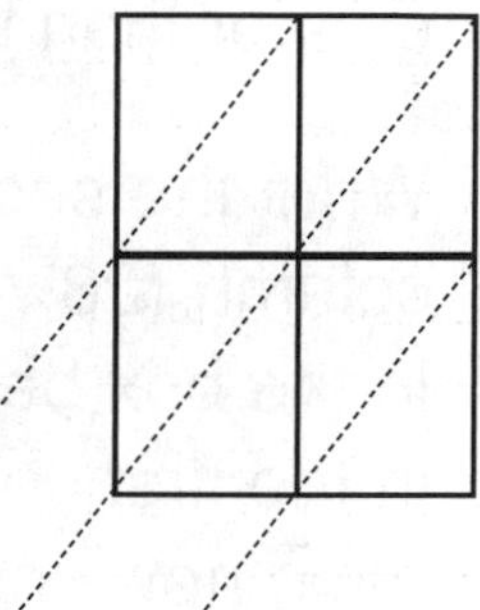

Practice

On the back of this page, use your favorite method to solve these problems.

4. 55 × 49 = ________

5. 91 × 33 = ________

Copyright © Wright Group/McGraw-Hill

Name Date Time

LESSON 9·12

Egyptian Multiplication

With a partner, carefully study the Egyptian multiplication algorithm below. Then solve a problem using this method.

Example: 13 × 28

Step 1: Write the first factor in the first column (13). Then write 1 in the first row below the factor. Double 1 and write 2 in the row below. Continue to double the number above until you get a number that is equal to or greater than the first factor. Cross out that number if it is greater than the first factor. 16 is crossed out.

1st factor: 13	2nd factor: ___
1	
2	
4	
8	
~~16~~	

Step 2: Write the second factor in the second column (28). Then write that number again in the box below. (It should be next to the 1 in the first column.) Double that number in each new line until the last number lines up with the last number of the first column (224 lines up with 8).

1st factor: 13	2nd factor: 28
1	28
2	56
4	112
8	224
~~16~~	

Step 3: Starting with the greatest number in column 1 (8), circle the numbers that add up to be the first factor (13). 8 + 4 + 1 = 13

Cross out the row of numbers that you did not use to make the first factor (2 and 56).

1st factor: 13	2nd factor: 28
(1)	28
~~2~~	~~56~~
(4)	112
(8)	224
~~16~~	

Step 4: Add the numbers in the second column that are not crossed out. 28 + 112 + 224 = 364

Answer: 13 × 28 = 364

Check the answer by solving the problem using an algorithm you already know.

1st factor: 13	2nd factor: 28
(1)	28
~~2~~	~~56~~
(4)	112
(8)	224
~~16~~	

Copyright © Wright Group/McGraw-Hill

Name Date Time

Egyptian Multiplication *continued*

Work with a partner to solve each problem following the steps of the Egyptian algorithm. Check your answers by solving the problems using an algorithm you already know.

1. 24 × 32

1st factor: 24	2nd factor: ____

Answer: 24 × 32 = ______

Try This

Do your own.

2. ___ × ___

1st factor: ____	2nd factor: ____

Answer: ___ × ___ = ___

Copyright © Wright Group/McGraw-Hill

Name Date Time

LESSON 9·12

Lattice Grids (2-Digit × 3-Digit)

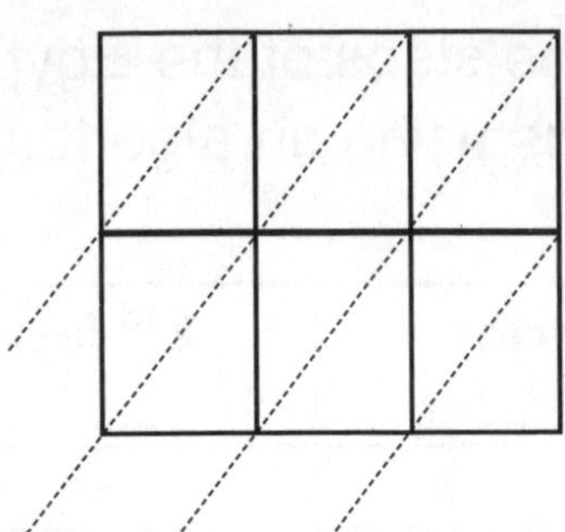

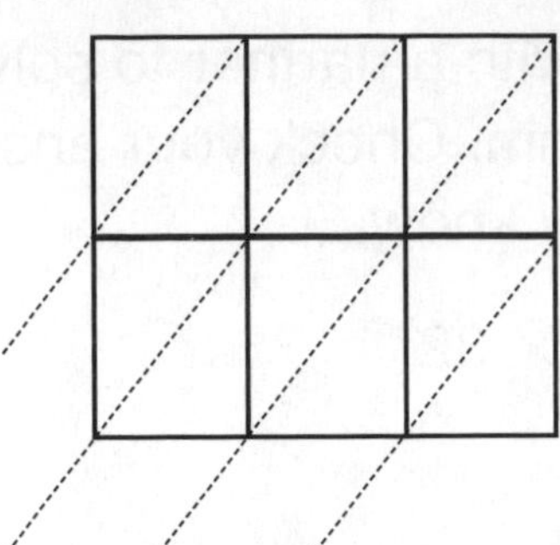

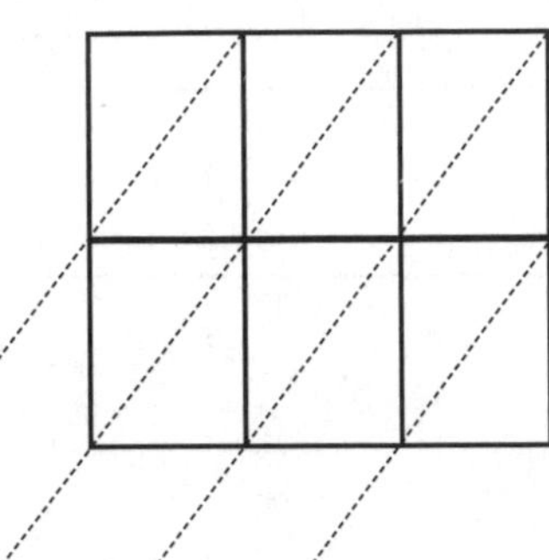

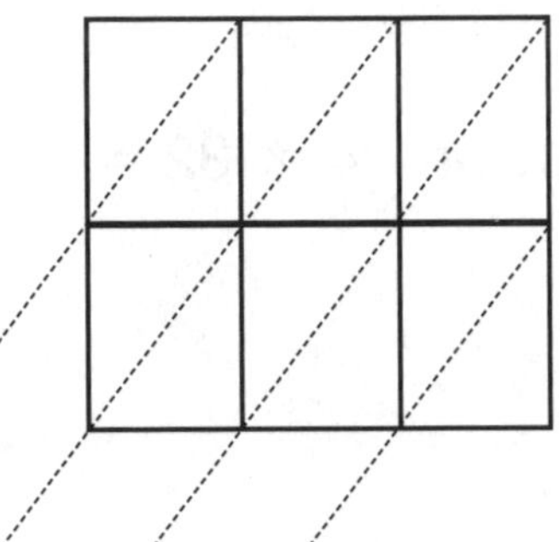

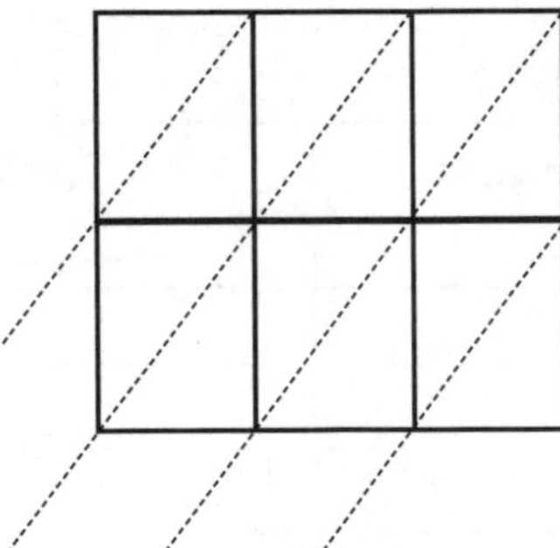

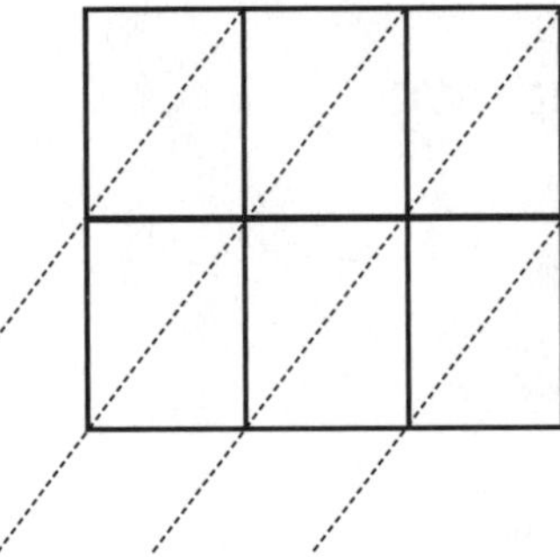

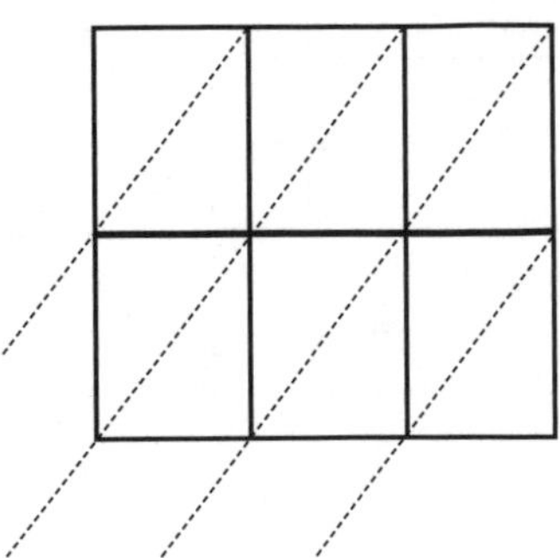

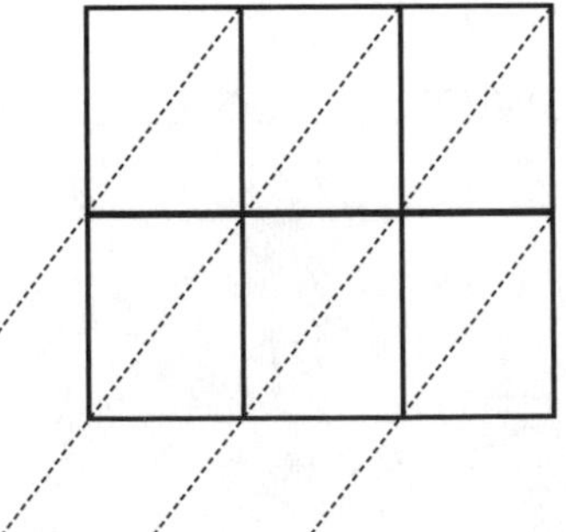

Copyright © Wright Group/McGraw-Hill

Name Date Time

Lattice Grids (2-Digit × 2-Digit)

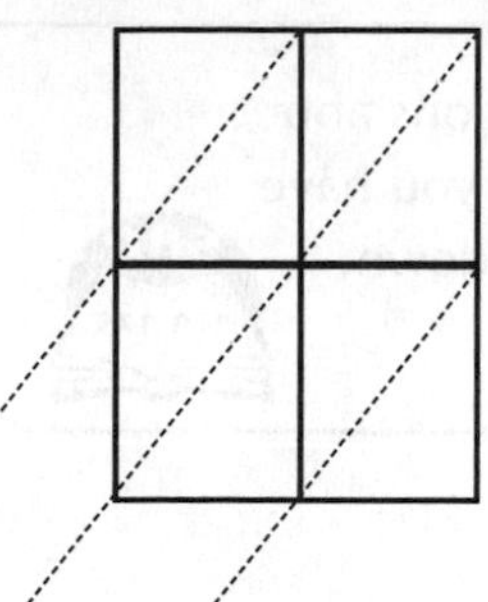

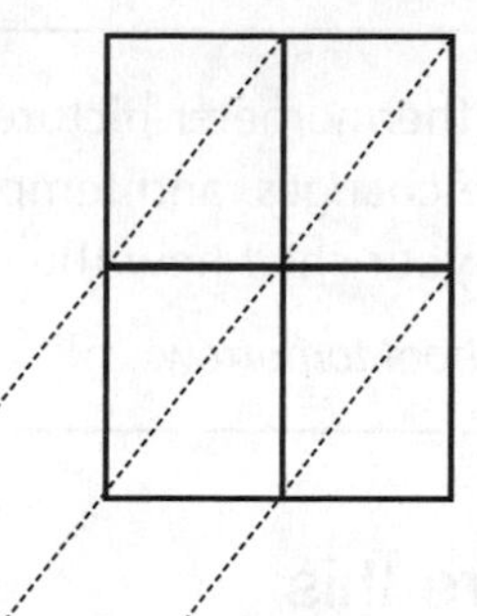

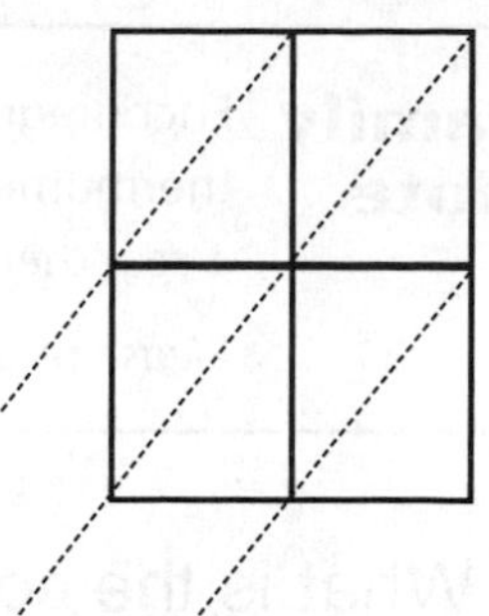

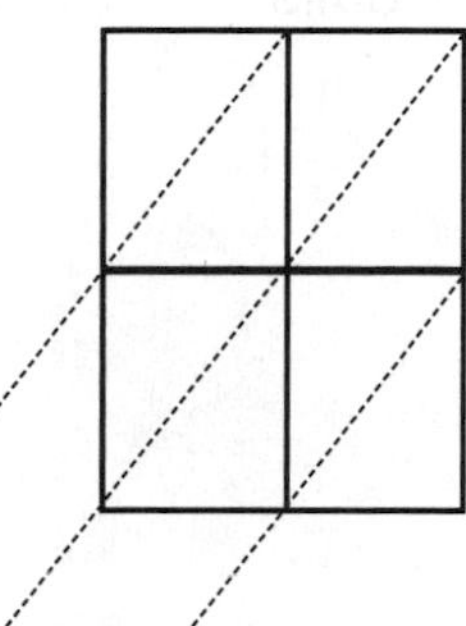

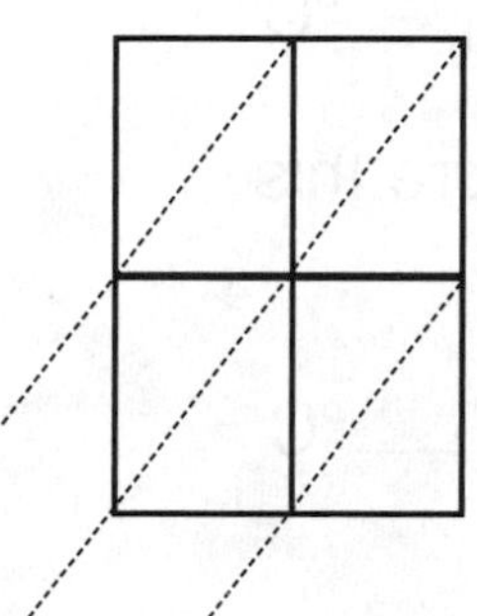

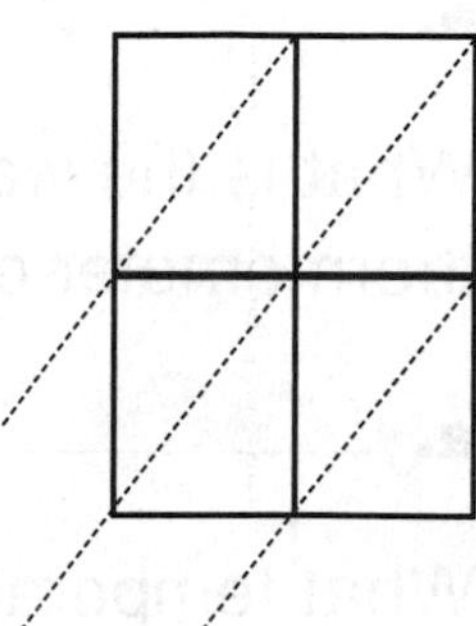

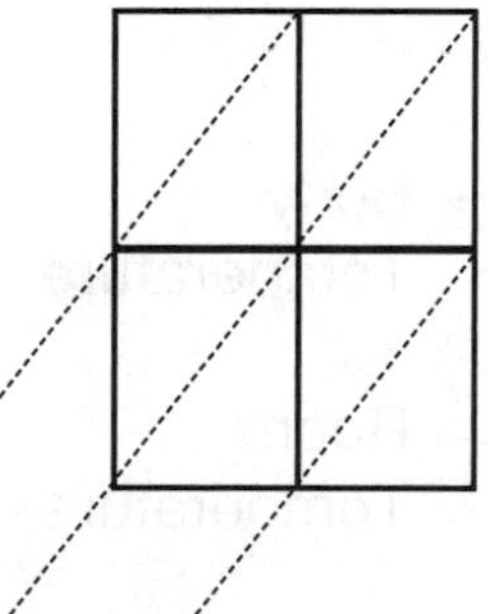

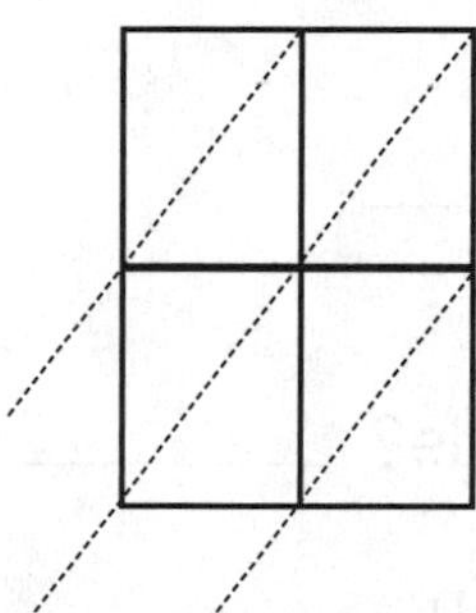

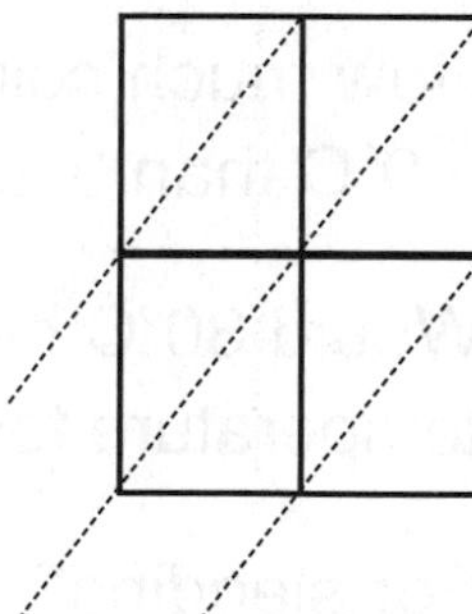

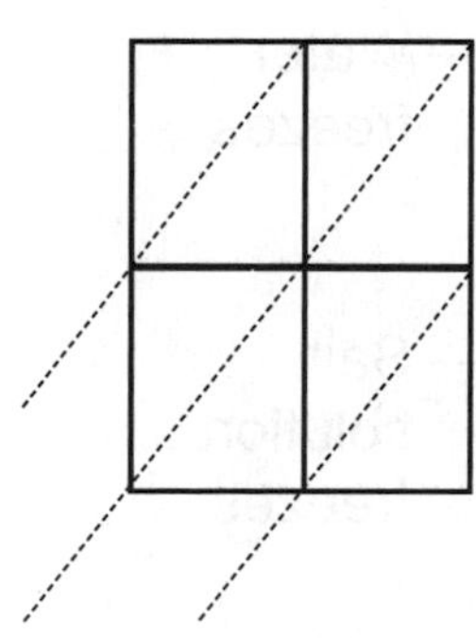

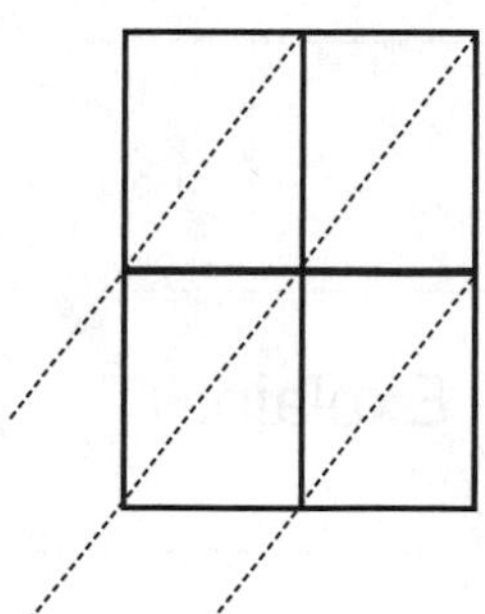

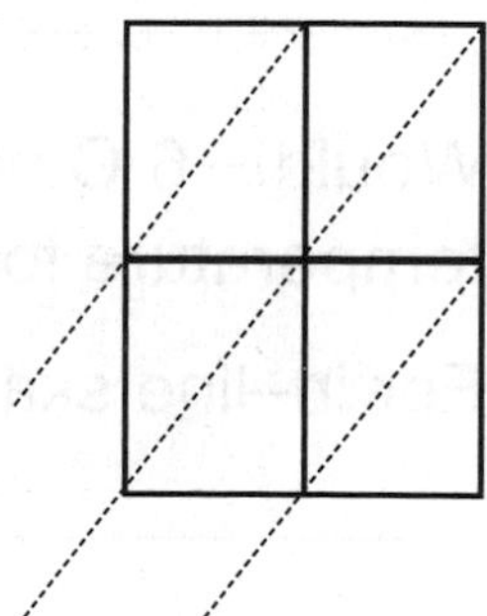

Copyright © Wright Group/McGraw-Hill

Name Date Time

HOME LINK 9•13

Positive and Negative Temperatures

Family Note Encourage your child to use the thermometer pictured here to answer questions about thermometer scales, temperature changes, and temperature comparisons. If you have a real thermometer, try to show your child how the mercury moves up and down.

Please return this Home Link to school tomorrow.

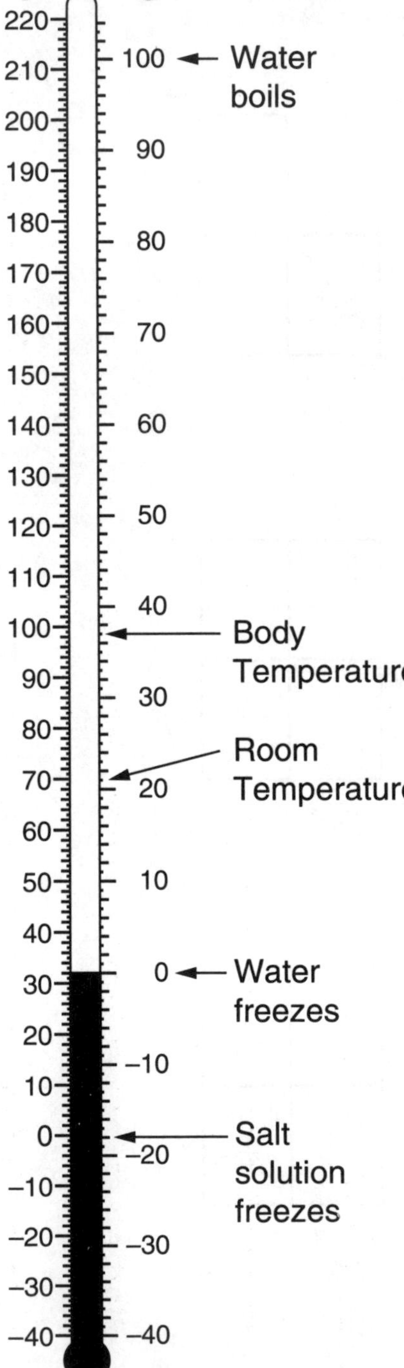

1. What is the coldest temperature this thermometer could show?

a. ________°F **b.** ________°C

2. What is the warmest temperature this thermometer could show?

a. ________°F **b.** ________°C

3. What temperature is 20 degrees warmer than −10°C? ________

4. How much colder is −9°C than 9°C? ________

5. Would 30°C be a good temperature for swimming outside? ________

For sledding? ________ Explain.

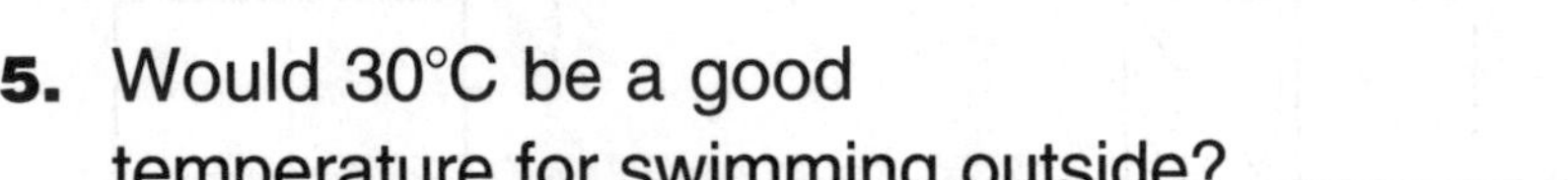

____

6. Would −6°C be a good temperature for ice-skating? ________

For in–line skating? ________ Explain.

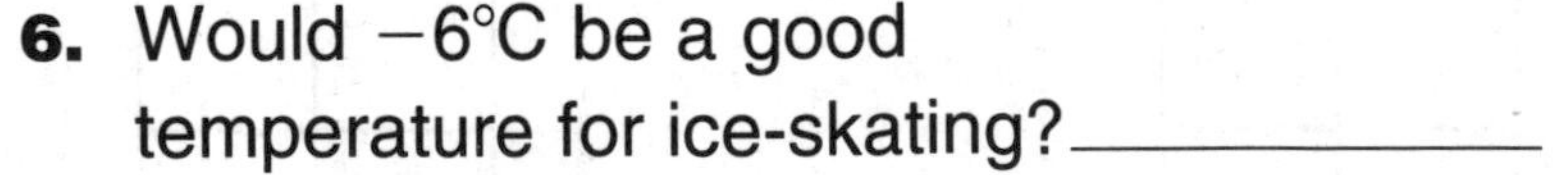

____

____

Copyright © Wright Group/McGraw-Hill

Name ______________________ Date ______________________ Time ______________________

LESSON 9·13

Negative Numbers on a Number Line

Copyright © Wright Group/McGraw-Hill

Show the jumps on the number lines.

1. Start at 10. Count back 13. Where did you land? ______

2. Start at −15. Count up 22. Where did you land? ______

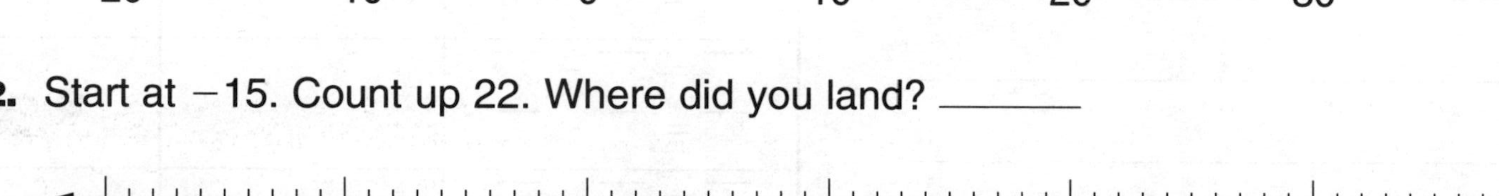

3. Start at 40. Count back 50. Where did you land? ______

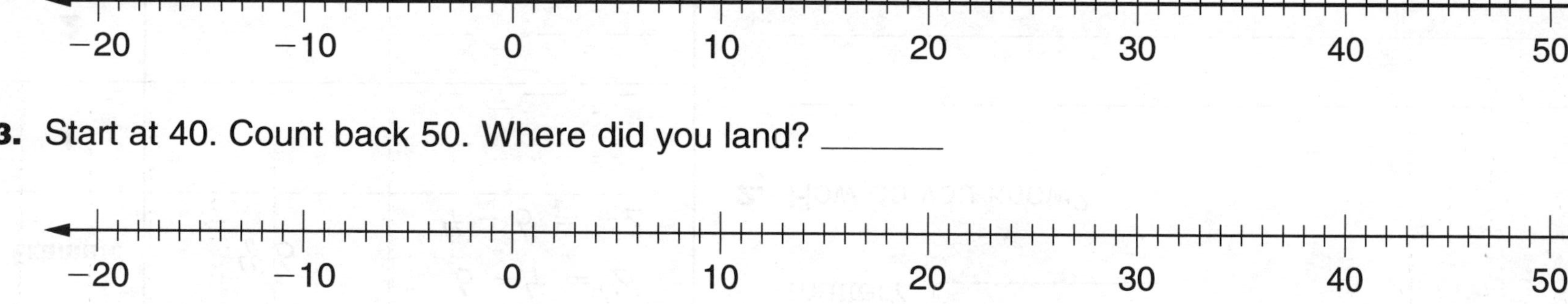

4. Do your own. Start at ______. Count ____________. Where did you land? ______

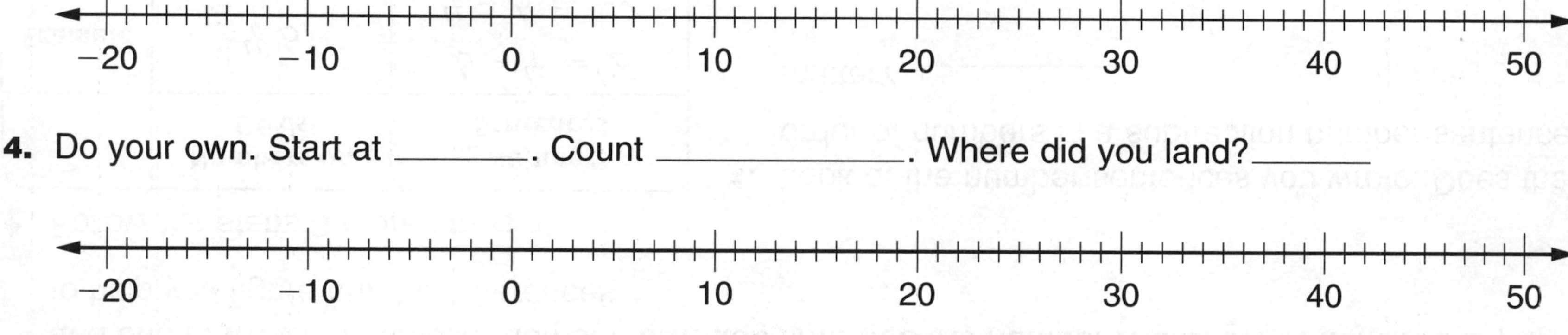

Try This

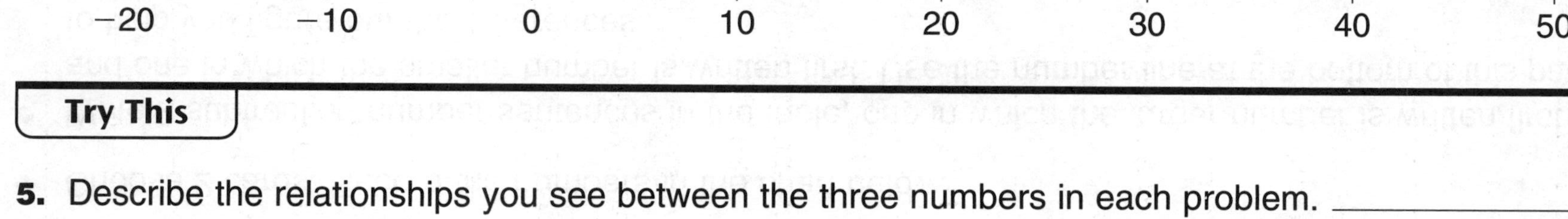

5. Describe the relationships you see between the three numbers in each problem. ____________

____

____

Name ______ Date ______ Time ______

LESSON 9·13

Exploring Order in Subtraction

You will need number cards 0–10 (2 of each).

- Place the cards number-side down.
- Choose 2 cards. Record the numbers in the chart below.
- Write 2 subtraction number sentences in the table, one in which the larger number is written first and one in which the smaller number is written first. Use the number line at the bottom of this page to help you figure out the differences.
- Follow the steps 3 more times.

	Numbers on Cards	Number Sentences
Example	4, 6	6 − 4 = 2 4 − 6 = −2
1		___ − ___ = ___ ___ − ___ = ___
2		___ − ___ = ___ ___ − ___ = ___
3		___ − ___ = ___ ___ − ___ = ___
4		___ − ___ = ___ ___ − ___ = ___

1. Look at the number sentences you wrote. Does the order of numbers in a subtraction number sentence matter? ______________

2. How do you know?

____

____

____

____

____

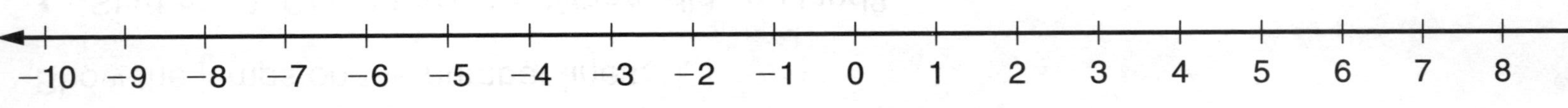

Copyright © Wright Group/McGraw-Hill

Name Date Time

HOME LINK 9•14

Unit 10: Family Letter

Measurement and Data

This unit has three main objectives:

- To review and extend previous work with measures of length, weight, and capacity by providing a variety of hands-on activities and applications. These activities will provide children with experience using U.S. customary and metric units of measurement.
- To extend previous work with the median and mode of a set of data and to introduce the mean (average) of a set of data.
- To introduce two new topics: finding the volume of rectangular prisms and using ordered pairs to locate points on a coordinate grid.

Children will repeat the personal measurements they made earlier in the year so that they may record their own growth. They will display these data in graphs and tables and find typical values for the class by finding the median, mean, and mode of the data.

They will begin to work with volumes of rectangular boxes, which have regular shapes, and will also compare the volumes of several irregular objects and investigate whether there is a relationship between the weight of these objects and their volumes.

Tables of Measures	
Length	1 kilometer = 1,000 meters 1 meter = 100 centimeters 1 centimeter = 10 millimeters 1 mile = 1,760 yards 1 yard = 3 feet 1 foot = 12 inches
Weight	1 kilogram = 1,000 grams 1 gram = 1,000 milligrams 1 ton = 2,000 pounds 1 pound = 16 ounces
Volume & Capacity	1 liter = 1,000 milliliters 1 gallon = 4 quarts 1 quart = 2 pints 1 pint = 2 cups 1 cubic yard = 27 cubic feet 1 cubic foot = 1,728 cubic inches

Copyright © Wright Group/McGraw-Hill

Please keep this Family Letter for reference as your child works through Unit 10.

Vocabulary

Important terms in Unit 10:

coordinate grid A reference frame for locating points in a plane by means of ordered pairs of numbers. A rectangular coordinate grid is formed by two number lines that intersect at right angles at their zero points.

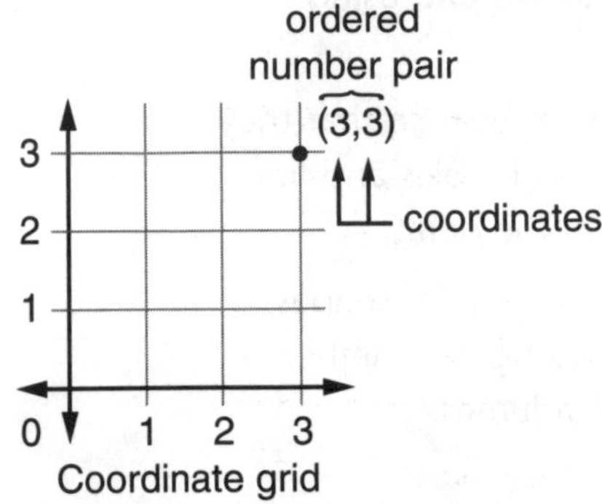

Coordinate grid

coordinate A number used to locate a point on a number line; a point's distance from an origin.

ordered number pair A pair of numbers used to locate a point on a coordinate grid.

height of a prism The length of the shortest line segment from a base of a prism to the plane containing the opposite face. The height is perpendicular to the base.

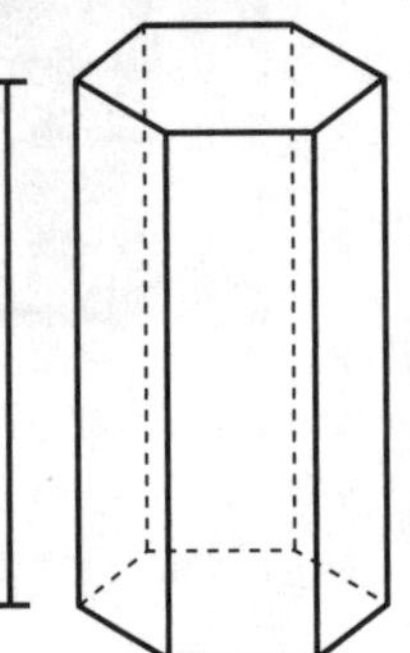

volume The amount of space occupied by a 3-dimensional shape.

square centimeter (square cm, cm^2) A unit to measure area. For example, a square centimeter is the area of a square with 1-cm long sides.

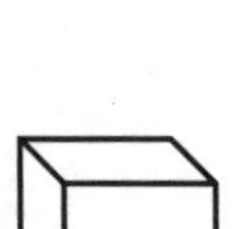

cubic centimeter (cubic cm, cm^3) A metric unit of volume or capacity equal to the volume of a cube with 1cm edges.

weight A measure of how heavy something is; the force of gravity on an object.

capacity (of a scale) The maximum weight a scale can measure. For example, most infant scales have a capacity of about 25 pounds.

capacity (of a container) The amount a container can hold. Capacity is often measured in units such as quarts, gallons, cups, or liters.

frequency table A table in which data are tallied and organized, often as a first step toward making a frequency graph.

Waist-to-floor measurement (inches)	Frequency	
	Tallies	Number
27	//	2
28		0
29	~~////~~	5
30	~~////~~ ///	8
31	~~////~~ //	7
32	////	4
	Total = 26	

mode The value or values that occur most often in a set of data. For example, in the frequency table above, 30 inches is the mode.

mean The sum of a set of numbers divided by the number of numbers in the set. Often called the average value of the set.

Copyright © Wright Group/McGraw-Hill

Do-Anytime Activities

To work with your child on the concepts taught in this unit and in previous units, try these interesting and rewarding activities:

1. Review equivalent names for measurements. For example: *How many inches in 1 foot? How many pints in 3 quarts? How many centimeters in 1 meter? How many grams in 1 kilogram?*
2. Review multiplication facts. For example: *How much is 6 times 3? 7 × 8? 4 [5s]?*
3. Review division facts. For example: *How many 2s in 12? What number multiplied by 4 equals 12? How much is 18 divided by 2?*
4. Practice multiplication with multiples of 10, 100, and 1,000. For example: *How much are 10 [30s]? How much is 4 × 100? What number times 100 equals 4,000?*
5. Practice division with multiples of 10, 100, and 1,000. For example: *How much is* $\frac{1}{10}$ *of 300? How many 50s in 5,000? How much is 200 divided by 50?*

Building Skills through Games

In Unit 10, your child will practice mental-math skills by playing the following games:

Memory Addition/Subtraction

Partners agree on a target number. They take turns adding or subtracting any number from 1 to 5 into the memory of their calculators while keeping track of the sums or differences in their heads. Then they press the MRC key to see if the final memory sums match their initial target number.

Multiplication Top-It

Players turn over two cards and call out the product. The player with the higher product keeps all the cards. The player with more cards at the end wins! *You will receive more detailed directions for* Multiplication Top-It *when we begin to play it in class.*

Copyright © Wright Group/McGraw-Hill

HOME LINK 9•14

Unit 10: Family Letter *cont.*

As You Help Your Child with Homework

As your child brings home assignments, you may want to go over the instructions together, clarifying them as necessary. The answers listed below will guide you through this unit's Home Links.

Home Link 10•1

1. 60; 96 **2.** 9; 12; 17

3. 33; 6; 12 **4.** 2; 4; 6

5. $\frac{1}{2}$; $\frac{1}{320}$; $\frac{1}{8}$; $\frac{1}{4}$; $\frac{1}{2}$ **6.** 90; 152; 117

Home Link 10•2

1. Boxes B, C, and D

2. Answers vary.

3. Answers vary.

Home Link 10•3

1. 2,052 **2.** 3,854

Home Link 10•5

1. inch **2.** gram

3. square yard **4.** centimeter

ch **6.** quart

8. 140

10. 864

Home Link 10•8

1. $20 \times 30 = 600$
$30 \times 20 = 600$
$600 \div 30 = 20$
$600 \div 20 = 30$

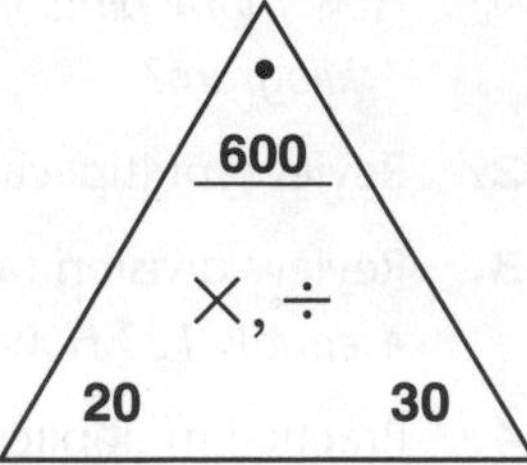

2. $40 \times 20 = 800$
$20 \times 40 = 800$
$800 \div 40 = 20$
$800 \div 20 = 40$

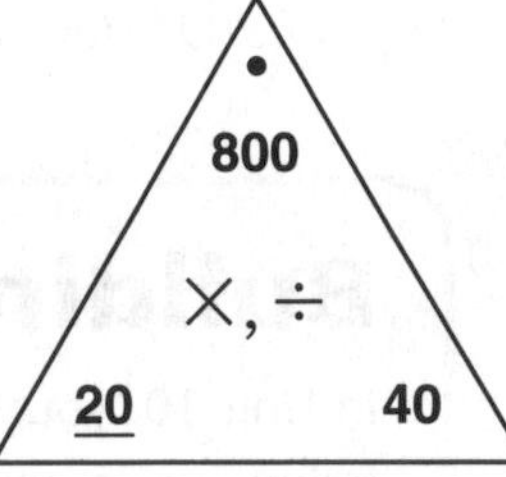

3. $100 \times 5 = 500$
$5 \times 100 = 500$
$500 \div 100 = 5$
$500 \div 5 = 100$

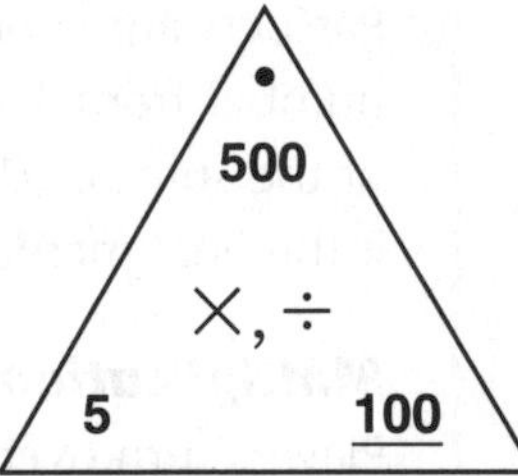

4. $600 \times 7 = 4{,}200$
$7 \times 600 = 4{,}200$
00 ÷ 600 = 7
÷ 7 = 600

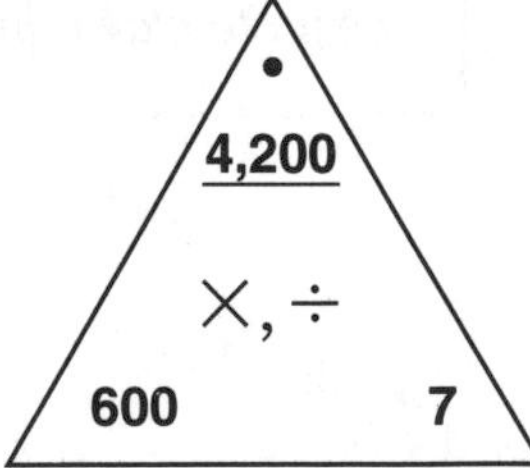

Home Link 10•10

1. (3,6) Algeria **2.** (6,3) Tanzania **3.** (5,5) Sudan

4. (4,5) Chad **5.** (5,6) Egypt **6.** (4,6) Libya

Copyright © Wright Group/McGraw-Hill

Name Date Time

LESSON 10•1

A Treasure Hunt

Jody and Jen heard a story about buried treasure at the Old Lighthouse. They decided to see for themselves. They couldn't agree on the route, so they took two different paths.

Find the length of each part of their paths.
(*Hint:* Measure in inches to the nearest $\frac{1}{4}$ inch.)

Whose route was shorter?

____

Try This

How much shorter?

About __________

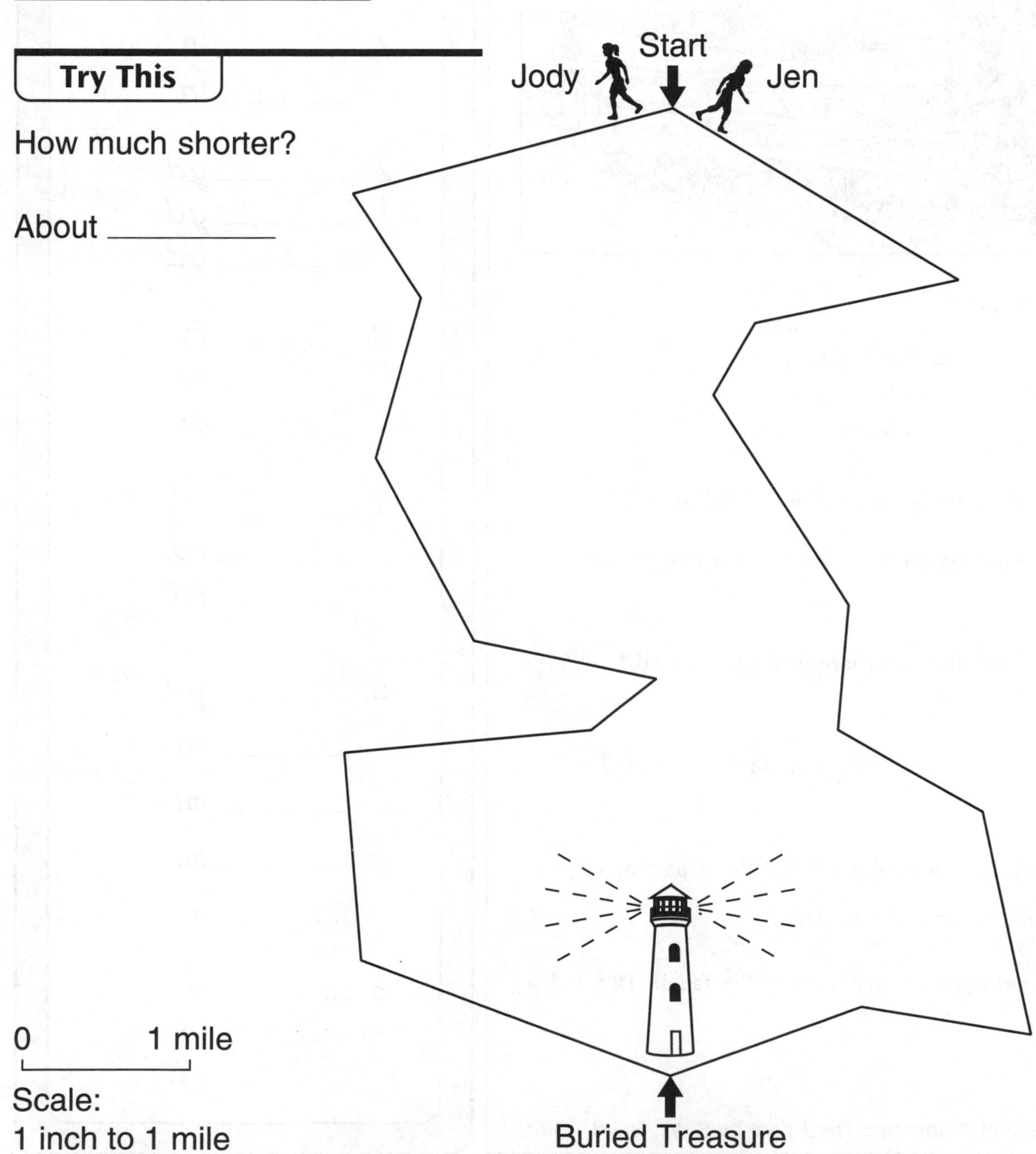

Scale:
1 inch to 1 mile

Copyright © Wright Group/McGraw-Hill

Old-Fashioned Equivalencies

Family Note Here is a page from a third-grade math book published in 1897. These are the kinds of measurement problems children were expected to do more than 100 years ago. The rod is a unit that is not often used today. It was used to measure land.

Please return this Home Link to school tomorrow.

Solve the problems yourself. Write your answers on the "slate."

12 inches (in.)	= 1 foot (ft.)
3 feet	= 1 yard (yd.)
$16\frac{1}{2}$ feet	= 1 rod (rd.)
$5\frac{1}{2}$ yards	= 1 rod
320 rods	= 1 mile (mi.)

1. How many inches are there in 5 ft.? in 8 ft.?

2. How many yards are there in 27 ft.? in 36 ft.? in 51 ft.?

3. How many feet are there in 2 rd.? in 2 yd.? in 4 yd.?

4. How many rods are there in 33 ft.? in 66 ft.? in 99 ft.?

5. What part of a yard is $1\frac{1}{2}$ ft.? What part of a mile is 1 rd.? 40 rd.? 80 rd.? 160 rd.?

6. How many inches are there in $7\frac{1}{2}$ ft.? in $12\frac{2}{3}$ ft.? in $9\frac{3}{4}$ ft.?

Graded Work in Arithmetic: Third Year by S. W. Baird, 1897.

1. ________ in.
________ in.

2. ________ yd
________ yd
________ yd

3. ________ ft
________ ft
________ ft

4. ________ rd
________ rd
________ rd

5. ________ yd
________ mi
________ mi
________ mi
________ mi

6. ________ in.
________ in.
________ in.

Copyright © Wright Group/McGraw-Hill

Name Date Time

Measurement Search

Use your estimating skills to find items in the classroom that are about the same length as the measurements below. List them. Use the line segments on the board as a reference.

1. about $4\frac{1}{2}$ feet in length or width

______ ______ ______

2. about 1.5 meters in length or width

______ ______ ______

3. about 2.5 centimeters in length or width

______ ______ ______

4. about 60 inches in girth (distance around)

______ ______ ______

5. a perimeter of about 200 centimeters

______ ______ ______

Use measuring tools to check your estimates. Draw a circle around the names of the items for which your estimate was close to your measurement.

Copyright © Wright Group/McGraw-Hill

Name Date Time

LESSON 10•1

Story with Measures

Make a list of 8 measurements of length. Use each of the following units at least once: inch, foot, yard, mile.

A. ______ ______ (unit)

B. ______ ______ (unit)

C. ______ ______ (unit)

D. ______ ______ (unit)

E. ______ ______ (unit)

F. ______ ______ (unit)

G. ______ ______ (unit)

H. ______ ______ (unit)

Match the letters in the story with the letters of your measures. Fill in each blank in the story with the measure that has the same letter.

This morning, after walking (A) ______ to school, I saw my friend Emma looking up into a tree. She was staring at a spot about (B) ______ above the ground. How in the world did her backpack get up there? I ran (C) ______ to my friend Henry's house. He had a stepladder (D) ______ tall. We raced back to school and set it up under the tree. I climbed up as far as I could go. If only I were (E) ______ taller, I could reach the backpack. Isaac came running with a stick that was (F) ______ long. I held it up, caught the backpack, and jiggled it free. It crashed to the ground with a thud!

Luckily, my locker is (G) ______ tall and (H) ______ wide. The ladder just fit. At the end of the day, we returned the ladder to Henry's house. Emma and I decided she was getting too big and strong to be tossing backpacks just for fun.

- Read the story. Is it silly or sensible?
- Discuss how you would change the measurements and distances to make the story more sensible.

Copyright © Wright Group/McGraw-Hill

Name Date Time

Box Patterns

A A A A

C C C C

B B B B

D D D D

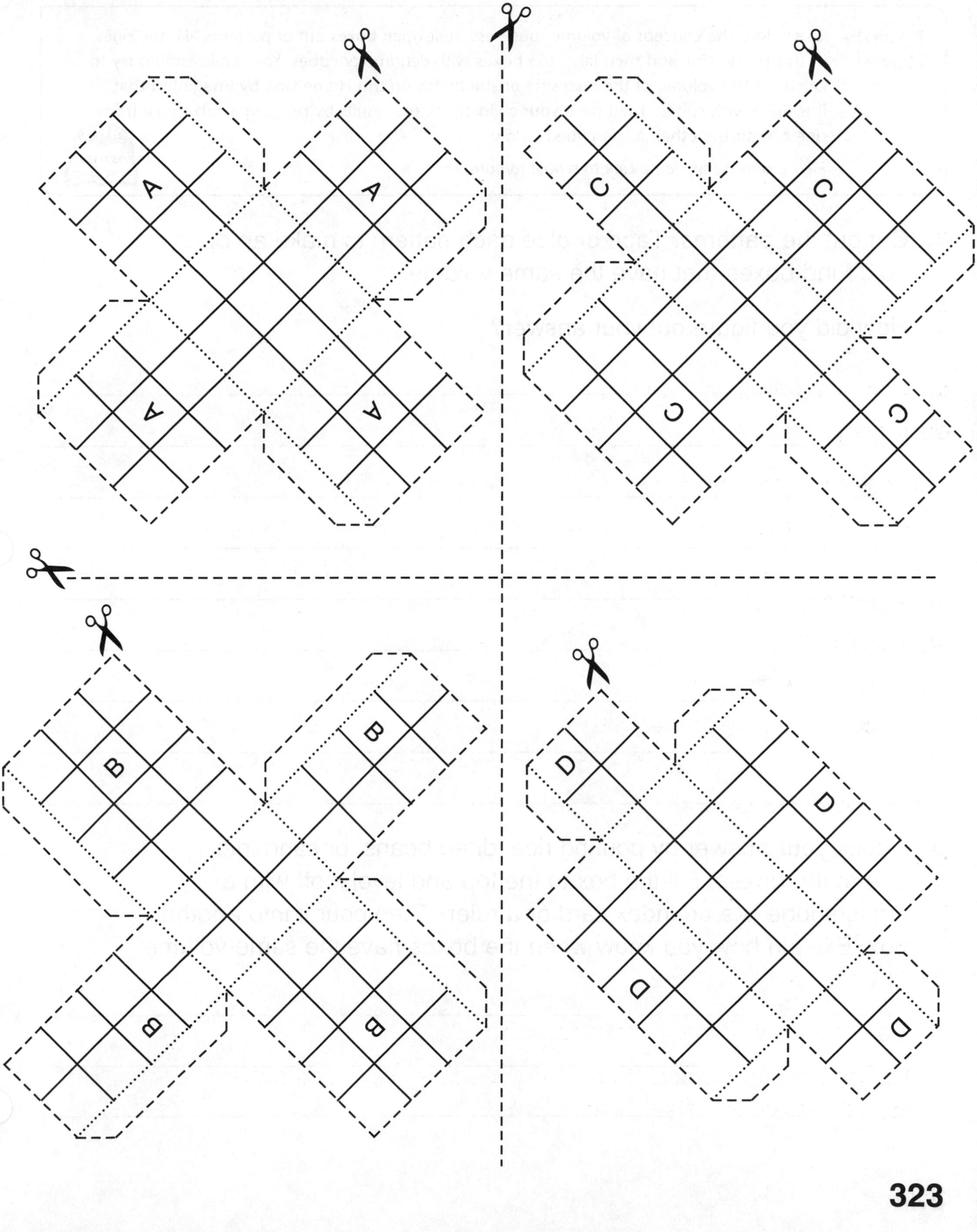

Copyright © Wright Group/McGraw-Hill

Name Date Time

Exploring the Volume of Boxes

Family Note To explore the concept of volume, our class built open boxes out of patterns like the ones in this Home Link and then filled the boxes with centimeter cubes. Your child should try to calculate the volume of the boxes he or she builds on this Home Link by imagining that it is filled with cubes. Then have your child check the results by pouring a substance from one box to the other, as described below.

Please return this Home Link to school tomorrow.

SRB 157–159

1. Cut out the patterns. Tape or glue each pattern to make an open box. Find boxes that have the same volume.

2. How did you figure out your answer?

____

____

____

____

____

____

____

____

____

3. Check your answer by pouring rice, dried beans, or sand into one of the boxes. Fill the box to the top and level it off with a straightedge like an index card or a ruler. Then pour it into another box. Explain how you know when the boxes have the same volume.

____

____

____

Copyright © Wright Group/McGraw-Hill

Name Date Time

HOME LINK 10•2

Exploring the Volume of Boxes *cont.*

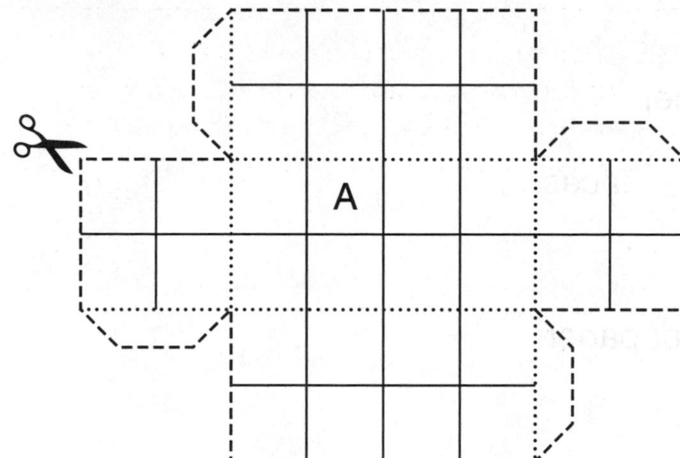

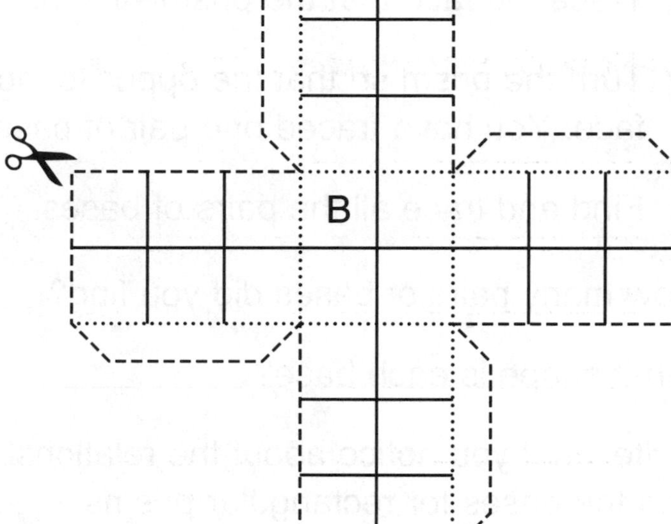

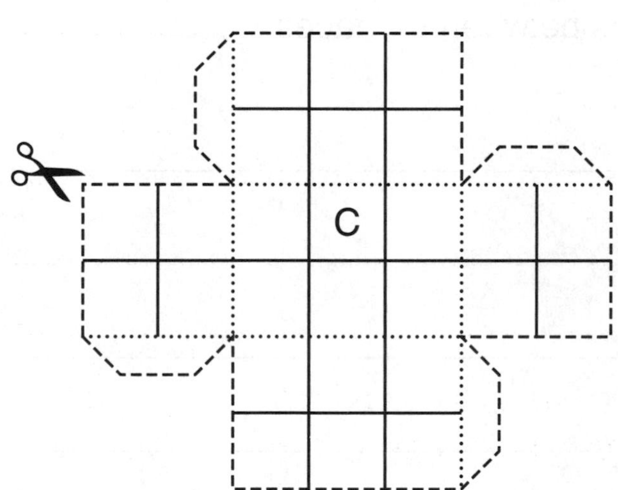

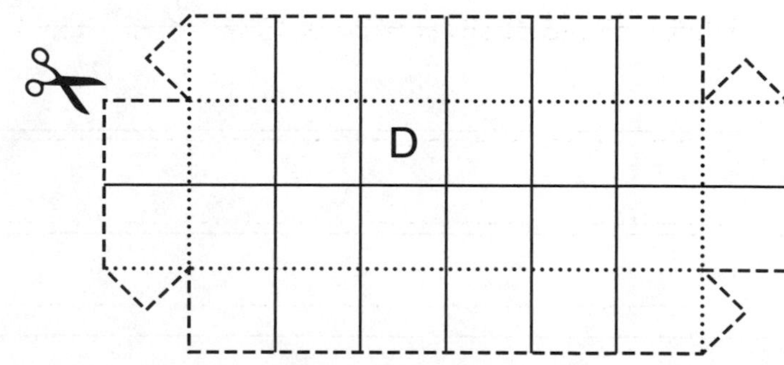

Copyright © Wright Group/McGraw-Hill

Name Date Time

LESSON 10•2

Bases of Rectangular Prisms

Work with a partner.

Get a rectangular prism from your teacher.

Count the number of faces. It has ______ faces.

What shape is each face? ____________

Place the rectangular prism on a sheet of paper.

1. Trace the face that the prism sits on.
2. Turn the prism so that the opposite face is on the paper. Trace that face. You have traced one pair of bases.
3. Find and trace all the pairs of bases.

How many pairs of bases did you find? ______

What shape is each base? ____________

Write what you notice about the relationships between the faces and the bases for rectangular prisms.

____

____

____

____

____

____

____

____

Copyright © Wright Group/McGraw-Hill

Name Date Time

Exploring the Volume of Cubes

Do the following activities. Remember that all faces of a cube are the same size.

1. Use centimeter cubes to build a cube whose faces each have an area of 4 square centimeters.

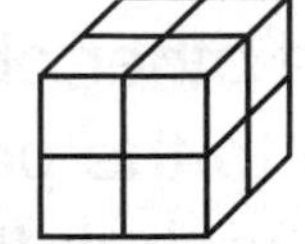

How many layers does the cube have? ______________

What is the volume of the cube? ______ cubic centimeters

2. Build a cube whose faces each have an area of 9 square centimeters.

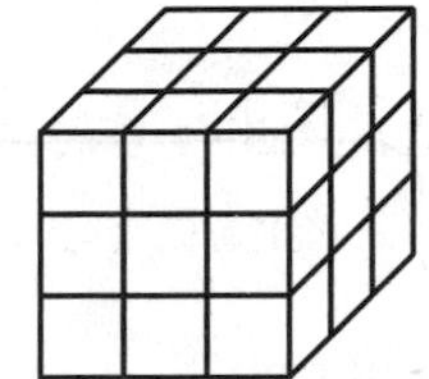

How many layers does the cube have? ______________

What is the volume of the cube? ______ cubic centimeters

3. Build a cube whose faces each have an area of 16 square centimeters.

How many layers does the cube have? ______________

What is the volume of the cube? ______ cubic centimeters

4. What do you think is the area of one face of the next larger cube? ______ square centimeters

What is the volume of the cube? ______ cubic centimeters

Explain how you found the volume.

____

____

____

____

5. Check the volume by building such a cube.

Copyright © Wright Group/McGraw-Hill

Name Date Time

LESSON 10·3 Comparing Weights

Use a scale to weigh a package of pasta.

The package weighs ______ pound(s).

Find other objects that weigh about the same amount. Compare each one to the package of pasta by holding the object in one hand and the package in the other.

List the objects that weigh about the same as the package of pasta in the first column of the table below.

Name of Object	Weight of Object (in pounds)

After you have listed at least 4 objects, weigh them and record the weights to the nearest pound in the second column. How close were your estimates?

Copyright © Wright Group/McGraw-Hill

Name Date Time

The Meaning of Weight

Family Note Today the children discussed weight. They examined different scales, discussed objects that might be weighed with each kind of scale, and read weights on scales.

Please return this Home Link to school tomorrow.

Which do you think weighs more: a pound of feathers or a pound of books? Explain your reason.

____

____

Practice

Solve each problem using the partial products and lattice algorithms.

1. partial products:

$$\begin{array}{r} 38 \\ \times\ 54 \\ \hline \end{array}$$

lattice:

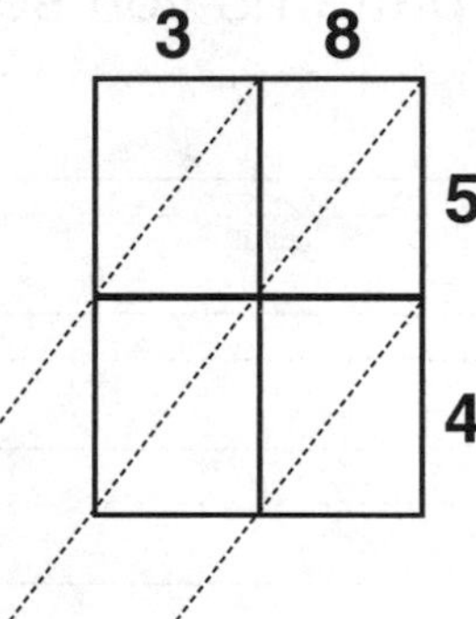

2. partial products:

$$\begin{array}{r} 82 \\ \times\ 47 \\ \hline \end{array}$$

lattice:

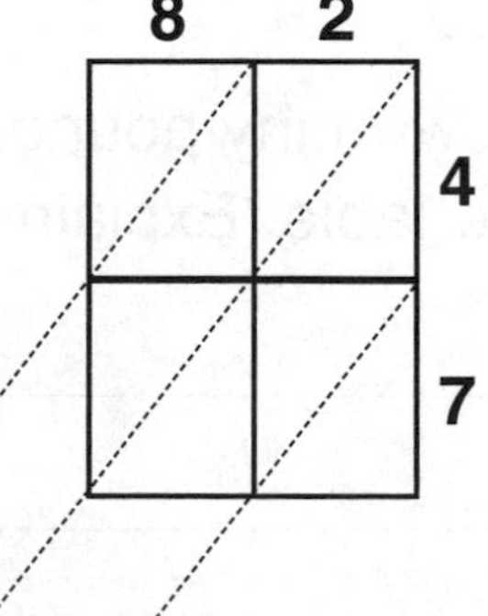

Copyright © Wright Group/McGraw-Hill

Name Date Time

Comparing Units of Measure

Units of Measure	
Kilograms (kg)	**Pounds (lb)**
5	11
10	22
15	33
20	44
25	55
60	

Describe the patterns you see in the table.

Try This

Figure out how many pounds are equal to 60 kg. Enter the number of pounds in the table. Explain how you figured it out.

Copyright © Wright Group/McGraw-Hill

Name Date Time

Ordering Objects by Volume

Exploration A

Find the *actual* order of the 4 objects on display from largest to smallest volume. Work with a partner. You will need the following materials:

- 4 objects from Lesson 10-1
- coffee can filled with water
- clear wide-mouthed jar, masking tape
- paper towels, large tub
- permanent marker

1. Attach a strip of tape to the side of the jar from top to bottom. This is your measuring jar.
2. Place the coffee can inside the tub. Make sure the can is filled to the rim with water.
3. Slowly place one of the four objects into the can. If the object floats, push it down gently until it is completely, but just barely, underwater. The tub will catch the displaced water.
4. Take the object out of the can and the can out of the tub. Pour the displaced water from the tub into the measuring jar.
5. Use a permanent marker. Mark the water level on the tape on the measuring jar. Label the mark with the name of the object.
6. Place the can back inside the tub and pour the water from the jar back into the can. If necessary, add more water to the can to fill it to the rim.

Repeat Steps 3–6 for each of the other objects.

Record the order of the objects from largest to smallest volume in Part 4 on journal page 241.

When you have finished, take the tape off the side of the jar. Wipe up spilled water and dry off the wet objects. Leave the area ready for the next group.

Copyright © Wright Group/McGraw-Hill

Name Date Time

HOME LINK 10•4

Collecting Food Container Labels

Family Note Today our class measured the weight and volume of several objects. We tried to decide whether an object that weighs more than another object always has the greater volume. Ask your child, "Which takes up more space, a pound of popped popcorn or a pound of marbles?"

Help your child practice multiplication facts by playing the game *Multiplication Top-It.* Directions for the game are below.

Please send the collected food labels to school tomorrow.

A. Ask someone at home to help you find food containers showing nutritional information. For example, you might look on canned goods, cereal boxes, bags of cookies, or bottles of cooking oil. Bring the labels or empty containers to school. Be sure they are clean.

B. Play a game of *Multiplication Top-It* with 1 or 2 people at home. *Multiplication Top-It* is similar to the card game *War.*

Directions

1. Remove the face cards from a regular deck of cards. The aces are the 1-cards.
2. Shuffle the cards. Place the deck facedown on a table.
3. Each player turns over two cards and calls out the product of the numbers. The player with the higher product wins the round and takes all the cards.
4. In case of a tie, each player turns over two more cards and calls out the product. The player with the higher product then takes all the cards from both plays.
5. Play ends when not enough cards are left for both players to turn over two cards. The player with more cards wins.

Example Colleen turns over a 6 and a 2. She calls out 12.
Danny turns over a 10 and a 4. He calls out 40.
Danny has the higher product. He takes all 4 cards.

Copyright © Wright Group/McGraw-Hill

Name Date Time

Same Volume, Different Prisms

Exploration B

Work with a partner. Use cm cubes to build 7 different rectangular prisms whose volume is 36 cubic centimeters. The base of the prism must have at least 2 rows of cubes with at least 2 cubes in each row. The prism must have at least 2 layers of cubes (2 cm high).

For each prism:

1. Use a straightedge to draw its base on the grid.

2. Label each base A–G.

3. Write the measures in the table.

Prism	Area of Base (sq cm)	Height (cm)	Volume (cu cm)
A			36
B			36
C			36
D			36
E			36
F			36
G			36

Copyright © Wright Group/McGraw-Hill

Name Date Time

Doubling with Volume

For each problem, build a prism with centimeter cubes to help you find the volume.

1. a. What is the volume of a rectangular prism that is 1 cm wide, 1 cm long, and 1 cm high? ______

   b. What is the volume of a rectangular prism with twice the dimensions from Problem 1? (2 cm wide, 2 cm long, and 2 cm high) ______

   c. What is the volume of a rectangular prism with twice the dimensions from Problem 3? (4 cm wide, 4 cm long, and 4 cm high) ______

2. a. What is the volume of a rectangular prism that is 3 cm wide, 3 cm long, and 3 cm high? ______

   b. Predict the volume of a rectangular prism with twice the dimensions from Problem 2a. (6 cm wide, 6 cm long, and 6 cm high) ______

Try This

3. Write a rule for how to find the volume of a rectangular prism when you double all of the dimensions.

______

______

______

Copyright © Wright Group/McGraw-Hill

Name Date Time

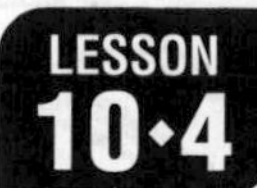

Weighing Objects on Scales

Exploration C

Work with a partner. Weigh items in the classroom using the different scales your teacher has provided.

For each item:

1. Decide which scale you and your partner will use to weigh each item. Discuss why that scale is the best one to use for that item.
2. If possible, weigh the item in both U.S. customary and metric units.
3. Record your results in the chart below.

Object	Scale	U.S. Customary Units (ounces, pounds)	Metric Units (grams, kilograms)

Try This

4. Talk to your partner and figure out a strategy to weigh an object that will not easily fit on a bath scale. On the back of this paper, describe how you weighed the object.

Copyright © Wright Group/McGraw-Hill

Name Date Time

LESSON 10•5

Capacity in Nonstandard Units

Work with a partner. Follow these steps.

1. Choose a container.
2. Predict the number of paper cups full of rice, beans, or sand that will fill the container. Find the row in the table below that matches the letter on your container. Record your prediction.
3. Check your prediction. Fill a paper cup with rice, sand, or beans. Pour it into the container, counting each paper cup as you go. Record your results in the table.
4. Repeat the steps for each of the containers.

Letter on Container	Prediction of Capacity (full paper cups)	Measured Capacity (full paper cups)
A		
B		
C		
D		
E		

5. Compare the capacities of the containers. Write at least 2 things you notice about the capacities.

____

____

____

____

Copyright © Wright Group/McGraw-Hill

Name Date Time

Matching Units of Measure

Family Note Today our class explored units of capacity—cups, pints, quarts, gallons, milliliters, and liters. For the list below, your child should choose an appropriate unit for measuring each item. Some of the items refer to capacity, but units of length, weight, area, and volume are also included. Do not expect your child to know all of the units. Remind your child that *square units* refer to area measurement and *cubic units* to volume measurement.

Please return this Home Link to school tomorrow.

SRB 146 154 157 160 162

Fill in the oval to mark the unit best used to measure each object.

	Object	Units		
1.	height of a chair	⬭ mile	⬭ inch	⬭ pound
2.	weight of a penny	⬭ pound	⬭ inch	⬭ gram
3.	area of a football field	⬭ square inch	⬭ square yard	⬭ cubic meter
4.	perimeter of your journal	⬭ kilometer	⬭ gallon	⬭ centimeter
5.	diameter of a dinner plate	⬭ foot	⬭ cubic centimeter	⬭ inch
6.	amount of juice in a carton	⬭ meter	⬭ quart	⬭ square liter

7. About how much water could you drink in 1 day?

⬭ 1 cup ⬭ 1 milliliter ⬭ 1 liter ⬭ 1 gallon

Practice

Solve.

8. $\begin{array}{r} 35 \\ \times\ 4 \\ \hline \end{array}$

9. $\begin{array}{r} 62 \\ \times\ 3 \\ \hline \end{array}$

10. $\begin{array}{r} 27 \\ \times\ 32 \\ \hline \end{array}$

Copyright © Wright Group/McGraw-Hill

Name Date Time

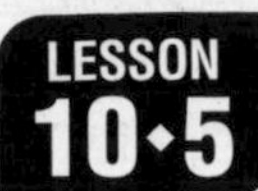

Finding the Volume & Weight of Popcorn

Part 1

Make predictions.

- Does popcorn weigh about the same before and after it is popped? ______
- Does it have the same volume? ______

Part 2

1. Measure the volume and weight of the unpopped corn kernels. Record your data in the data chart below.
2. Measure the volume and weight of the popped popcorn. Record your data in the data chart.

	Unpopped Kernels	**Popped Kernels**
Weight		
Volume		

3. Were your predictions correct? Explain.

Copyright © Wright Group/McGraw-Hill

Name Date Time

LESSON 10•6

Predicting Dice Rolls

If you roll a die 20 times, predict how many times you think you will roll a 1. ______

Roll a die 20 times. Record your results in the table to the right. Use the grid below to make a bar graph showing your results. Remember to label your graph and give it a title.

Dice Roll	Tallies
1	
2	
3	
4	
5	
6	

Title: ______

Copyright © Wright Group/McGraw-Hill

Name Date Time

HOME LINK 10•6 Mean, or Average, Number of Fish

Family Note Many of us learned that to find the mean (average) of a set of numbers, we add all the numbers and then divide the total by how many numbers we added. In today's lesson, the class tried a different method of finding the mean. After your child has completed the page, ask him or her to explain how this method works. In the next lesson, we will introduce finding the mean by adding the numbers and dividing to find the answer.

SRB 83–85

Please return this Home Link to school tomorrow.

The table below lists how many goldfish each child won at the school fun fair.

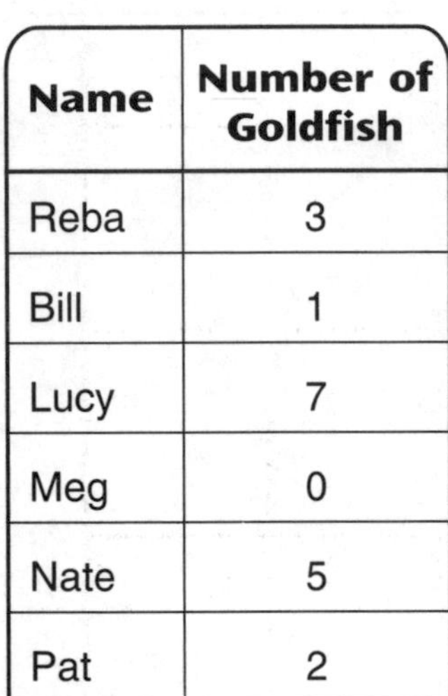

Name	Number of Goldfish
Reba	3
Bill	1
Lucy	7
Meg	0
Nate	5
Pat	2

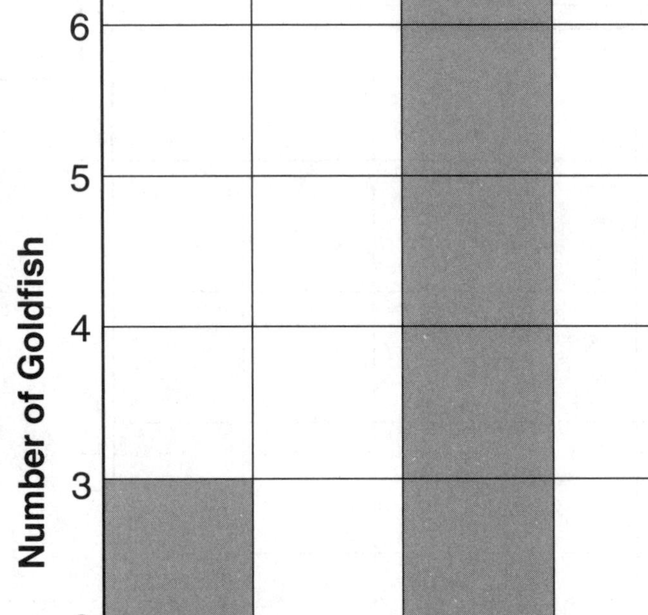

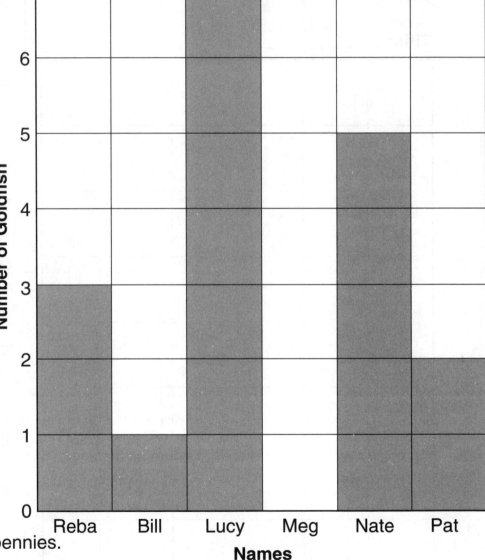

1. Put a penny over each shaded square in the bar graph.
2. Move the pennies so that each column has the same number of pennies.
3. Draw a horizontal line across your graph to show the height of the pennies when all of the columns are the same height.
4. The mean (average) number of goldfish won by children at the fun fair is ______.

Copyright © Wright Group/McGraw-Hill

Name Date Time

Graphing a Data Set

Make a bar graph for your set of data.

Title: ______________________

Copyright © Wright Group/McGraw-Hill

Name Date Time

LESSON 10·6

Making a Data Set

Altogether, 5 children have 15 cookies in their lunch bags.

- The median number of cookies is 2.
- The range of the number of cookies is 5.
- The mode of the number of cookies is 2.

How many cookies could each child have?

Use counters and the drawings of lunch bags below to organize your data. Draw cookies in the lunch bags to match the description above.

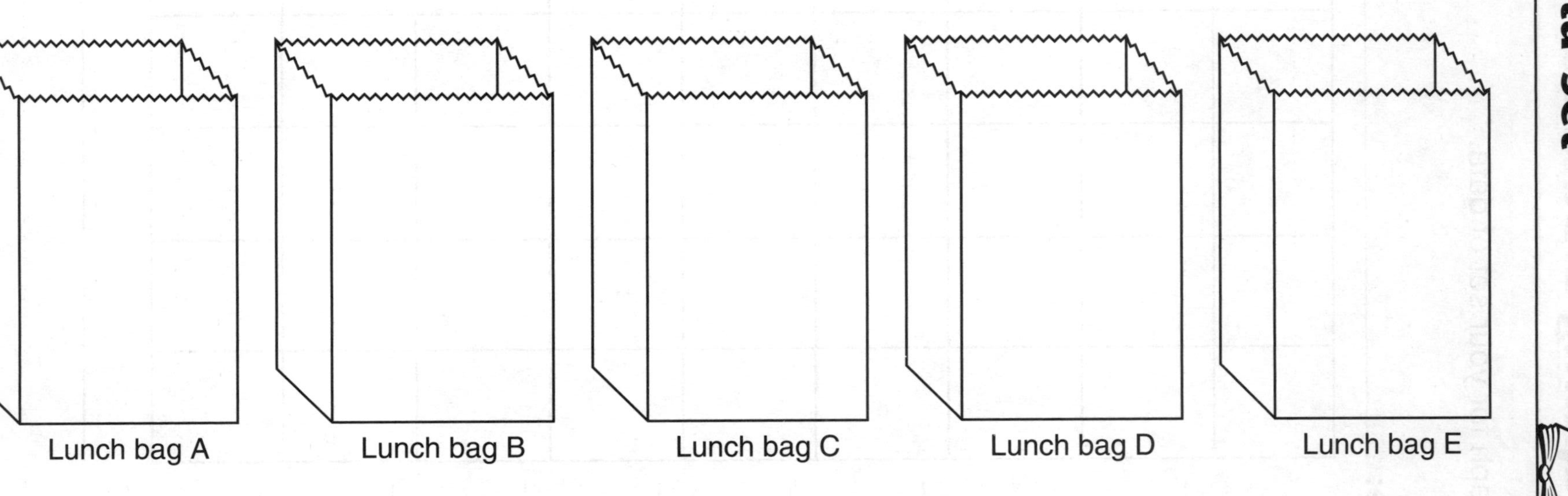

Graph your results on *Math Masters,* page 341. Remember to include labels and a title.

Copyright © Wright Group/McGraw-Hill

Name Date Time

Finding the Mean

Family Note The median and mean (average) indicate typical values in a set of data. The median is the middle value when the data numbers are listed in order. The mean (average) is found by the process described below. Your child may use a calculator to solve the problems. (In third grade, we ignore any digits to the right of the tenths place.)

Please return this Home Link to school tomorrow.

SRB 80 83–85

To find the mean (average):

1. Find the sum of the data numbers.
2. Count the data numbers.
3. Use a calculator to divide the sum by the number of data numbers.
4. Drop any digits after tenths.

Example:

Basketball Scores: 80, 85, 76

1. 80 + 85 + 76 = 241
2. There are 3 scores.
3. 241 ÷ 3 = 80.333333...
4. Mean: 80.3

Baseball Home Run Leaders		
1998	Mark McGwire	70
1999	Mark McGwire	65
2000	Sammy Sosa	50
2001	Barry Bonds	73
2002	Alex Rodriguez	57
2003	Jim Thome, Alex Rodriguez	47

1. Mean number of home runs: ______

Baseball Home Run Leaders		
1901	Sam Crawford	16
1902	Socks Seybold	16
1903	Buck Freeman	13
1904	Harry Davis	10
1905	Fred Odwell	9

2. Mean number of home runs: ______

Source: *World Almanac*, 2004

3. List some data for people in your home—for example, their ages, shoe sizes, or heights. Find the median and mean of the data.

Kind of data ______________________

Data ______________________

Median: __________ Mean: __________

Copyright © Wright Group/McGraw-Hill

Name Date Time

LESSON 10•7

Comparing Height & Arm-Span Measures

You will need:

- $\frac{1}{4}$-inch grid paper (*Math Masters,* page 437)
- median height and median arm span of adults in your group from *Math Journal 2,* page 256
- median height and median arm span of children in your group from *Math Journal 2,* page 256
- crayons and pencil

Follow these steps:

1. Use $\frac{1}{4}$-inch grid paper. The length of each square or unit on the grid represents 4 inches. Draw and color a rectangle (or square) to represent the median height and median arm span of the *adults* in your group.

- Use the median adult height for the *length* of the rectangle. Use the median adult arm span for the *width* of the rectangle.

2. Draw and color a second rectangle (or square) to represent the median height and median arm span of the *children* in your group.

- Use the median child height for the *length* of the rectangle. Use the median child arm span for the *width* of the rectangle.

3. Compare the rectangles. Which rectangle seems to be more square—the children's or the adults'?

4. Draw a rectangle for your own height and arm span.

Copyright © Wright Group/McGraw-Hill

Name Date Time

Matching Tally Charts to Bar Graphs

Work with a partner.

1. Match each tally chart with the bar graph that best describes the data. Write a title that tells about each graph. Fill in the missing labels.

Number of Books Read	Number of Children
0	
1	///
2	~~////~~ ///
3	~~////~~ /
4	~~////~~

Number of Pockets	Number of Children
0	~~////~~ /
1	
2	~~////~~ /
3	//
4	~~////~~
5	///

Title: ______________________

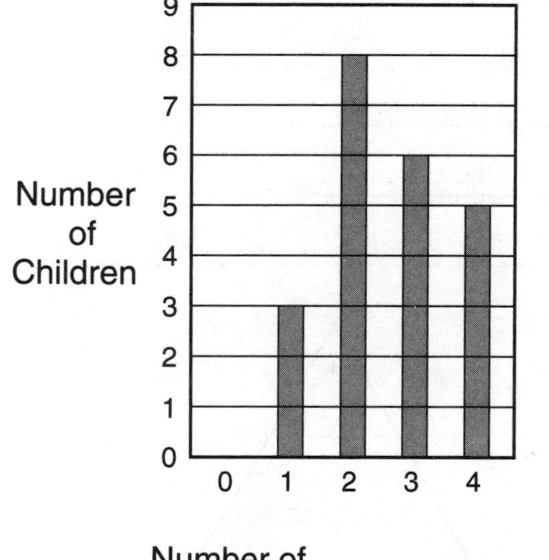

Title: ______________________

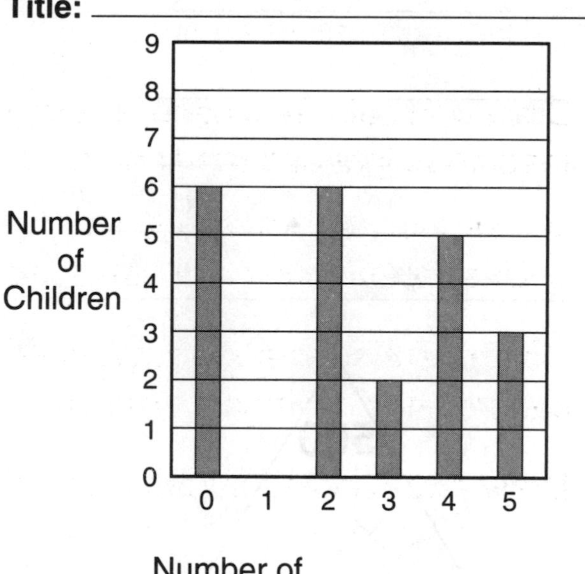

2. There are 22 children total. If you were to meet one of them on the street, predict how many pockets he or she would have. _______

Predict how many books he or she might have read. _______

Explain your predictions on the back of this page.

Copyright © Wright Group/McGraw-Hill

Name Date Time

HOME LINK 10•8

Fact Triangles

Family Note In today's lesson, we learned about the memory keys on our calculators. If you have a calculator, ask your child to show you how to store a number in the calculator's memory. If your calculator is different from the ones we use in class, you might need to help your child figure out how to use it.

In this Home Link, your child is reviewing fact extensions.

Please return this Home Link to school tomorrow.

Fill in the missing number in each Fact Triangle. Then write the number families for the three numbers in the Fact Triangle.

1. 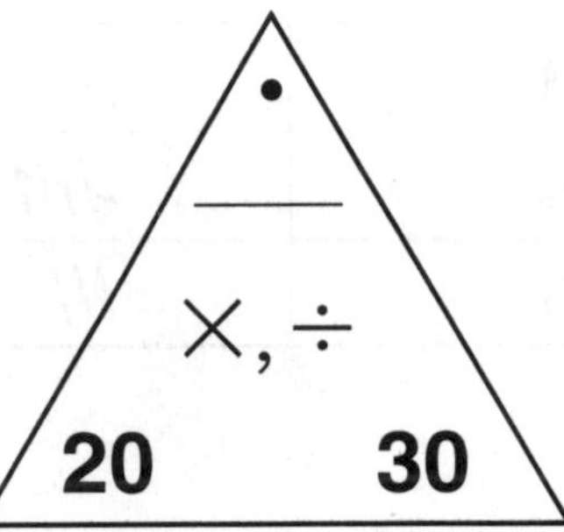

______

______

______

______

2. 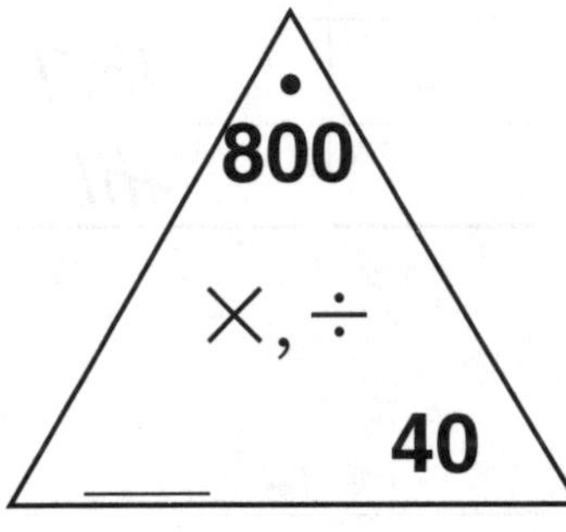

______

______

______

______

3. 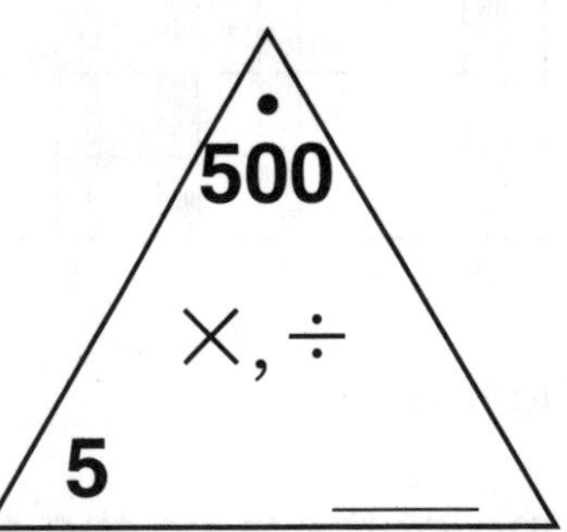

______

______

______

______

4. 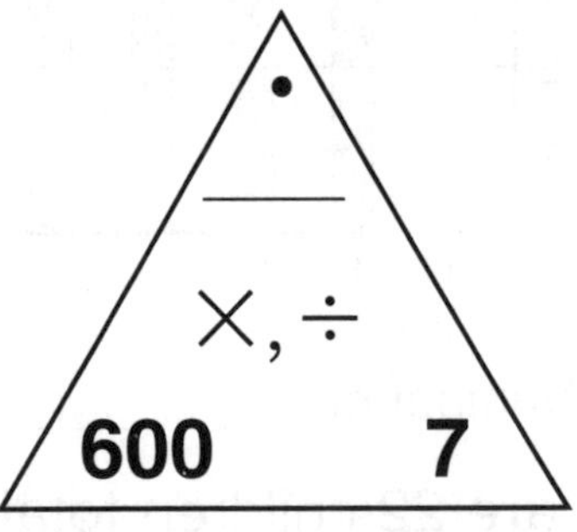

______

______

______

______

Copyright © Wright Group/McGraw-Hill

Name Date Time

Math Message

You will need your calculator. Refer to the table below.

- Begin with the first row. Press the keys on your calculator.
- Write what is in the display after each step.
- **Do not** clear your calculator between steps.

Press	Display
MRC MRC ON/C or AC	0.
5 M+	
7 M+	
MRC	
3 M+	
MRC	

What do you think M+ does?

____

Copyright © Wright Group/McGraw-Hill

Name Date Time

LESSON 10·8

Calculator Riddles

Calculators can send messages! If you enter any number from 0 to 9 and rotate your calculator, the display will show a letter.

(0) looks like O	(5) looks like S
(1) looks like I	(6) looks like g
(2) looks like Z	(7) looks like L
(3) looks like E	(8) looks like B
(4) looks like h	(9) looks like G

Example A calculator greeting just for you!

Enter 7 tenths [+] 7 hundredths [+] 3 thousandths [+] 0.0004 (=).

Turn your calculator around. What word do you see? *hELLO (0.7734)*

1. What do baby snakes say? ______________________

To find out, enter five thousand [+] ten [+] four [+] five hundred (=).

2. What do their big brothers and sisters say? ______________________

To find out, enter nine tenths [+] five hundred [+] four [+] two thousand [+] eight thousandths [+] three thousand [+] one hundredth [+] ten (=).

3. According to stories, what could George Washington never do? You can guess this one! Enter one thousand (−) three (−) eighty (−) six hundred.

____

Try This

4. Find a way to change an EGG (993) into a GOOSE (35009).

Tell how you solved the problem.

____

____

Copyright © Wright Group/McGraw-Hill

Name Date Time

Computing with Calculators

For each problem, predict whether the number sentence is true or false. Then use your calculator to check your predictions. Remember to use ON/C or AC to clear the calculator before you begin each problem.

Number Sentence	Prediction (True/False)	Actual (True/False)
1. $5 + 9 + 8 + 6 = 28$	______	______
2. $10 - 2 - 1 = 7$	______	______
3. $12 + 5 + 50 + 3 = 53$	______	______
4. $100 - 40 - 9 = 51$	______	______
5. $98 + 3 + 128 + 3 = 198$	______	______

Try This

6. Explain how you made your guess for Problem 5.

______

______

______

Copyright © Wright Group/McGraw-Hill

Name Date Time

Comparing Waist-to-Floor Measurements

1. Use the floor-to-waist data from the Math Message. Divide the data into two groups, one for boys' data and one for girls' data.

2. Make two frequency tables (one for each set of data) on the back of this page.

3. Make a graph for each data set on copies of *Math Masters,* page 352.

4. Find and record the landmarks (median, mean, and mode) for each data set. Use your calculator to help you.

   Median:

   Girls ______________ Boys ______________

   Mean:

   Girls ______________ Boys ______________

   Mode:

   Girls ______________ Boys ______________

5. Compare the two graphs and the landmarks. What do you know from these results?

   ____

   ____

   ____

   ____

Copyright © Wright Group/McGraw-Hill

Name Date Time

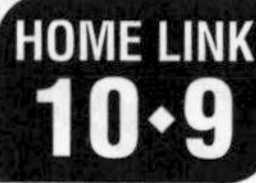

A Frequency Table

Family Note Today we learned how to organize data in a frequency table. For today's Home Link, help your child count the number of electrical outlets in at least 8 different rooms. It would be best if the rooms were all in the same kind of building—for example, rooms in a house or apartment; rooms in the local library; or rooms in a school.

Please return this Home Link to school tomorrow.

SRB 80–85

1. Make a frequency table for the number of electrical outlets in at least 8 different rooms.

Number of Electrical Outlets

Room	Frequency	
	Tallies	Number

2. What is the *median* (middle) number of outlets? ______

3. What is the *mean* (average) number of outlets? (You may use a calculator to calculate the answer. Drop any digits to the right of the tenths place.) ______

4. What is the *mode* of the data in the table? (*Reminder:* The mode is the number that occurs most often in a set of data.) ______

Copyright © Wright Group/McGraw-Hill

Name Date Time

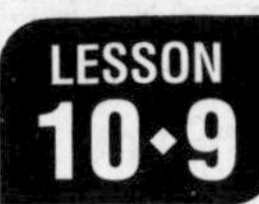

Bar Graph

Title:

Copyright © Wright Group/McGraw-Hill

Name Date Time

Locating Points on a Map

Family Note In an ordered pair, such as (3,6), the first number indicates how far the point is to the right (or left) of 0. The second number indicates how far it is above (or below) 0.

Please return this Home Link to school tomorrow.

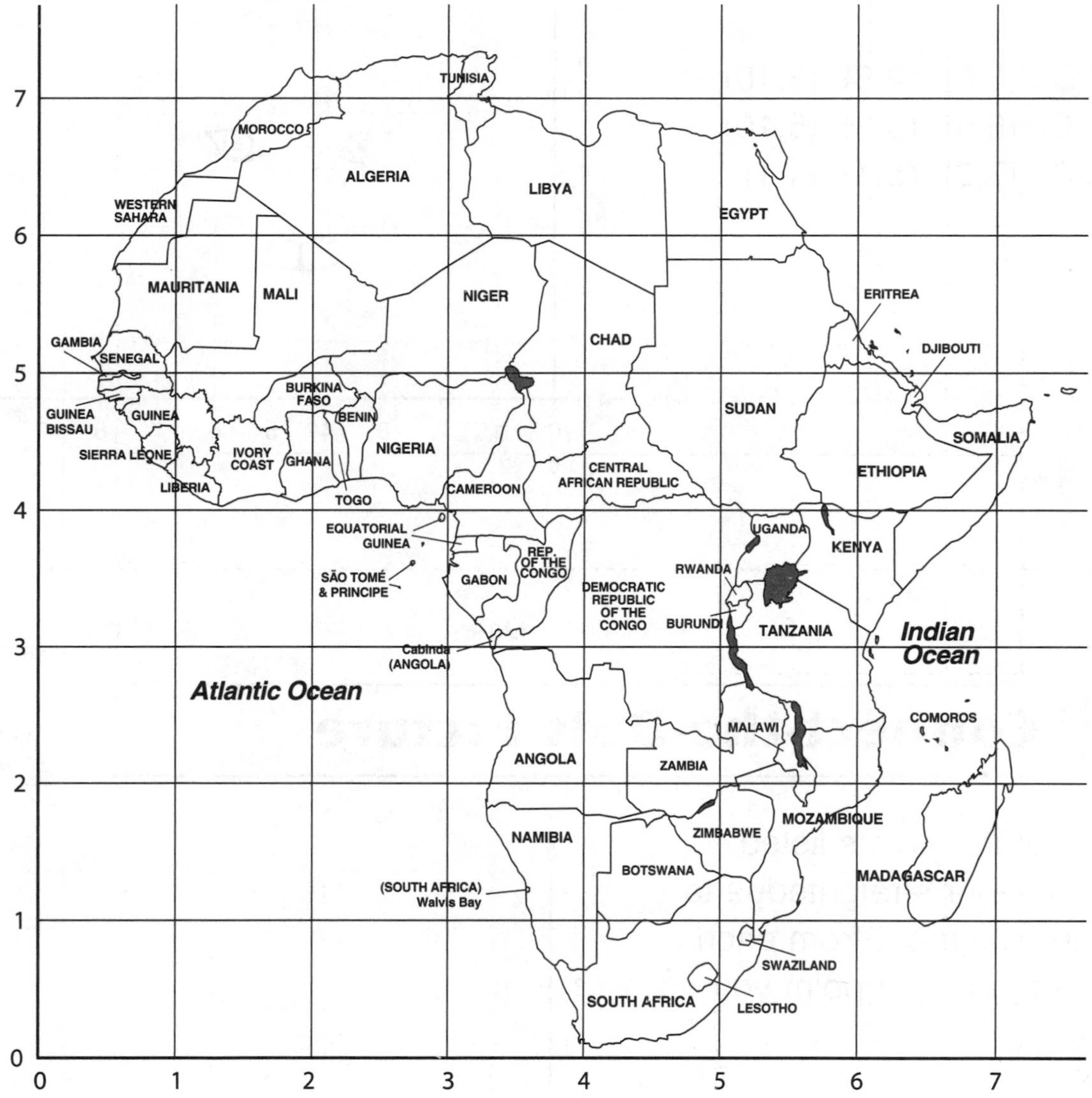

Here is a map of Africa. Write the name of the country in which each point is located.

1. (3,6) ______ **2.** (6,3) ______ **3.** (5,5) ______

4. (4,5) ______ **5.** (5,6) ______ **6.** (4,6) ______

Copyright © Wright Group/McGraw-Hill

Name Date Time

LESSON 10•10 Connect-the-Dots Picture

Plot each of the points listed below. Use your straightedge to draw a line segment from each new point to the last point you plotted.

(4,1), (2,3), (3,6), (2,8), (3,10), (4,8), (3,6), (6,6), (5,8), (6,10), (7,8), (6,6), (7,3), (5,1), (4,1)

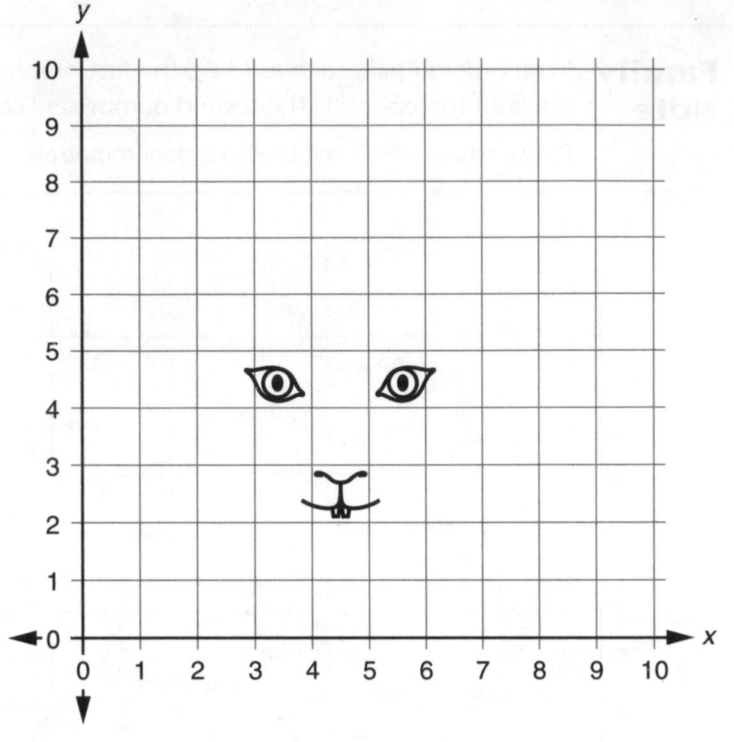

Copyright © Wright Group/McGraw-Hill

Name Date Time

LESSON 10•10 Connect-the-Dots Picture

Plot each of the points listed below. Use your straightedge to draw a line segment from each new point to the last point you plotted.

(4,1), (2,3), (3,6), (2,8), (3,10), (4,8), (3,6), (6,6), (5,8), (6,10), (7,8), (6,6), (7,3), (5,1), (4,1)

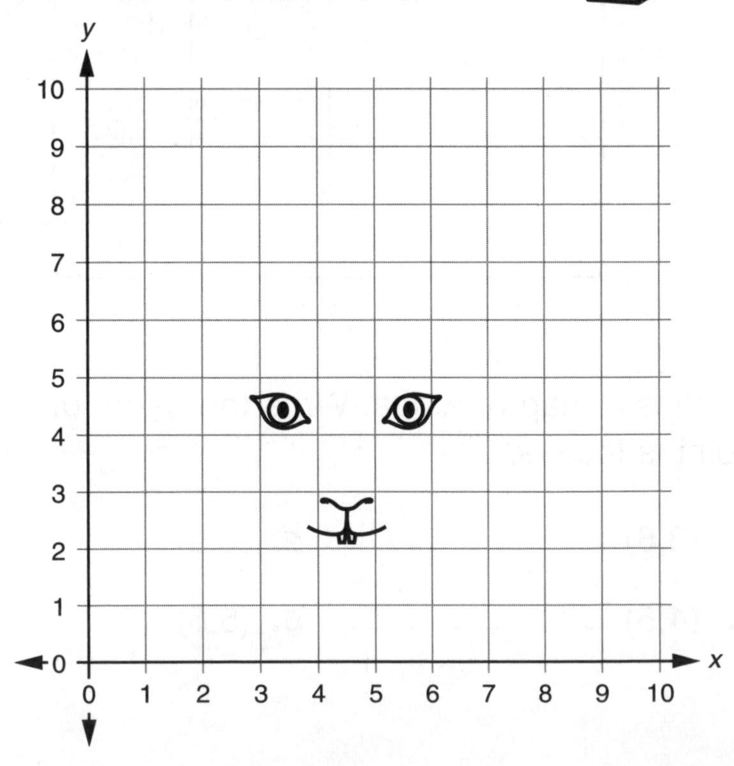

Copyright © Wright Group/McGraw-Hill

Name Date Time

Geoboard Polygons

You need:

- ◆ one geoboard and several rubber bands per partnership
- ◆ straightedge
- ◆ dry-erase marker
- ◆ *Math Masters,* page 438 for each partner

1. Use a dry-erase marker to draw numbers on the horizontal and vertical lines of the geoboard. Use the picture to help you. Your geoboard can now be used as a coordinate grid.

2. Without letting your partner see, make a polygon on the geoboard coordinate grid with a rubber band.

3. Tell your partner the coordinate points of the vertices of the polygon. For example, the coordinate points of the triangle in this picture are (2,4), (4,4), and (4,2).

4. Your partner plots the points on one of the grids on *Math Masters,* page 438 and uses a straightedge to draw the line segments you name.

5. Compare the polygon made on the geoboard with the polygon drawn on the paper. Are they the same? If not, work together to find out why.

6. Continue until both partners have each taken 4 turns.

Copyright © Wright Group/McGraw-Hill

Name Date Time

Unit 11: Family Letter

Probability; Year-Long Projects, Revisited

In this year's final unit, children will have the opportunity to bring closure to the yearlong data-collection projects about lengths of days and temperature changes. They will look at patterns in data and draw conclusions.

Unit 11 also contains informal spinner activities relating to chance and probability.

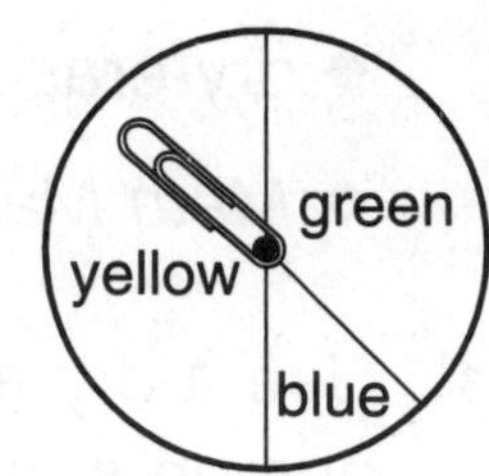

Some of these activities call for children to compare the likelihood of several possible outcomes of an event: why one thing is more likely to happen than another. For example, children will make predictions about where a paper clip on a spinner is more likely to land when the spinner is divided into unequal parts.

Other activities ask children to estimate the chance that something will happen. For example, children design a spinner so that a paper clip is twice as likely to land on one color as another.

Please keep this Family Letter for reference as your child works through Unit 11.

Copyright © Wright Group/McGraw-Hill

Unit 11: Family Letter *cont.*

Vocabulary

Important terms in Unit 11:

equally likely outcomes Outcomes of a chance experiment or situation that have the same probability of happening. For example, any number 1–6 landing up are the equally likely outcomes of rolling a die.

winter solstice The shortest day of the year, when the sun is farthest south of the Earth's equator. The number of hours of daylight depends on your latitude. In the Northern Hemisphere, the winter solstice occurs on or about December 21.

summer solstice The longest day of the year, when the sun is farthest north of the Earth's equator. The number of hours of daylight depends on your latitude. In the Northern Hemisphere, the summer solstice occurs on or about June 21.

Do-Anytime Activities

To work on the concepts taught in this unit and in previous units, try these interesting and rewarding activities:

1. When you are in the car or walking with your child, search for geometric figures. Identify them by name if possible and talk about their characteristics. For example, a stop sign is an octagon, which has 8 sides and 8 angles. Many skyscrapers are rectangular prisms; their faces are rectangles.

2. Draw name-collection boxes for various numbers and together with your child write five to ten equivalent names in each box. Include name-collection boxes for fractions and decimals. For example, a $\frac{1}{2}$ name-collection box might include $\frac{2}{4}$, $\frac{10}{20}$, 0.5, 0.50, and $\frac{500}{1,000}$ because these are also names for $\frac{1}{2}$. Then create name-collection boxes that include equivalent measures. For example, a 1 ft name-collection box might contain 12 in., $\frac{1}{3}$ yd, $\frac{1}{5,280}$ mile, $\frac{12}{36}$ yd, and so on.

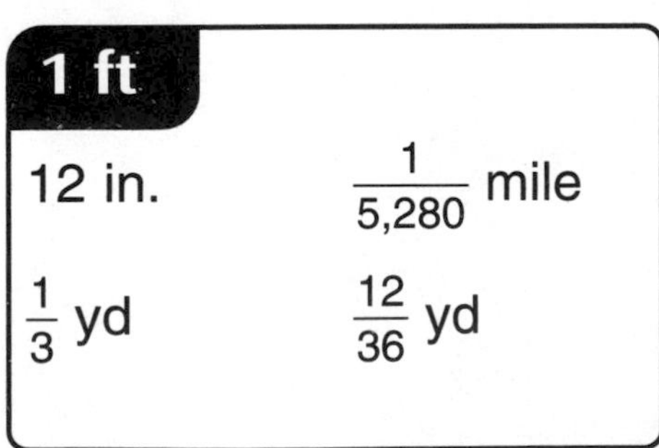

1 ft
12 in.
$\frac{1}{5,280}$ mile
$\frac{1}{3}$ yd
$\frac{12}{36}$ yd

3. Make predictions about the likelihood of pulling an item of one color out of a bag filled with the same items of different colors. Then check your predictions. For example, place 2 red blocks and 4 blue blocks in a bag. There are 4 out of 6 chances to pull a blue block.

Copyright © Wright Group/McGraw-Hill

Building Skills through Games

In Unit 11, your child will practice skills related to chance and probability by playing the following games. For detailed instructions, see the *Student Reference Book.*

Block Drawing Game

Without letting the other players see the blocks, a Director puts five blocks in a paper bag and tells the players how many blocks are in the bag. A player takes a block out of the bag. The Director records the color of the block for all players to see. The player replaces the block. At any time, a player may say *Stop!* and guess how many blocks of each color are in the bag. If a player guesses incorrectly, that player is out of the game. The first player to guess correctly wins the game.

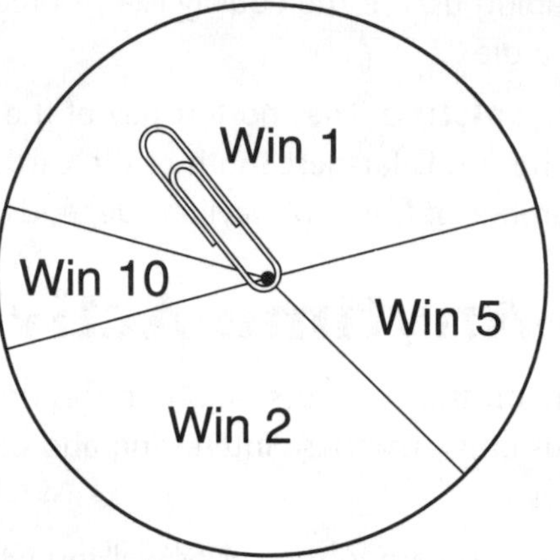

Spinning to Win

Each player claims one section of the spinner. Players take turns spinning the spinner. If the spinner lands on a player's number, the player takes that number of pennies. The player with the most pennies after 12 spins wins the game.

Copyright © Wright Group/McGraw-Hill

HOME LINK 10•11

Unit 11: Family Letter *cont.*

As You Help Your Child with Homework

As your child brings home assignments, you may want to go over the instructions together, clarifying them as necessary. The answers listed below will guide you through this unit's Home Links.

Home Link 11•2

Numbers	Add	Subtract	Multiply	Divide
30 and 7	37	23	210	4R2
50 and 5	55	45	250	10
40 and 6	46	34	240	6 R4
150 and 3	153	147	450	50
3,000 and 50	3,050	2,950	150,000	60
12,000 and 60	12,060	11,940	720,000	200

Home Link 11•5

1. 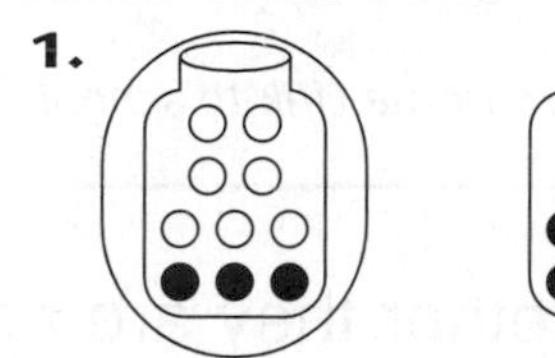

2. 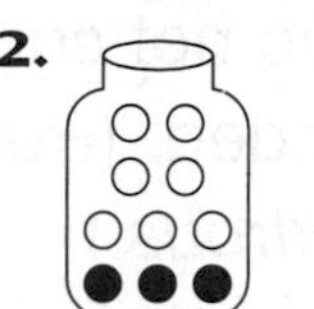 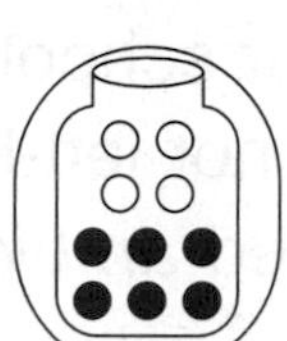

3. 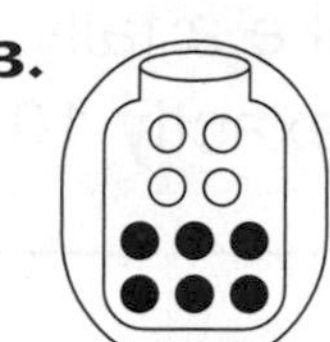 

4. 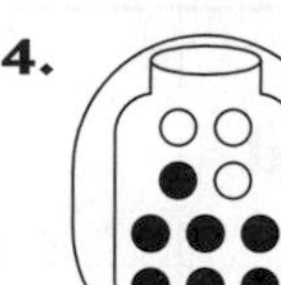 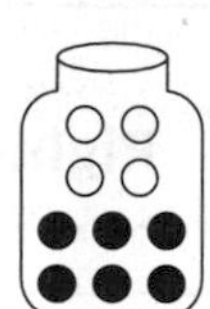

Copyright © Wright Group/McGraw-Hill

Name Date Time

A Survey

Family Note Have your child survey 10 people—family members, neighbors, and out-of-school friends—to find out how many are right-handed and how many are left-handed. Do not count people who say they are ambidextrous (able to use both hands with equal ease). Take a few days to help your child complete the survey. The results will be used in Lesson 11-5.

Please return this Home Link to school.

1. Ask 10 people whether they are right-handed or left-handed. Do not ask people at your school. Do not count people who say they are neither right-handed nor left-handed. (People who can use both hands with equal ease are called *ambidextrous.*)

2. On the chart below, make a tally mark for each person. Be sure that you have exactly 10 marks.

	Tallies
Right-handed	
Left-handed	

3. When you have finished your survey, record the results at the bottom of the page. Bring the results to school.

Name ____________________

Survey Results

Number of right-handed people: ________

Number of left-handed people: ________

Total: 10

Copyright © Wright Group/McGraw-Hill

Name Date Time

LESSON 11•1

How Many Hours and Minutes?

Solve each problem. Use your tool-kit clock to help you.

1. The basketball game lasted 100 minutes, including time-outs and halftime.

How many whole hours are in 100 minutes?

_______ hour(s)

How many minutes are left over?

_______ minute(s)

2. The bus trip to the basketball game took 45 minutes. The return trip took another 45 minutes. How many minutes were spent on the bus in all?

_______ minutes

How many whole hours?

_______ hour(s)

How many minutes are left over?

_______ minute(s)

3. How many minutes in all did the basketball team play in the game and ride on the bus?

_______ minutes

How many whole hours?

_______ hour(s)

How many minutes are left over?

_______ minute(s)

4. Describe how you figured out the answer to Problem 3.

____

____

____

____

____

Copyright © Wright Group/McGraw-Hill

Name Date Time

LESSON 11•1

Planning a Field Trip

Use the schedule below to plan a field trip for Mr. Murer's third-grade class. The children will arrive at the City Zoo at 9:30 A.M. and must leave by 2:00 P.M.

Create a plan that includes

- ◆ the Predator or Prey? show,
- ◆ the Rainforest Animals show,
- ◆ the Endangered Reptiles exhibit,
- ◆ one or two other activities,
- ◆ and a 30-minute lunch break.

In your plan, show the times at which each activity will begin and end. Write your plan on another sheet of paper.

City Zoo Schedule		
Title	**Start time**	**Length***
Predator or Prey? show	9:25 A.M. 9:55 10:25 10:55 11:25	30 min
Rainforest Animals show	9:00 9:45 10:30 11:15 12:00 P.M.	45 min
African Journey (long tour)	Any time	90 min
African Journey (short tour)	Any time	25 min
Big Cats Habitat	Any time	45 min
Great Ape House	Any time	25 min
Sea Lion Pool	Any time	20 min
Endangered Reptiles exhibit	Any time	90 min

*The length of each activity includes travel time and bathroom breaks.

Copyright © Wright Group/McGraw-Hill

Name Date Time

Computation Round-Up

Family Note Please observe as your child adds, subtracts, multiplies, and divides pairs of whole numbers. Encourage your child to use and explain his or her favorite strategies.

Please return this Home Link to school.

For each of the number pairs below, use mental arithmetic or other strategies to perform the operations indicated in each column in the table. Show any work on the back of this page. Explain your favorite strategies to someone at home.

Numbers	Add	Subtract	Multiply	Divide
30 and 7	$30 + 7 = 37$	$30 - 7 = 23$	$30 \times 7 = 210$	$30 \div 7 \rightarrow 4$ R2
50 and 5				
40 and 6				
150 and 3				
3,000 and 50				
12,000 and 60				

Copyright © Wright Group/McGraw-Hill

Name Date Time

LESSON 11·2 Finding Differences

−19	−18	−17	−16	−15	−14	−13	−12	−11	−10
−9	−8	−7	−6	−5	−4	−3	−2	−1	0
1	2	3	4	5	6	7	8	9	10
11	12	13	14	15	16	17	18	19	20
21	22	23	24	25	26	27	28	29	30
31	32	33	34	35	36	37	38	39	40
41	42	43	44	45	46	47	48	49	50
51	52	53	54	55	56	57	58	59	60
61	62	63	64	65	66	67	68	69	70
71	72	73	74	75	76	77	78	79	80
81	82	83	84	85	86	87	88	89	90
91	92	93	94	95	96	97	98	99	100
101	102	103	104	105	106	107	108	109	110

1. Describe how you can use the number grid to find the difference between −5 and 51.

____

____

____

____

Find the difference between each pair of numbers.

2. 22 and 46 ______

3. 91 and 36 ______

4. 104 and 17 ______

5. −16 and 65 ______

6. 83 and −9 ______

7. 101 and −13 ______

Copyright © Wright Group/McGraw-Hill

Name Date Time

LESSON 11•2

Comparing Seasonal Temperature Differences

1. Organize the temperature differences from the National High/Low Temperatures Project on journal page 175 by month. For example, group together all of the differences for the month of October. Then group the differences for November, and so on.

2. Use your calculator to find the mean (average) temperature difference for each month for which you have data. Record your results below.

3. Use copies of *Math Masters,* page 352 to create two graphs showing seasonal temperature differences. One graph should show data for fall and winter months (October through March). The other graph should show the data for spring and summer months (April through September).

   Reminder: Be sure to label your graphs clearly.

4. Compare the 2 bar graphs. Record at least 2 things you know from looking at your graphs.

____

____

____

____

____

____

Fall/Winter Months	Mean Temperature Difference
October	
November	
December	
January	
February	
March	
Spring/Summer Months	**Mean Temperature Difference**
April	
May	
June	
July	
August	
September	

Copyright © Wright Group/McGraw-Hill

LESSON 11·3 Math Message

Color each circle to match the description.

1. $\frac{3}{4}$ red, $\frac{2}{8}$ blue

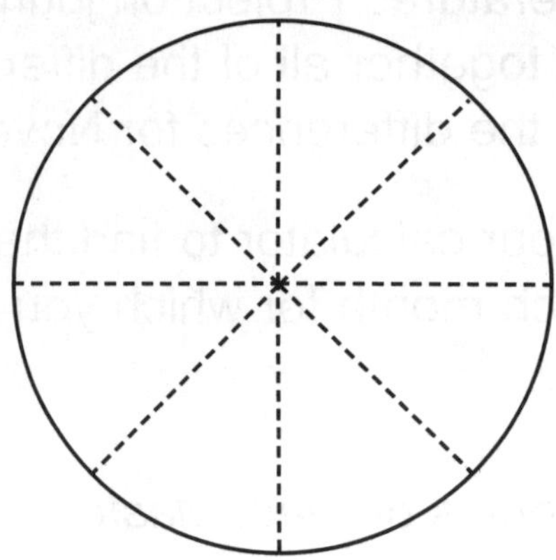

2. $\frac{1}{2}$ red, $\frac{1}{3}$ yellow, $\frac{1}{6}$ blue

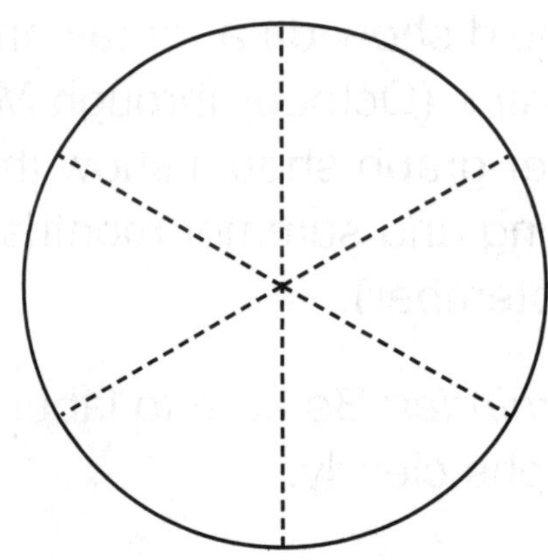

3. $\frac{2}{5}$ red, $\frac{2}{5}$ blue, $\frac{1}{5}$ yellow

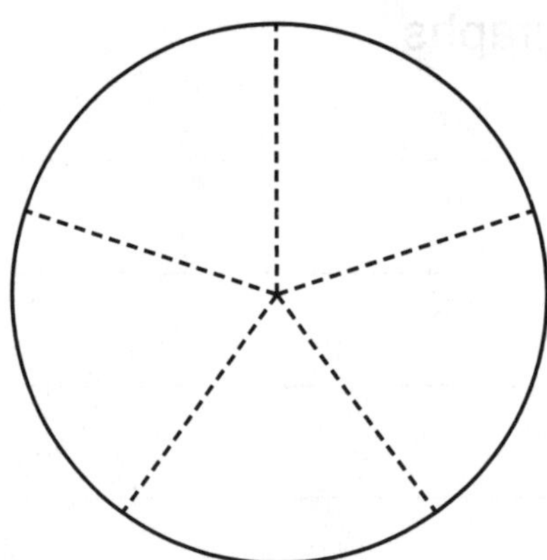

Copyright © Wright Group/McGraw-Hill

Name Date Time

LESSON 11•3

Spinners

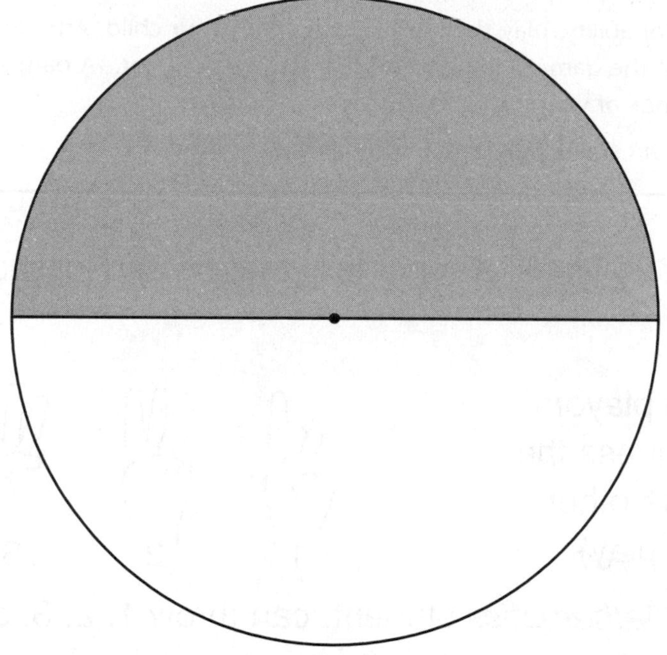

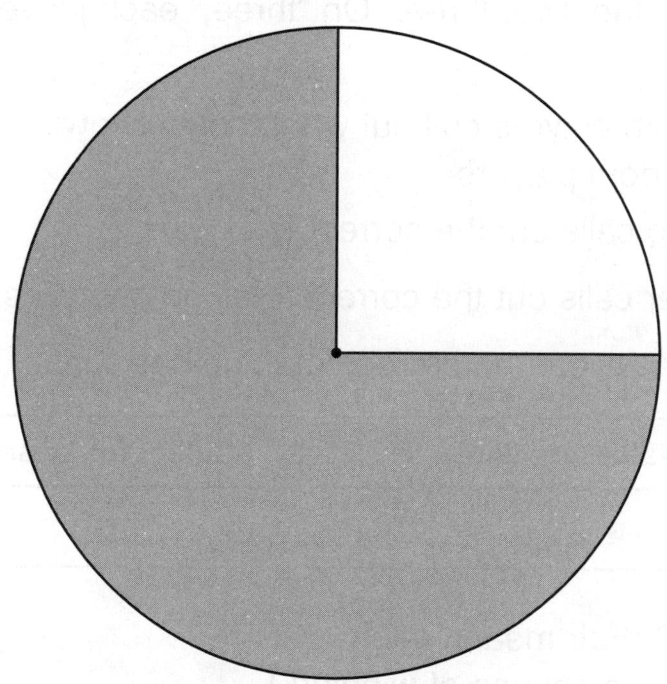

Copyright © Wright Group/McGraw-Hill

Name Date Time

HOME LINK 11·3

A Fair Game?

Family Note To explore probability, play the game *Fingers* with your child. After 20 games, have your child decide if the game is fair and explain why or why not. (A game is fair if all players have an equal chance of winning or losing.)

Please return this Home Link to school tomorrow.

Play *Fingers* at least 20 times. Keep a tally of wins and losses in the table below.

Rules for *Fingers*

This is a game for 2 players. One player tries to guess the number of fingers the other player will throw (display).

1

2

3

4

You, the *Everyday Mathematics* student, can throw 1, 2, 3, or 4 fingers. The other player can throw only 1 or 2 fingers.

Players face each other. Each one puts a closed fist on his or her chest.

One player counts, "One, two, three." On "three," each player throws some number of fingers.

At the same time, both players call out what they think will be the total number of fingers thrown by both players.

- The player who calls out the correct total wins.
- If *neither* player calls out the correct total, no one wins.
- If *both* players call out the correct total, no one wins.

Tallies for Wins	Tallies for Losses

1. Is this game fair? (Fair means each player has the same chance of winning.) ______________

2. On the back of this page explain your answer.

Adaptation of rules for *Mora* in *Family Fun and Games,* The Diagram Group, Sterling Publishing, 1992, p. 365

Copyright © Wright Group/McGraw-Hill

Name Date Time

Equivalent Fractions

- Cut the Fraction Circles from *Math Masters,* page 370 into parts along the dotted lines.
- Tape or glue the cut-out pieces onto the circles on this page as directed.
- Write the missing numerators to complete the equivalent fractions.

1. Cover $\frac{3}{4}$ of the circle with **eighths.**

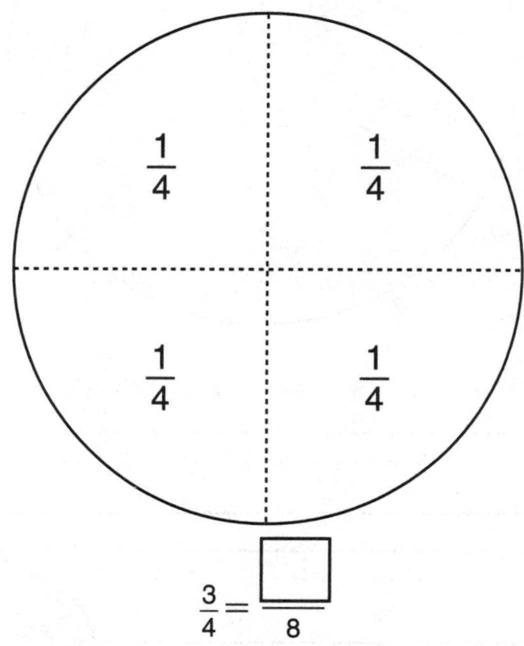

$\frac{3}{4} = \frac{\square}{8}$

2. Cover $\frac{1}{4}$ of the circle with **eighths.**

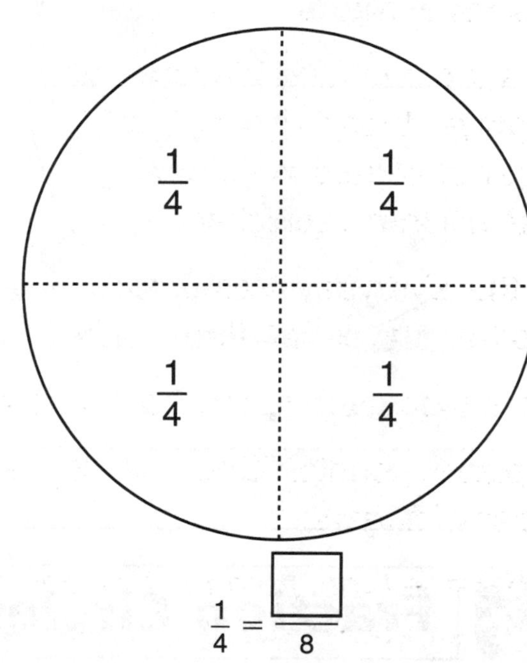

$\frac{1}{4} = \frac{\square}{8}$

3. Cover $\frac{1}{2}$ of the circle with **sixths.**

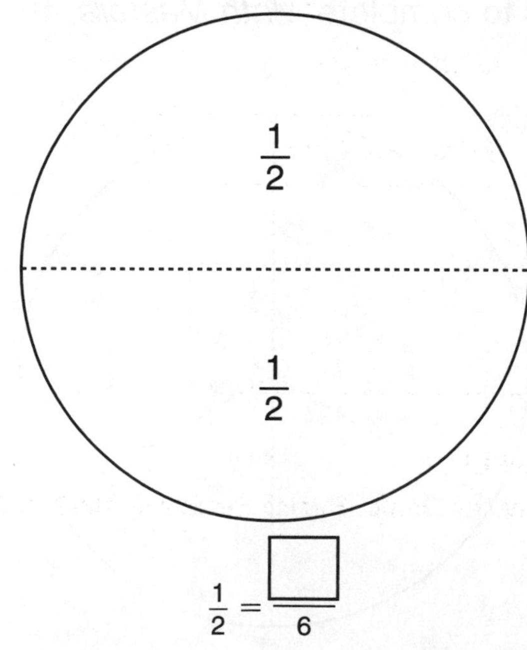

$\frac{1}{2} = \frac{\square}{6}$

4. Cover $\frac{1}{3}$ of the circle with **sixths.**

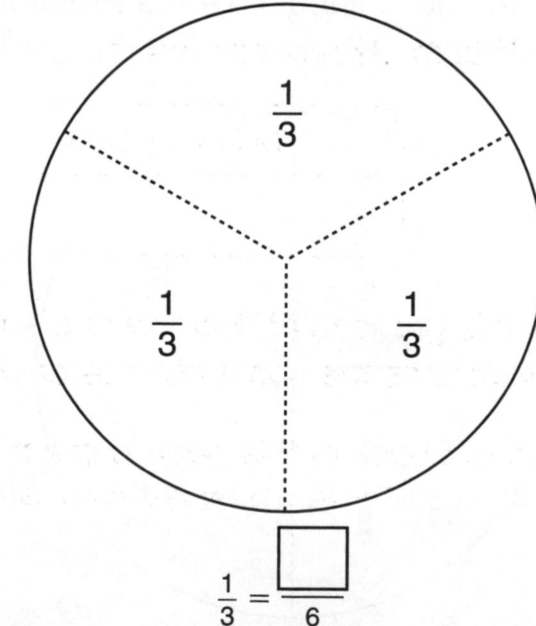

$\frac{1}{3} = \frac{\square}{6}$

Copyright © Wright Group/McGraw-Hill

Name Date Time

LESSON 11•3

Fraction Circles

First, label the parts of each circle with a fraction. Then cut out each circle along the solid lines. Use the Fraction Circles to complete *Math Masters,* page 369.

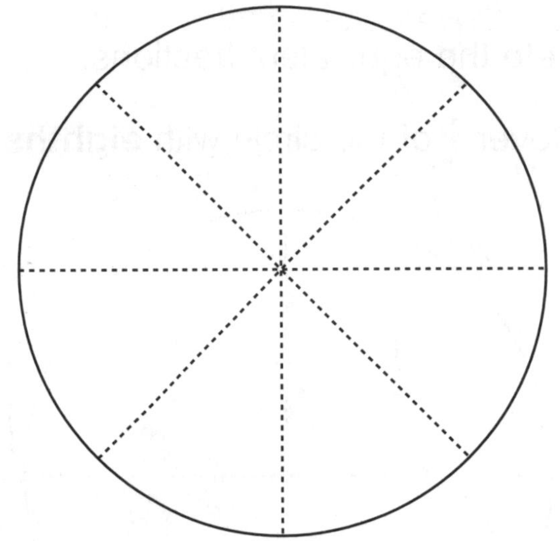

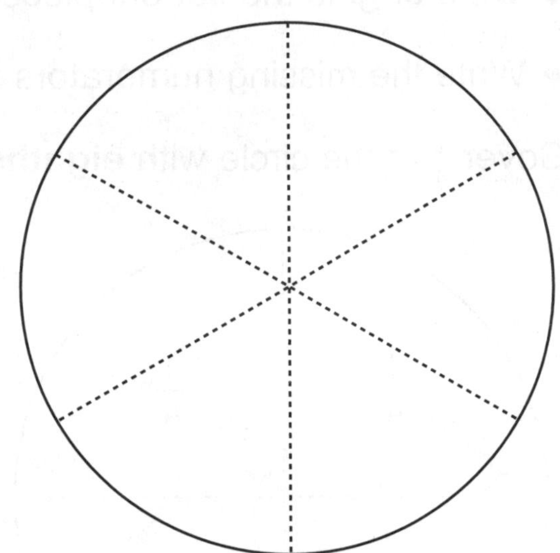

Copyright © Wright Group/McGraw-Hill

Name Date Time

LESSON 11•3

Fraction Circles

First, label the parts of each circle with a fraction. Then cut out each circle along the solid lines. Use the Fraction Circles to complete *Math Masters,* page 369.

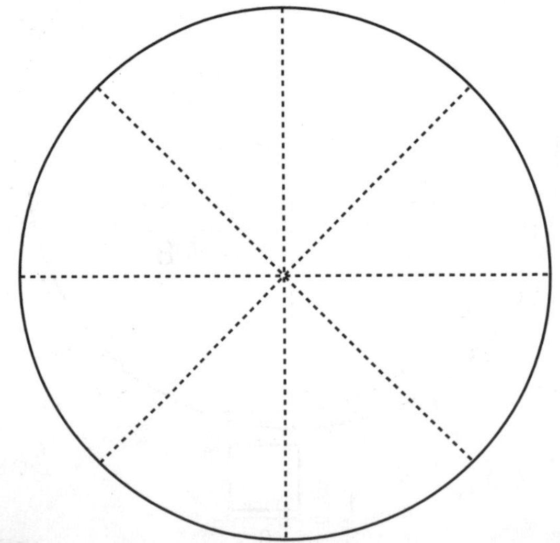

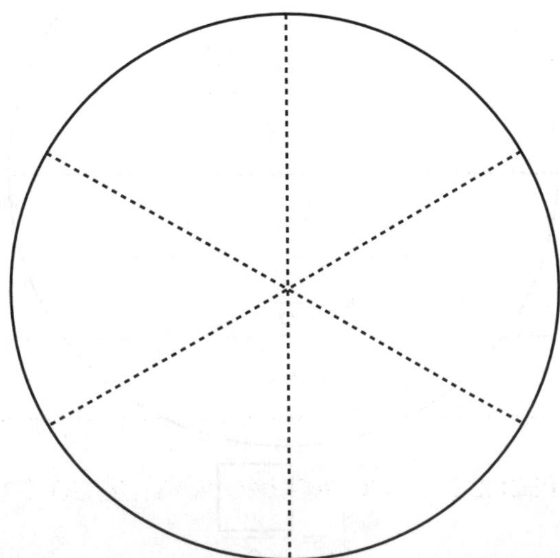

Copyright © Wright Group/McGraw-Hill

Name Date Time

LESSON 11·3

Spinners and Tallies

1. Use a straightedge and divide the spinner into two *unequal* parts. Shade one part so a paper clip is more likely to land on the unshaded part than on the shaded part.

2. Test your spinner at least 20 times and tally the results below.

Lands On	Tallies
Shaded part	
Unshaded part	

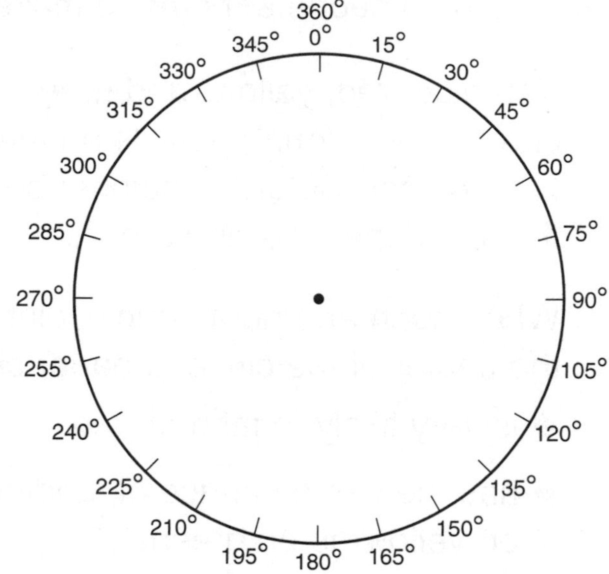

3. Explain your results on the back of this page.

4. Design another spinner with *more than two unequal* parts. Color the parts different colors. Predict what the results might be for 20 or more spins. Check your prediction. Record your results below.

Lands On	Tallies

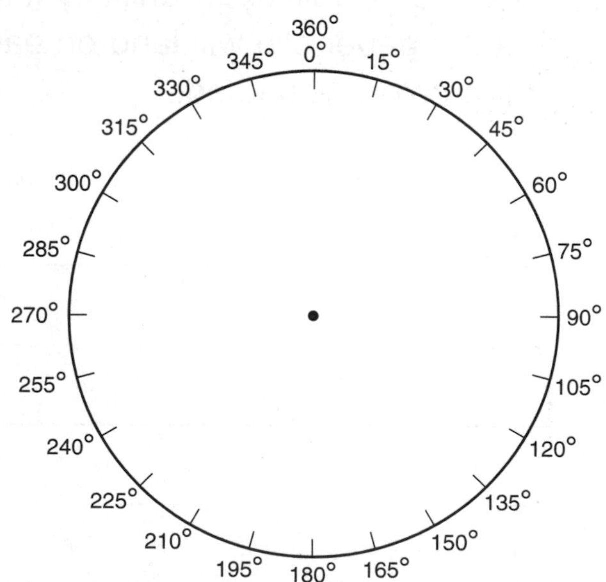

Discuss your results with a partner.

Copyright © Wright Group/McGraw-Hill

Name Date Time

HOME LINK 11•4

Spinners

Family Note To study probability, help your child design a spinner that meets the conditions in Part 1 below. Then help your child design another spinner by dividing the circle into parts (wedges) and coloring the parts.

Please return this Home Link to school tomorrow.

Work with someone at home to make two spinners.

1. Use blue, red, yellow, and green crayons or coloring pencils on the first spinner. Color the spinner so that all of the following are true:

When spun around a pencil point in the center of the circle, a paper clip

- ◆ is very likely to land on red.
- ◆ has the same chance of landing on yellow as on green.
- ◆ may land on blue but is very unlikely to land on blue.

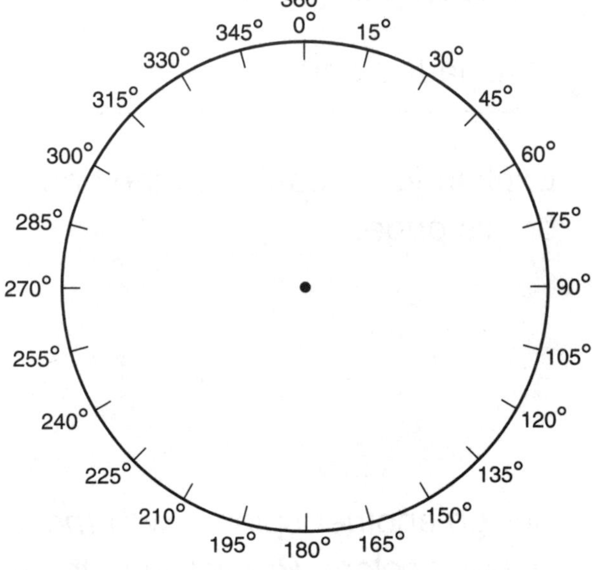

2. Design and color your own spinner. Then tell how likely or unlikely it is that the paper clip will land on each of the colors you used.

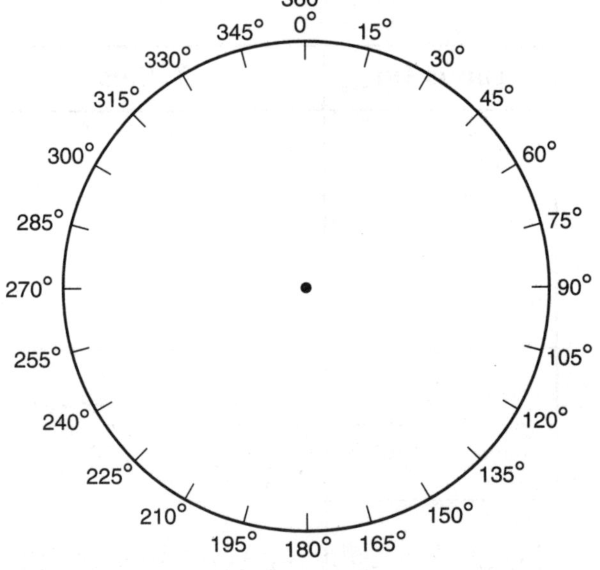

Copyright © Wright Group/McGraw-Hill

Name Date Time

Shading Fractions on Spinners

Divide each spinner into fractional parts according to the instructions.

1.

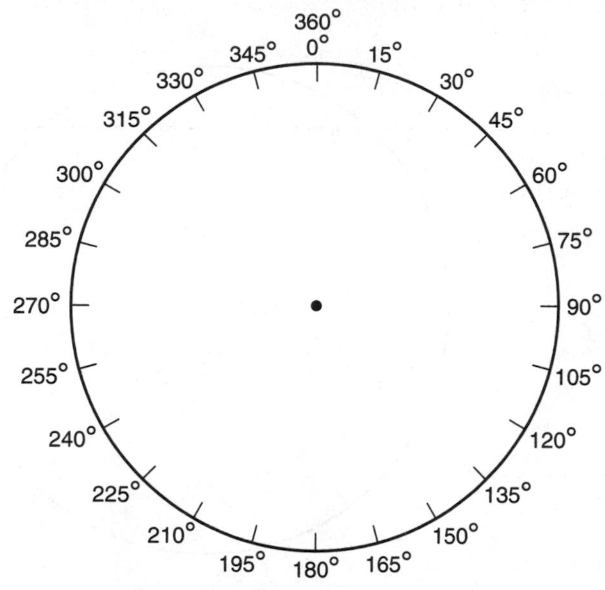

Color the spinner so that $\frac{3}{6}$ is green, $\frac{2}{6}$ is blue, and $\frac{1}{6}$ is red.

2.

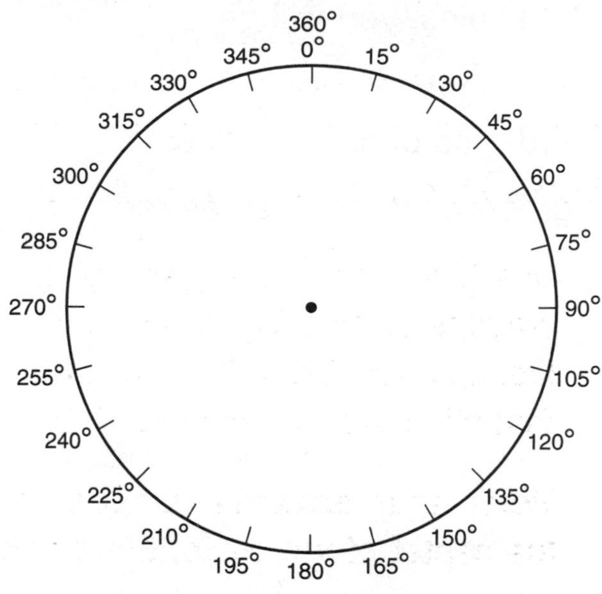

Color the spinner so that $\frac{1}{2}$ is red, $\frac{1}{3}$ is green, and $\frac{1}{6}$ is blue.

3.

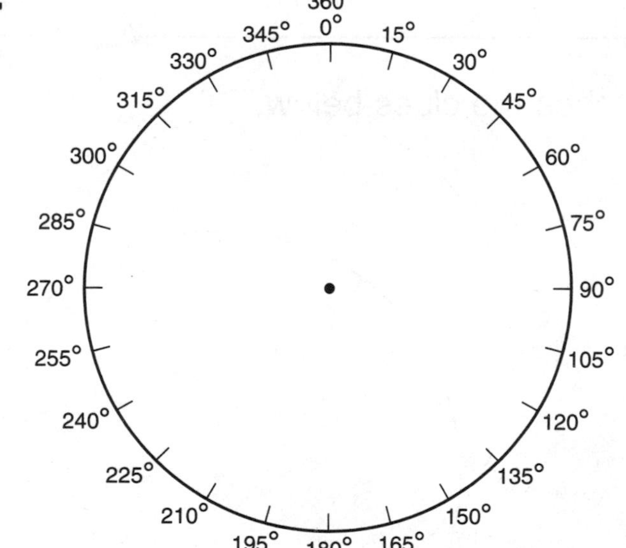

Color the spinner so that $\frac{1}{2}$ is blue, $\frac{1}{4}$ is red, and $\frac{2}{8}$ are green.

Try This

4.

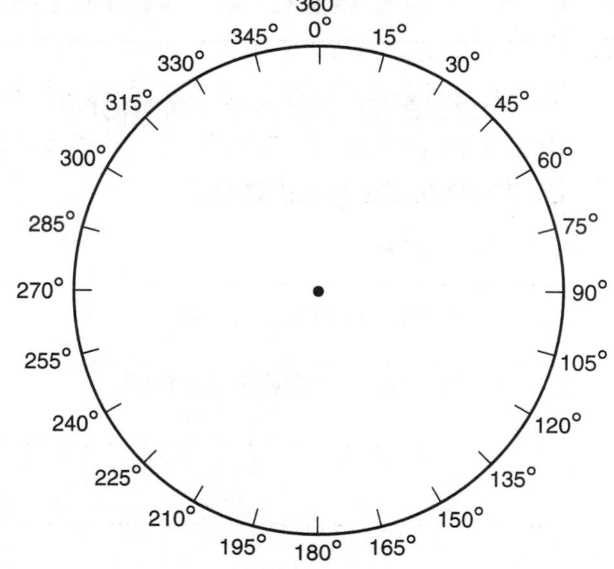

Color the spinner so that it has 6 sections: $\frac{1}{12}$ and $\frac{1}{6}$ are red, $\frac{1}{8}$ and $\frac{1}{4}$ are blue, $\frac{3}{12}$ and $\frac{1}{8}$ are green.

Copyright © Wright Group/McGraw-Hill

Name Date Time

LESSON 11·4

Create a Spinner

Use the circle to make a spinner that matches the clues below.

In 100 spins, you will get:

a. blue 50 times.

b. red $\frac{1}{2}$ as often as yellow.

c. green twice as often as red.

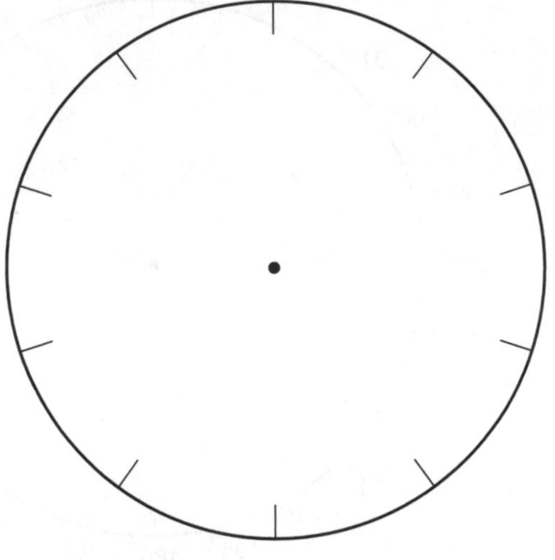

Copyright © Wright Group/McGraw-Hill

Name Date Time

LESSON 11·4

Create a Spinner

Use the circle to make a spinner that matches the clues below.

In 100 spins, you will get:

a. blue 50 times.

b. red $\frac{1}{2}$ as often as yellow.

c. green twice as often as red.

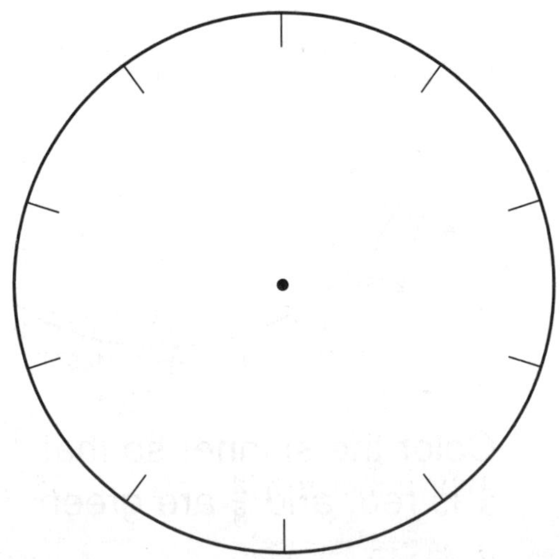

Copyright © Wright Group/McGraw-Hill

Name Date Time

More Random-Draw Problems

Family Note This Home Link focuses on predicting the contents of a jar by drawing out marbles. Don't expect your child to be an expert. Explorations with probability will continue through sixth grade. This is a first exposure.

Please return this Home Link to school tomorrow.

In each problem there are 10 marbles in a jar. The marbles are either black or white. A marble is drawn at random (without looking) from the jar. The type of marble drawn is tallied. Then the marble is returned to the jar.

- Read the description of the random draws in each problem.
- Circle the picture of the jar that best matches the description.

Example: From 100 random draws, you get:

a black marble ● 81 times.
a white marble ○ 19 times.

1. From 100 random draws, you get:

a black marble ● 34 times.
a white marble ○ 66 times.

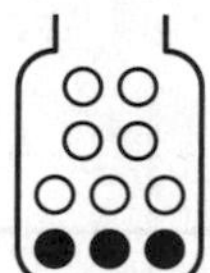

2. From 100 random draws, you get:

a black marble ● 57 times.
a white marble ○ 43 times.

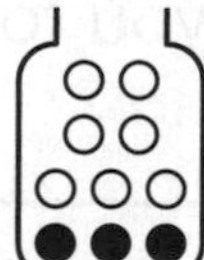

Try This

3. From 50 random draws, you get:

a black marble ● 28 times.
a white marble ○ 22 times.

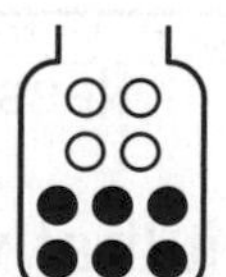

4. From 50 random draws, you get:

a black marble ● 35 times.
a white marble ○ 15 times.

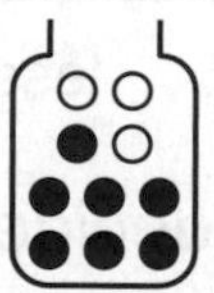

Copyright © Wright Group/McGraw-Hill

Name Date Time

LESSON 11·5

How Likely?

Make an X on the line to show the likelihood of an event happening.

Example:

How likely is it that a glass falling off a table will hit the ceiling?

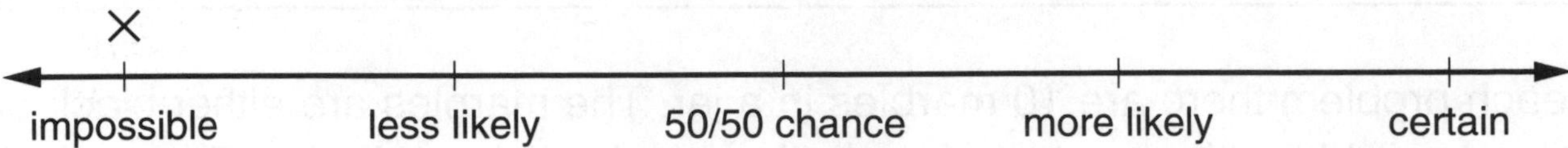

1. How likely is it that a cow will jump over the moon?

impossible less likely 50/50 chance more likely certain

2. How likely is it that the paper clip will land on green?

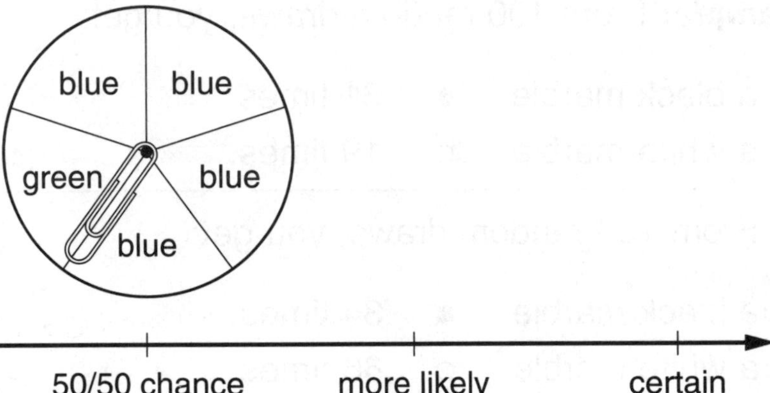

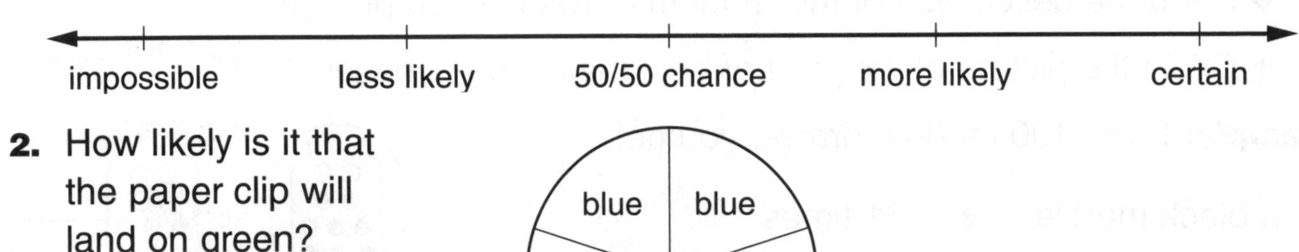

3. How likely are you to see a friend today?

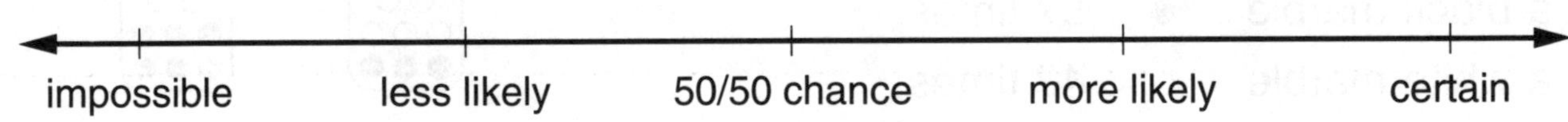

4. How likely is it that a tossed coin will land on heads 23 times out of 50?

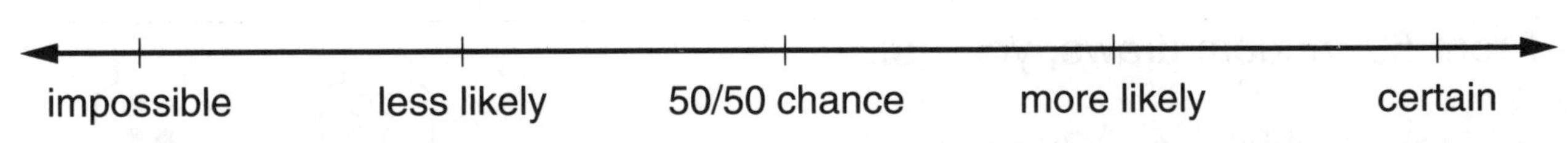

5. How likely is it that you will roll a sum greater than 3 with a pair of dice?

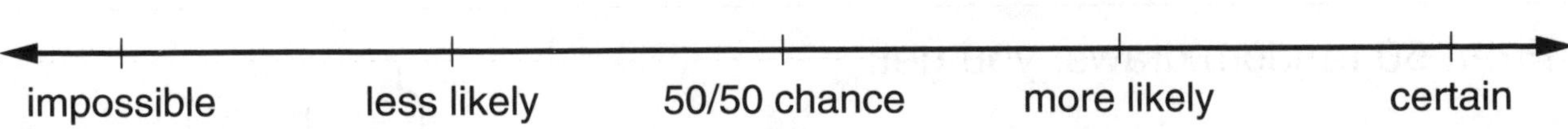

6. How did you decide where to put the mark in the box in Problem 5? Write your answer on the back of this page.

Copyright © Wright Group/McGraw-Hill

Name Date Time

Matching Spinners with Outcomes

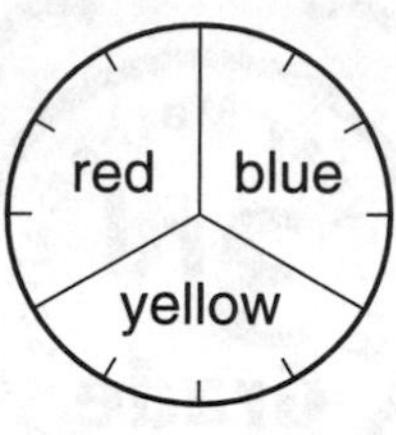

Spinner A

red blue yellow

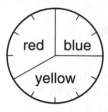

Spinner B

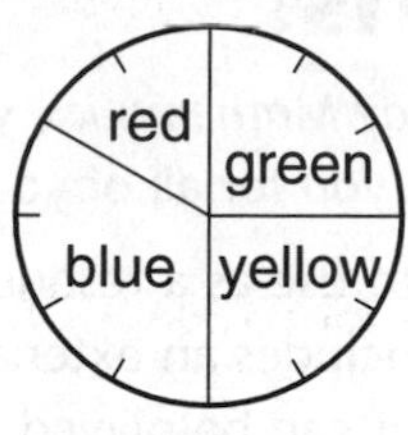

Spinner C

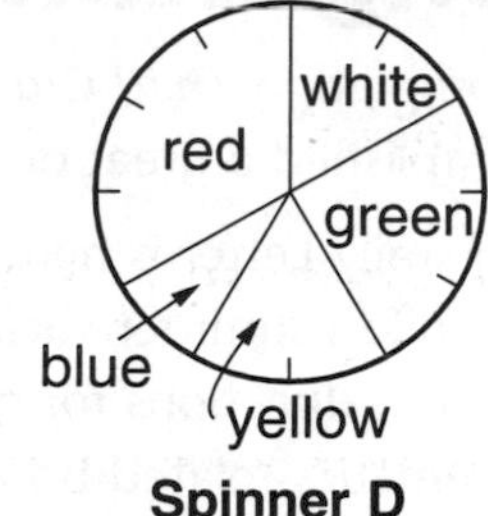

Spinner D

For each statement below, write the letter of the spinner that best matches the outcome.

1. You get yellow about half of the time. Spinner _____
2. You get blue about twice as often as red. Spinner _____
3. You are about 4 times as likely to get red as blue. Spinner _____
4. You get either red or blue about half of the time. Spinner _____
5. You don't get green, but *no* color is a favorite. Spinner _____
6. The paper clip lands on yellow 23 times out of 100 spins. Spinner _____
7. The paper clip lands on yellow 22 times out of 50 spins. Spinner _____

Make up your own.

8. ____

____

____

Spinner _____

9. ____

____

____

Spinner _____

Copyright © Wright Group/McGraw-Hill

Family Letter

Congratulations!

By completing *Third Grade Everyday Mathematics,* your child has accomplished a great deal. Thank you for all of your support!

This Family Letter is here for you to use as a resource throughout your child's summer vacation. It includes an extended list of Do-Anytime Activities, directions for games that can be played at home, a list of mathematics-related books to check out over vacation, and a sneak preview of what your child will be learning in *Fourth Grade Everyday Mathematics.* Enjoy your vacation!

Do-Anytime Activities

Mathematics means more when it is rooted in real-life situations. To help your child review many of the concepts he or she has learned in third grade, we suggest the following activities for you and your child to do together over vacation. These activities will help your child build on the skills he or she has learned this year and help prepare him or her for *Fourth Grade Everyday Mathematics.*

1. If you receive a daily newspaper, continue with the length-of-day project by recording the time of sunrise and sunset once a week. Draw conclusions about the length of a day during vacation months.
2. Over a period of time, have your child record the daily temperatures in the morning and in the evening. Keep track of the findings in chart or graph form. Ask questions about the data—for example, to find the differences in temperatures from morning to evening or from one day to the next.
3. As you are driving in the car or going on walks, search for geometric figures and identify them by name along with some of their characteristics. For example: A stop sign is an octagon, which has eight sides and eight angles; an orange construction cone is a cone, which has one flat surface that is shaped like a circle, a curved surface, and an apex; a brick is a rectangular prism in which all faces are rectangles.
4. Continue to practice addition, subtraction, multiplication, and division facts. Using short drill sessions with Fact Triangles, fact families, and games helps your child build on previous knowledge.
5. Provide multidigit addition and subtraction problems for your child to solve; encourage your child to write number stories to go along with the number models.

Copyright © Wright Group/McGraw-Hill

Building Skills through Games

The following section lists rules for games that can be played at home. The number cards used in some games can be made from 3" by 5" index cards.

Division Arrays

Materials
- ☐ number cards 6–18 (3 of each)
- ☐ 18 counters, such as pennies
- ☐ 1 regular die
- ☐ scratch paper for each player

6	7	8	9	10

Players 2 to 4

Directions

Shuffle the cards and place the deck facedown on the playing surface.

At each turn, a player draws a card and takes the number of counters shown on the card. Next, the player rolls the die. The number on the die specifies the number of equal rows the player must have in the array he or she makes using the counters. The player's score is the number of counters in each row. If there are no leftover counters, the player's score is double the number of counters in each row.

Players take turns. They keep track of their scores on scratch paper. The player with the highest total at the end of five rounds wins.

Three Addends

Materials
- ☐ paper and pencil (for each player)
- ☐ number cards 1–20 (1 of each)

Players 2

Directions

Shuffle the cards and place the deck facedown on the playing surface.

In turn, players draw three cards from the top of the deck. Both players write addition models using the three numbers on their sheets of paper. (The numbers can be written in whatever order they find easiest for solving the problem.) Players solve the problem and then compare answers.

Option: For a harder version, players take turns drawing four cards from the top of the deck. Players thus solve problems with four addends.

Copyright © Wright Group/McGraw-Hill

Unit 12: Family Letter *cont.*

Baseball Multiplication

Materials
- ☐ 2 regular dice
- ☐ 4 pennies
- ☐ score sheet (see below)
- ☐ calculator

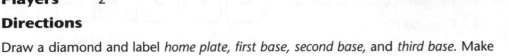

Players 2

Directions

Draw a diamond and label *home plate, first base, second base,* and *third base.* Make a score sheet that looks like the one below.

SCORE SHEET

Innings	1	2	3	4	5	6	Total
Player 1 outs							
Runs							
Player 2 outs							
Runs							

1. Take turns being the pitcher and the batter.
2. At the start of the inning, the batter puts a penny on home plate.
3. The pitcher rolls the dice. The batter multiplies the two numbers that come up and tells the answer. The pitcher checks the answer with a calculator.
4. If it is correct, the batter looks up the product in the Hitting Table. The batter either makes an out or moves a penny along the diamond for a single, double, triple, or home run.

   An incorrect solution is a strike, and another pitch (dice roll) is thrown. Three strikes make an out.
5. A run is scored each time a penny crosses home plate.
6. A player remains the batter for 3 outs. Then players switch roles. The inning is over when both players have made 3 outs.
7. After making the third out, a batter records the number of runs scored in that inning on the score sheet.
8. The player who has more runs at the end of six innings wins the game.

HITTING TABLE

36 =	Home Run
26–35 =	Triple
16–25 =	Double
6–15 =	Single
5 or less =	Out

Copyright © Wright Group/McGraw-Hill

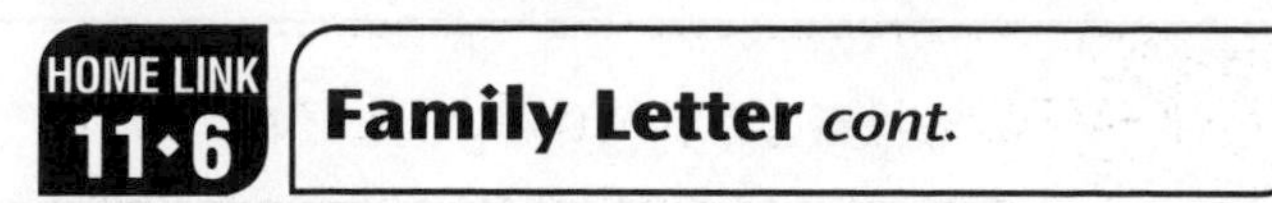

Vacation Reading with a Mathematical Twist

Books can contribute to children's learning by presenting mathematics in a combination of real-world and imaginary contexts. The titles listed below were recommended by teachers who use *Everyday Mathematics* in their classrooms. They are organized by mathematical topic. Visit your local library and check out these mathematics-related books with your child.

Geometry

A Cloak for the Dreamer by Aileen Friedman

Fractals, Googols, and Other Mathematical Tales by Theoni Pappas

Sir Cumference and the First Round Table: A Math Adventure by Wayne Geehan

Measurement

How Tall, How short, How Far Away by David Adler

Math Curse by Jon Scieszka

The Story of Money by Betsy Maestro

If You Made a Million by David Schwartz

Measuring on Penny by Loren Leedy

Numeration

Fraction Fun by David Adler

How Much Is a Million? by David Schwartz

Operations

The Grapes of Math by Gregory Tang

The King's Chessboard by David Birch

The I Hate Mathematics! Book by Marilyn Burns

A Remainder of One by Elinor J. Pinczes

Anno's Mysterious Multiplying Jar by Masqichiro Anno

Patterns, Functions, and Algebra

Eight Hands Round: A Patchwork Alphabet by Ann Whitford Paul

A Million Fish... More or Less by Patricia C. McKissack

Reference Frames

Pigs in a Blanket by Amy Axelrod

Three Days on a River in a Red Canoe by Vera B. Williams

Looking Ahead: *Fourth Grade Everyday Mathematics*

Next year, your child will ...

- go on a World Tour.
- continue to practice addition and subtraction skills.
- develop multiplication and division skills.
- investigate methods for solving problems using mathematics in everyday situations.
- work with number lines, coordinates, times, latitude and longitude, and dates.
- collect, organize, and interpret numerical data.
- continue to explore 3-dimensional objects and their properties, uses, and relationships.
- read, write, and use whole numbers, fractions, decimals, percents, and negative numbers.
- explore scientific notation.

Again, thank you for all of your support this year. Have fun continuing your child's mathematics experiences throughout the vacation!

Copyright © Wright Group/McGraw-Hill

Name Date

Notes

Copyright © Wright Group/McGraw-Hill

Name Date

Notes

Copyright © Wright Group/McGraw-Hill

Project Masters

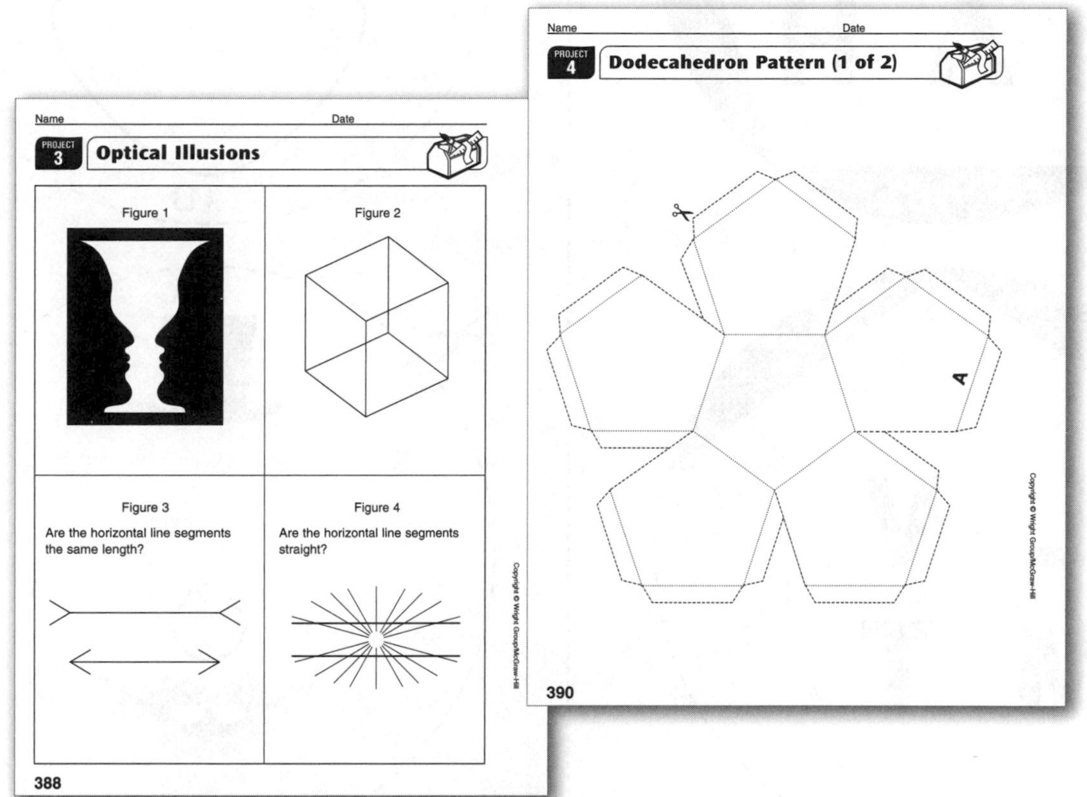

Copyright © Wright Group/McGraw-Hill

Name Date

PROJECT 3

Spinning Illusions

Set 1

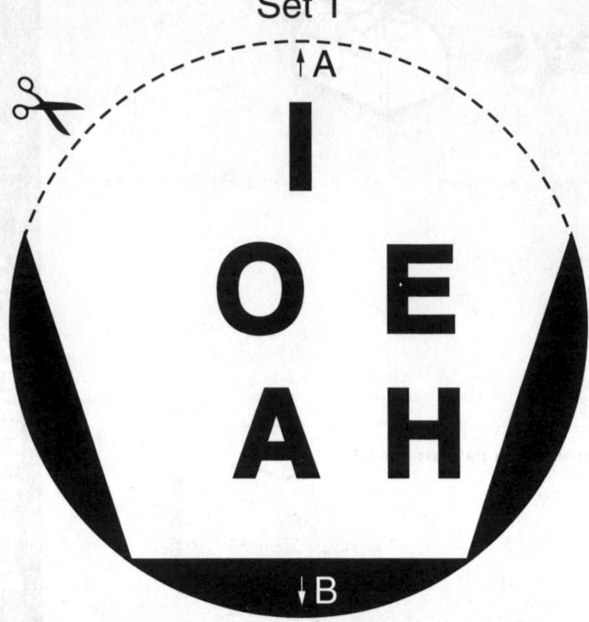

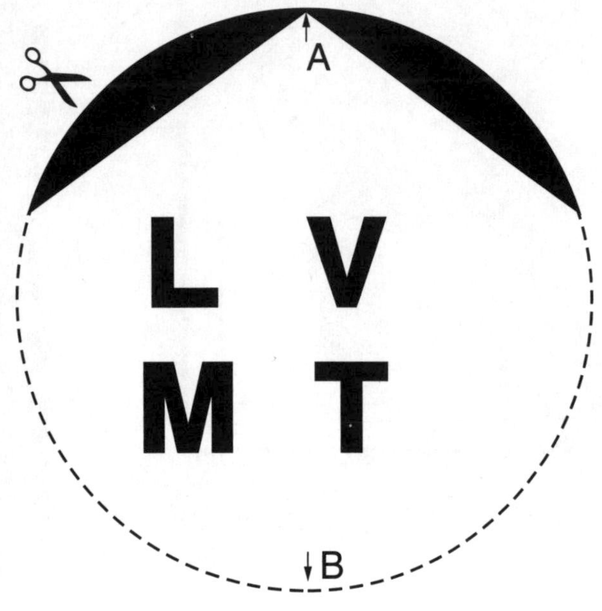

Set 2

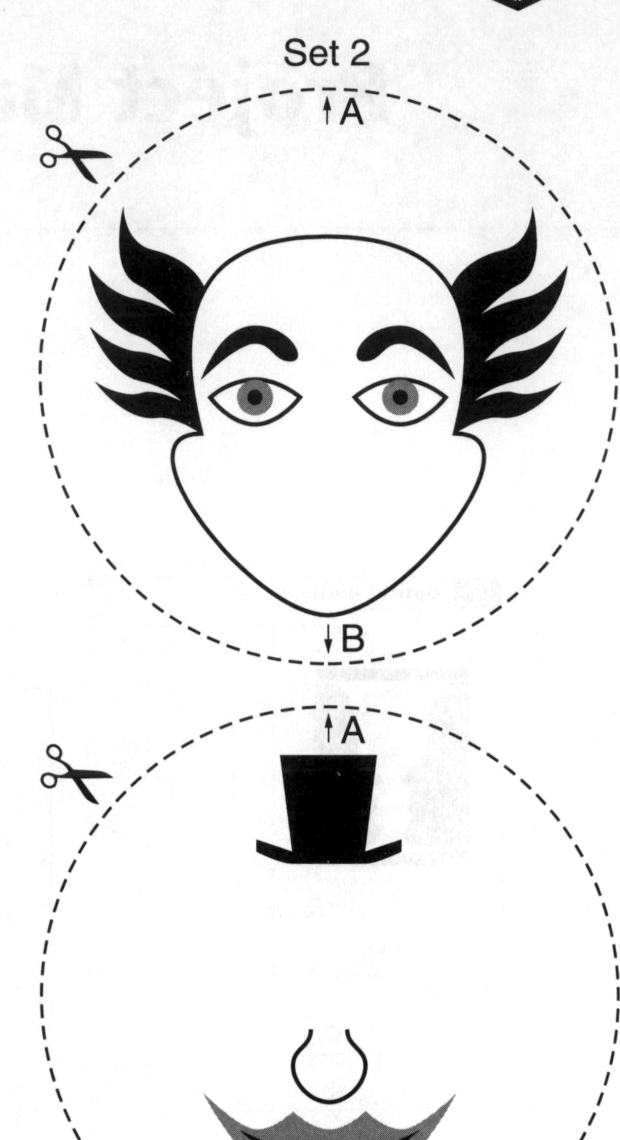

Copyright © Wright Group/McGraw-Hill

Name Date

PROJECT 3

Spinning Illusions Blank

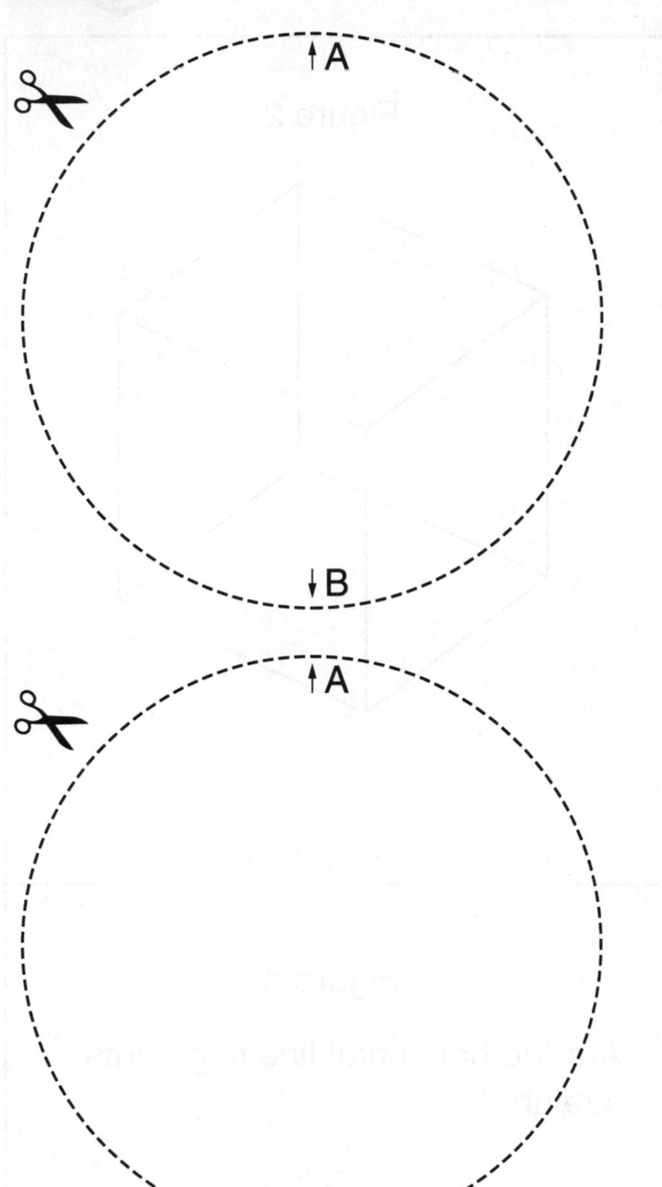

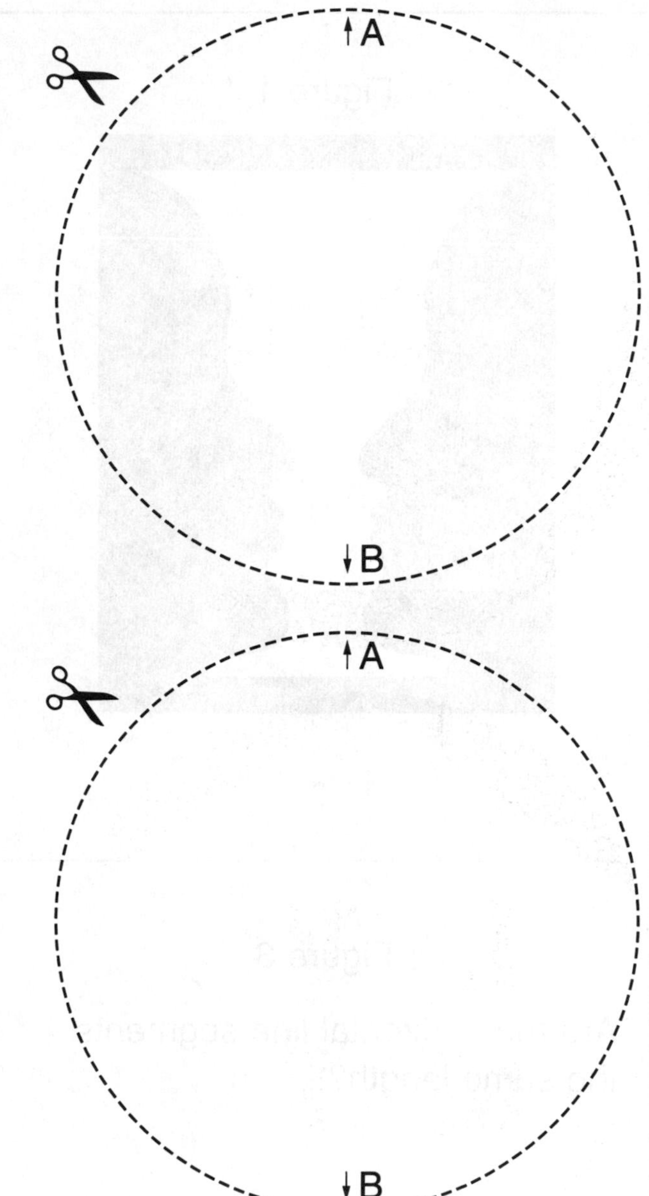

Copyright © Wright Group/McGraw-Hill

Name Date

Optical Illusions

Figure 1

Figure 2

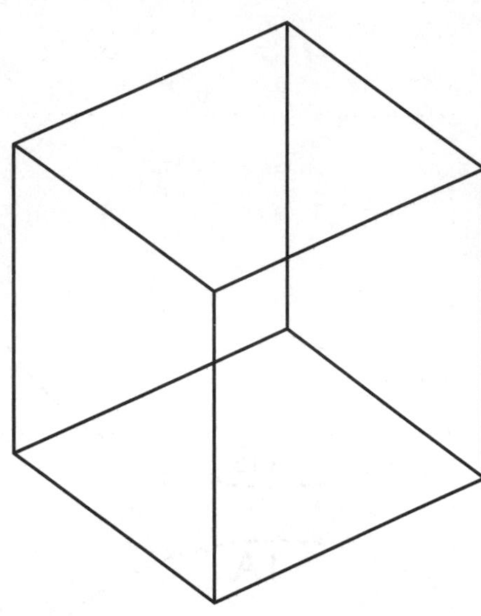

Figure 3

Are the horizontal line segments the same length?

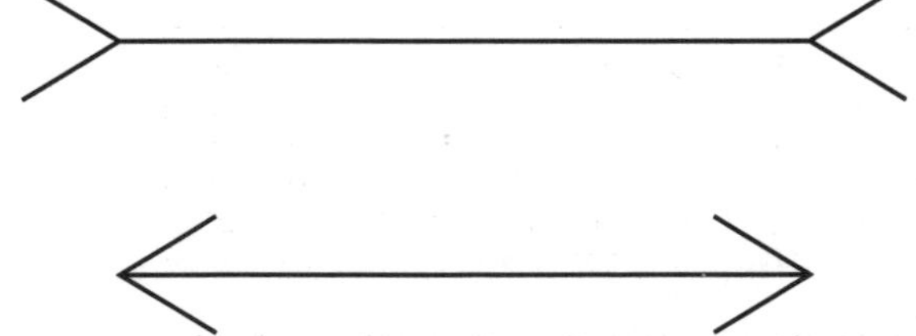

Figure 4

Are the horizontal line segments straight?

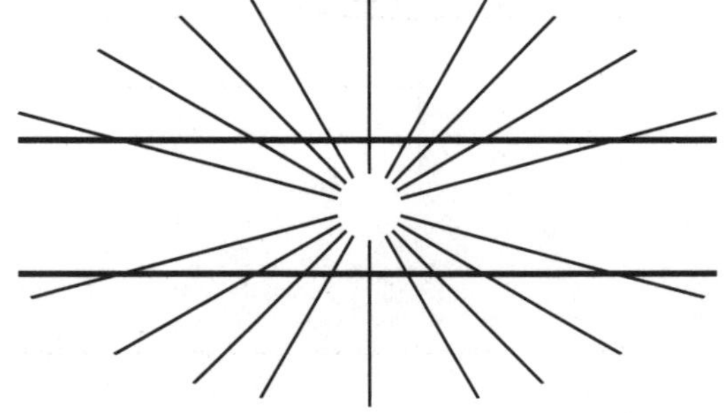

Copyright © Wright Group/McGraw-Hill

Name Date

PROJECT 4

Calendar Months and Names

S	M	T	W	T	F	S
1	2	3	4	5	6	7
8	9	10	11	12	13	14
15	16	17	18	19	20	21
22	23	24	25	26	27	28
29	30	31				

S	M	T	W	T	F	S
1	2	3	4	5	6	7
8	9	10	11	12	13	14
15	16	17	18	19	20	21
22	23	24	25	26	27	28
29	30	31				

S	M	T	W	T	F	S
1	2	3	4	5	6	7
8	9	10	11	12	13	14
15	16	17	18	19	20	21
22	23	24	25	26	27	28
29	30	31				

S	M	T	W	T	F	S
	1	2	3	4	5	6
7	8	9	10	11	12	13
14	15	16	17	18	19	20
21	22	23	24	25	26	27
28	29	30	31			

S	M	T	W	T	F	S
	1	2	3	4	5	6
7	8	9	10	11	12	13
14	15	16	17	18	19	20
21	22	23	24	25	26	27
28	29	30	31			

S	M	T	W	T	F	S
	1	2	3	4	5	6
7	8	9	10	11	12	13
14	15	16	17	18	19	20
21	22	23	24	25	26	27
28	29	30	31			

S	M	T	W	T	F	S
		1	2	3	4	5
6	7	8	9	10	11	12
13	14	15	16	17	18	19
20	21	22	23	24	25	26
27	28	29	30	31		

S	M	T	W	T	F	S
		1	2	3	4	5
6	7	8	9	10	11	12
13	14	15	16	17	18	19
20	21	22	23	24	25	26
27	28	29	30	31		

S	M	T	W	T	F	S
		1	2	3	4	5
6	7	8	9	10	11	12
13	14	15	16	17	18	19
20	21	22	23	24	25	26
27	28	29	30	31		

S	M	T	W	T	F	S
			1	2	3	4
5	6	7	8	9	10	11
12	13	14	15	16	17	18
19	20	21	22	23	24	25
26	27	28	29	30	31	

S	M	T	W	T	F	S
			1	2	3	4
5	6	7	8	9	10	11
12	13	14	15	16	17	18
19	20	21	22	23	24	25
26	27	28	29	30	31	

S	M	T	W	T	F	S
			1	2	3	4
5	6	7	8	9	10	11
12	13	14	15	16	17	18
19	20	21	22	23	24	25
26	27	28	29	30	31	

S	M	T	W	T	F	S
				1	2	3
4	5	6	7	8	9	10
11	12	13	14	15	16	17
18	19	20	21	22	23	24
25	26	27	28	29	30	31

S	M	T	W	T	F	S
				1	2	3
4	5	6	7	8	9	10
11	12	13	14	15	16	17
18	19	20	21	22	23	24
25	26	27	28	29	30	31

S	M	T	W	T	F	S
				1	2	3
4	5	6	7	8	9	10
11	12	13	14	15	16	17
18	19	20	21	22	23	24
25	26	27	28	29	30	31

S	M	T	W	T	F	S
					1	2
3	4	5	6	7	8	9
10	11	12	13	14	15	16
17	18	19	20	21	22	23
24	25	26	27	28	29	30
31						

S	M	T	W	T	F	S
					1	2
3	4	5	6	7	8	9
10	11	12	13	14	15	16
17	18	19	20	21	22	23
24	25	26	27	28	29	30
31						

S	M	T	W	T	F	S
					1	2
3	4	5	6	7	8	9
10	11	12	13	14	15	16
17	18	19	20	21	22	23
24	25	26	27	28	29	30
31						

S	M	T	W	T	F	S
						1
2	3	4	5	6	7	8
9	10	11	12	13	14	15
16	17	18	19	20	21	22
23	24	25	26	27	28	29
30	31					

S	M	T	W	T	F	S
						1
2	3	4	5	6	7	8
9	10	11	12	13	14	15
16	17	18	19	20	21	22
23	24	25	26	27	28	29
30	31					

S	M	T	W	T	F	S
						1
2	3	4	5	6	7	8
9	10	11	12	13	14	15
16	17	18	19	20	21	22
23	24	25	26	27	28	29
30	31					

Copyright © Wright Group/McGraw-Hill

Name Date

Dodecahedron Pattern (1 of 2)

A

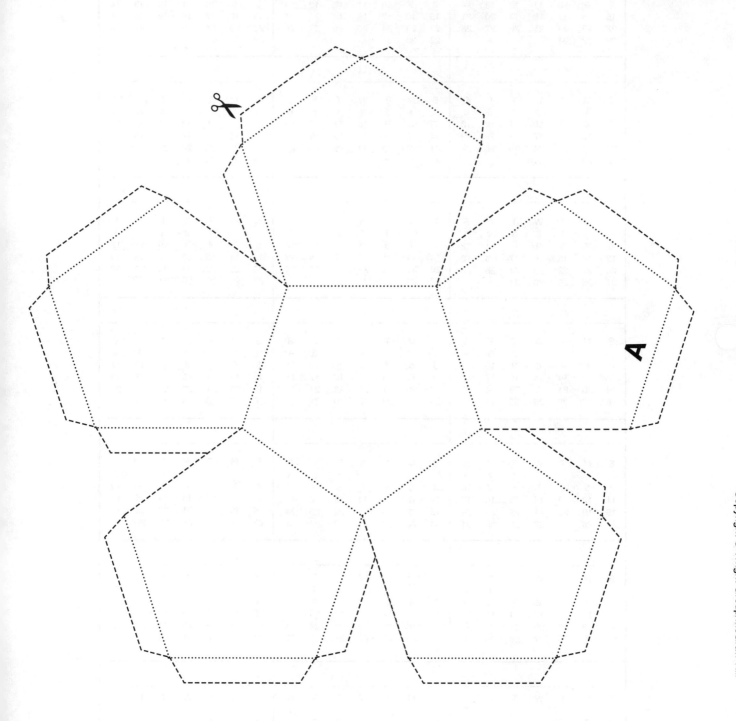

Copyright © Wright Group/McGraw-Hill

Name Date

PROJECT 4

Dodecahedron Pattern (2 of 2)

B

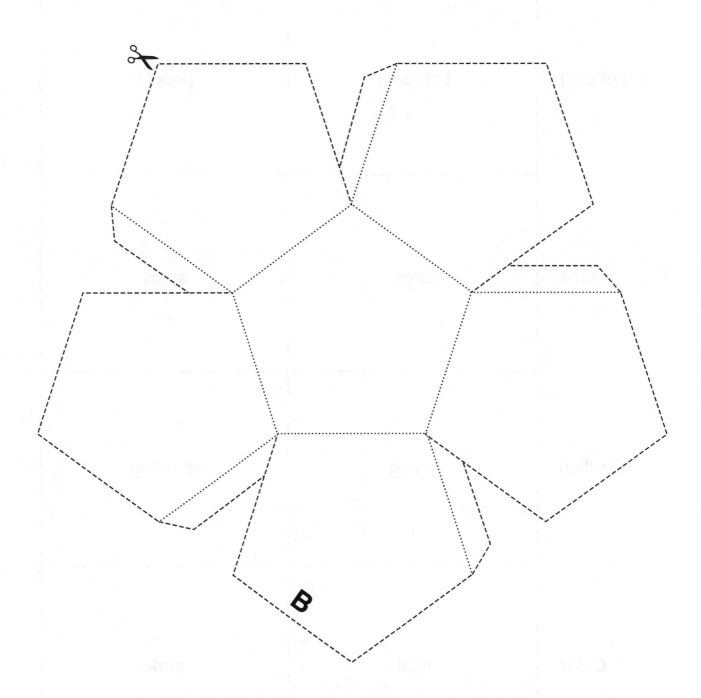

Copyright © Wright Group/McGraw-Hill

Name Date

PROJECT 5

Label Cards

Attributes	Values	
Kind of Dog	Labrador	poodle
Size	large	small
Position	sitting	standing
Color	light	dark

Cut on the dashed lines.

Copyright © Wright Group/McGraw-Hill

Name Date

Picture Cards

Cut on the dashed lines.

Copyright © Wright Group/McGraw-Hill

Name Date

PROJECT 6

How Far Can You Go in a Million Steps?

Powers of Ten

$10 \times 10 = 100$ (one hundred)

$10 \times 100 = 1{,}000$ (one thousand)

$10 \times 1{,}000 = 10{,}000$ (ten thousand)

$10 \times 10{,}000 = 100{,}000$ (one hundred thousand)

$10 \times 100{,}000 = 1{,}000{,}000$ (one million)

$10 \times 1{,}000{,}000 = 10{,}000{,}000$ (ten million)

$10 \times 10{,}000{,}000 = 100{,}000{,}000$ (one hundred million)

$10 \times 100{,}000{,}000 = 1{,}000{,}000{,}000$ (one billion)

1. We walk an average of ______________ (unit) in 10 steps.

2. This means we can walk about:

a. ______________ (unit) in 100 steps.

b. ______________ (unit) in 1,000 steps.

c. ______________ (unit) in 10,000 steps.

d. ______________ (unit) in 100,000 steps.

e. ______________ (unit) in 1,000,000 steps.

3. About how many miles or kilometers can we walk in 1,000,000 steps?

______________ (unit)

Try This

4. About how many miles or kilometers can we travel in 1,000,000,000 steps? ______________ (unit)

5. Earth is about 25,000 miles, or 40,000 kilometers, around its circumference. About how many times could we travel around Earth in 1,000,000,000 steps?

______________ (unit)

Copyright © Wright Group/McGraw-Hill

Teaching Aid Masters

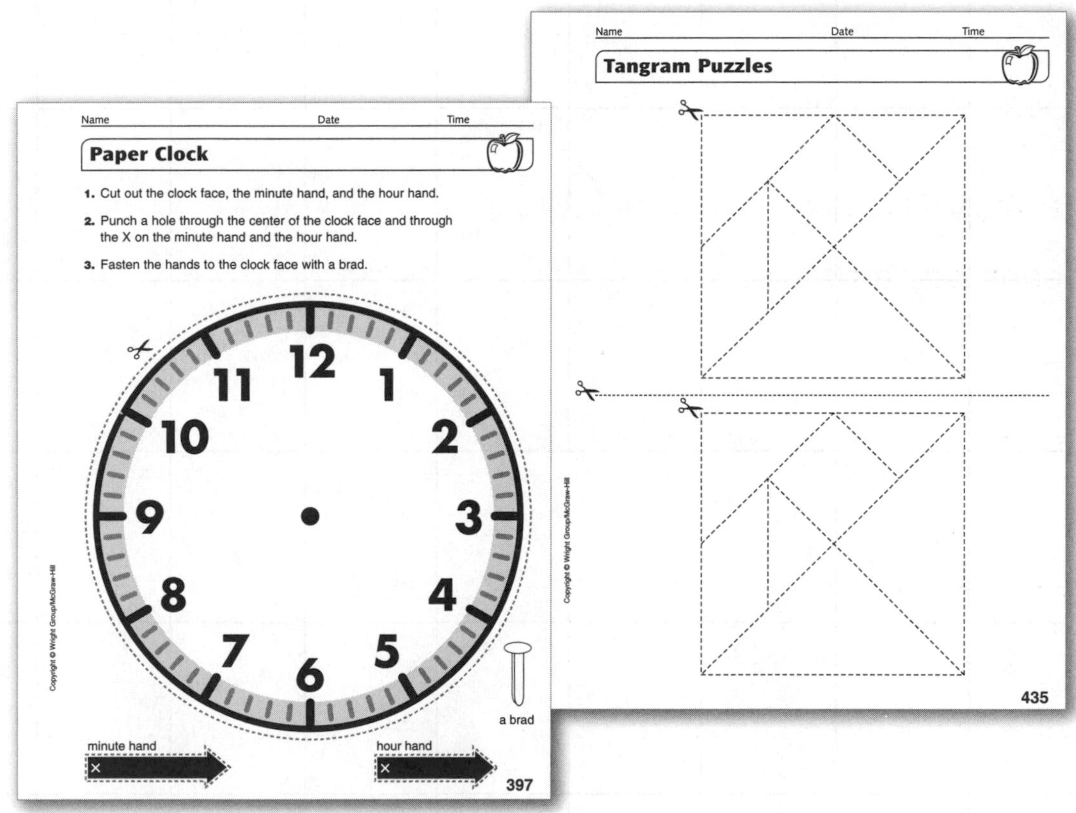

Copyright © Wright Group/McGraw-Hill

Teaching Aid Masters

Name Date Time

Number Grid

Copyright © Wright Group/McGraw-Hill

Name Date Time

Paper Clock

1. Cut out the clock face, the minute hand, and the hour hand.
2. Punch a hole through the center of the clock face and through the X on the minute hand and the hour hand.
3. Fasten the hands to the clock face with a brad.

12
11
1
10
2
9
3
8
4
7
5
6

a brad

minute hand
×

hour hand
×

Copyright © Wright Group/McGraw-Hill

Name Date Time

My Exit Slip

Copyright © Wright Group/McGraw-Hill

Name Date Time

My Exit Slip

Copyright © Wright Group/McGraw-Hill

Name Date Time

$1 Bills

Copyright © Wright Group/McGraw-Hill

Name Date Time

$1 Bills

Copyright © Wright Group/McGraw-Hill

Name Date Time

$10 and 100 Bills

Copyright © Wright Group/McGraw-Hill

Name Date Time

$10 and 100 Bills

Copyright © Wright Group/McGraw-Hill

Name Date Time

Coin Top-It

Ⓓ Ⓓ Ⓝ	  	Ⓠ Ⓝ Ⓟ 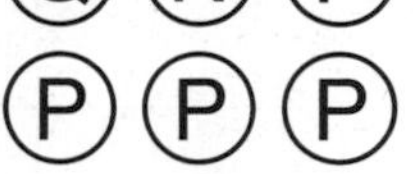	 Ⓟ Ⓟ Ⓟ
	Ⓠ Ⓓ Ⓓ Ⓟ Ⓟ		Ⓠ Ⓠ Ⓝ Ⓟ
	Ⓠ Ⓓ Ⓓ Ⓓ Ⓓ		Ⓠ Ⓠ Ⓠ
Ⓠ Ⓠ Ⓠ 	Ⓠ Ⓠ Ⓠ Ⓓ Ⓟ	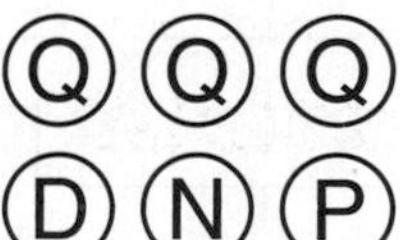	Ⓠ Ⓠ Ⓠ Ⓠ

Copyright © Wright Group/McGraw-Hill

Name Date Time

Sunrise and Sunset Record

Date	Time of Sunrise	Time of Sunset	Length of Day
			hr min
			hr min
			hr min
			hr min
			hr min
			hr min
			hr min
			hr min
			hr min
			hr min
			hr min
			hr min
			hr min
			hr min
			hr min
			hr min
			hr min
			hr min
			hr min
			hr min
			hr min

Copyright © Wright Group/McGraw-Hill

Name Date Time

Fact Triangle

•

+, −

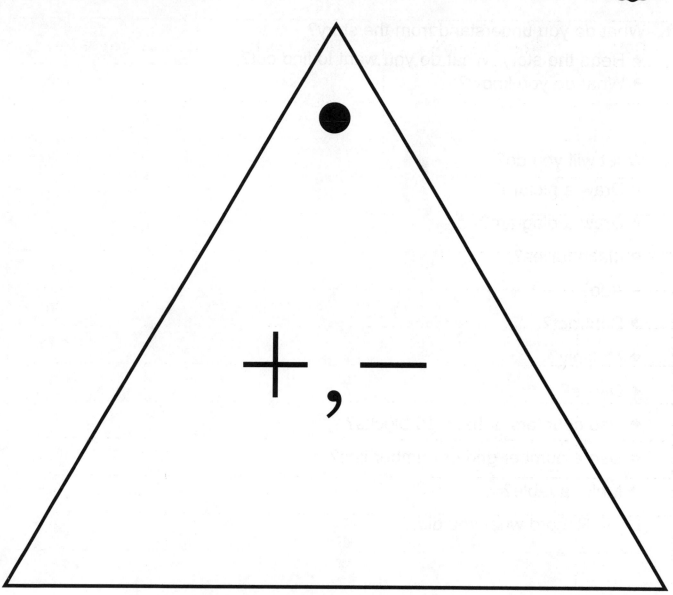

Copyright © Wright Group/McGraw-Hill

Name Date Time

Guide to Solving Number Stories

1. What do you understand from the story?
   - Read the story. What do you want to find out?
   - What do you know?

2. What will you do?
   - Draw a picture?
   - Draw a diagram?
   - Make tallies?
   - Add?
   - Subtract?
   - Multiply?
   - Divide?
   - Use counters or base-10 blocks?
   - ◆ Use a number grid or number line?
   - Make a table?

   Do it. Record what you did.

3. Answer the question.

   Write the units. Write a number model to show what you did.

4. **Check:** Does your answer make sense? How do you know?

Copyright © Wright Group/McGraw-Hill

Name Date Time

A Number Story

Unit

Copyright © Wright Group/McGraw-Hill

Name Date Time

Parts-and-Total Diagram

Total	
Part	Part

Copyright © Wright Group/McGraw-Hill

Name Date Time

Change Diagrams

Change

Start		End
	______	

Change

Start		End
	______	

Change

Start		End
	______	

Copyright © Wright Group/McGraw-Hill

Name Date Time

Comparison Diagrams

Quantity

Quantity

Difference

Quantity

Quantity

Difference

Copyright © Wright Group/McGraw-Hill

Name Date Time

3-Digit Place-Value Mat

Ones	
Tens	
Hundreds	

Copyright © Wright Group/McGraw-Hill

Name Date Time

Base-10 Flat

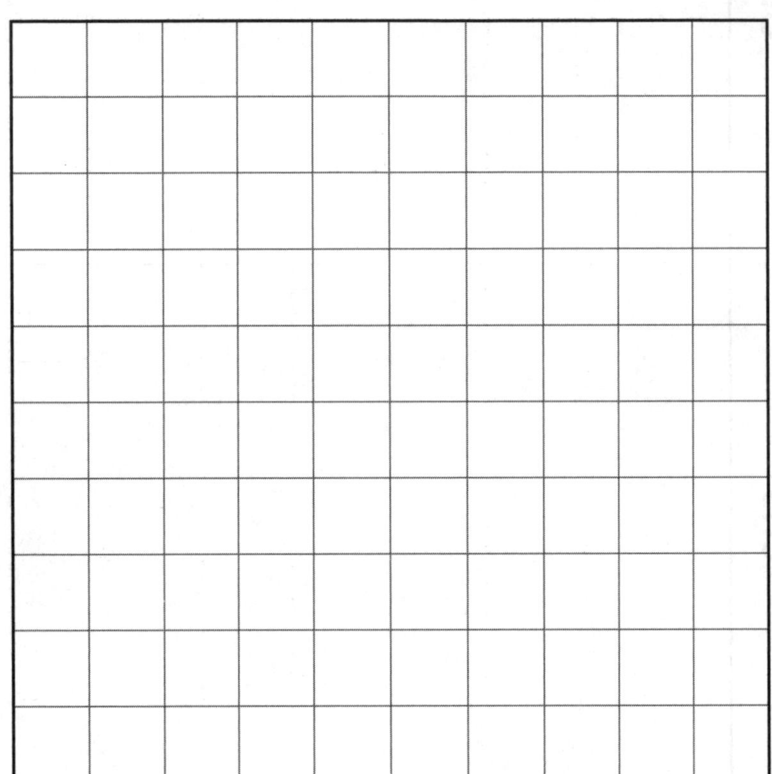

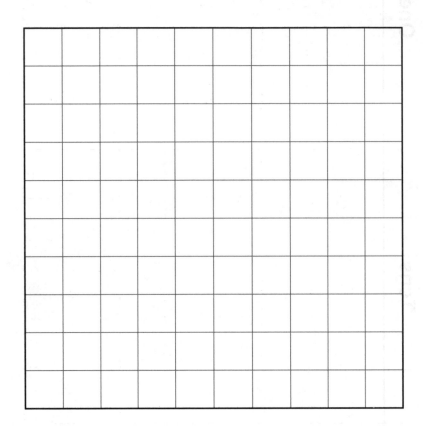

Copyright © Wright Group/McGraw-Hill

Name Date Time

Rulers

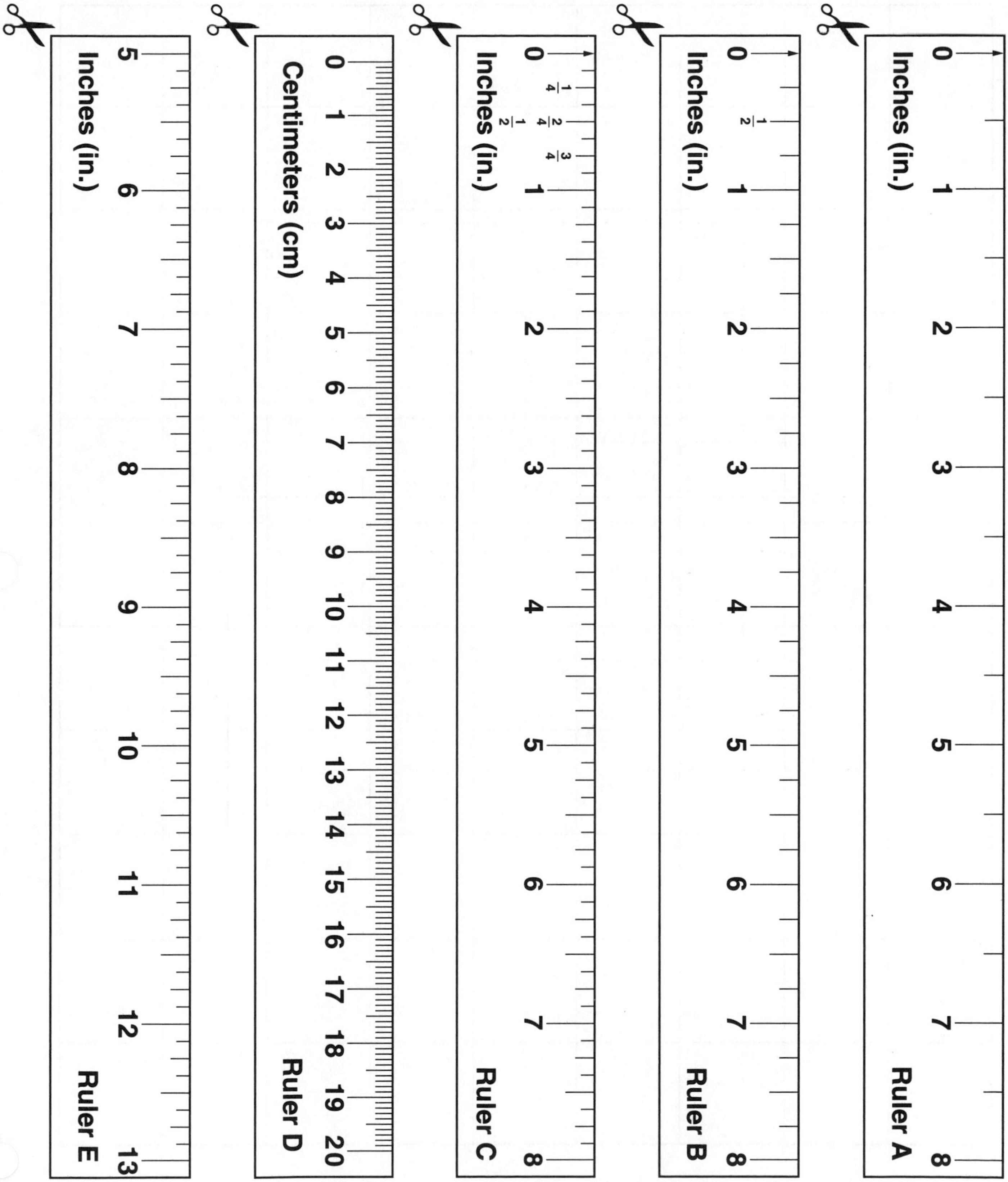

Inches (in.) Ruler A

0 1 2 3 4 5 6 7 8

Inches (in.) Ruler B

0 $\frac{1}{2}$ 1 2 3 4 5 6 7 8

Inches (in.) Ruler C

0 $\frac{1}{4}$ $\frac{2}{4}$ $\frac{1}{2}$ $\frac{3}{4}$ 1 2 3 4 5 6 7 8

Centimeters (cm) Ruler D

0 1 2 3 4 5 6 7 8 9 10 11 12 13 14 15 16 17 18 19 20

Inches (in.) Ruler E

5 6 7 8 9 10 11 12 13

Copyright © Wright Group/McGraw-Hill

Name Date Time

Grid

Copyright © Wright Group/McGraw-Hill

Name Date Time

Geoboard Dot Paper (10 × 10)

1.

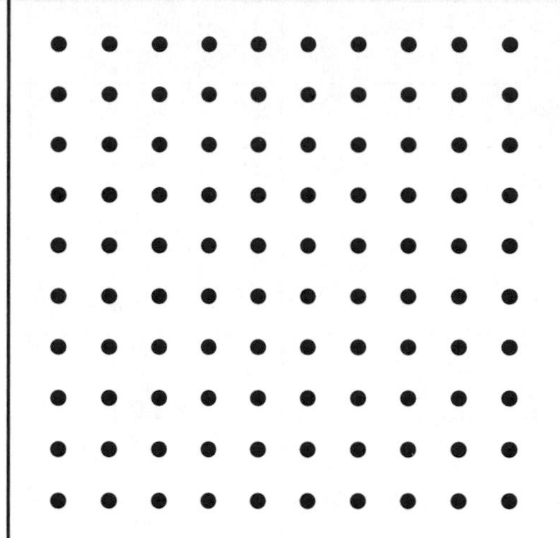

2.

3.

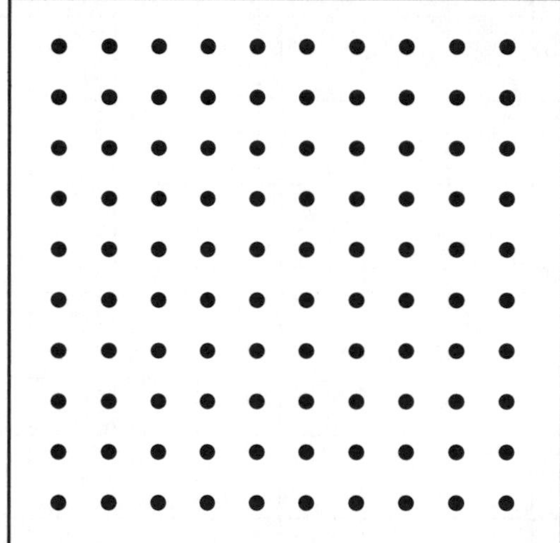

4.

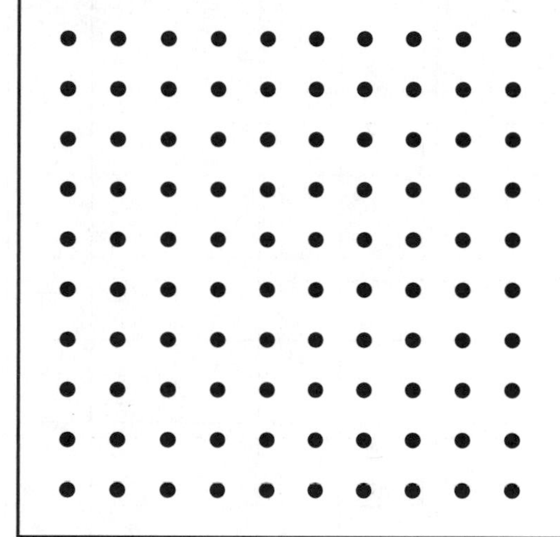

5.

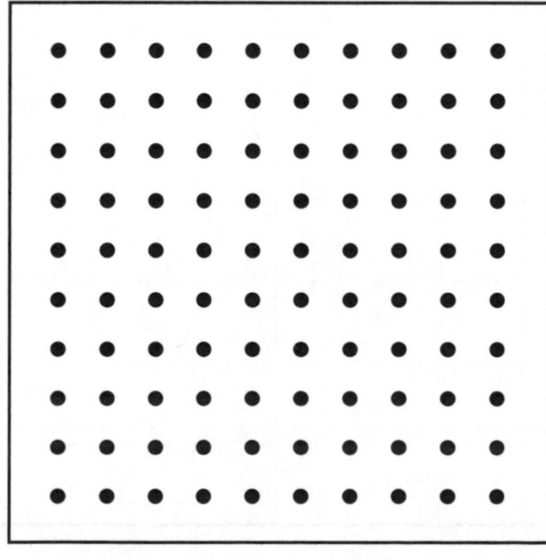

6.

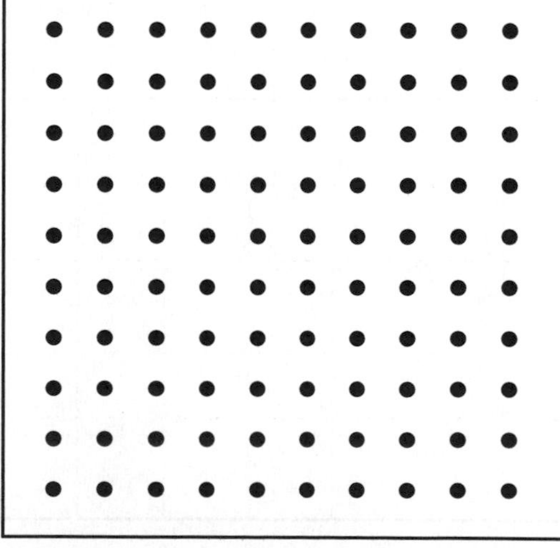

Copyright © Wright Group/McGraw-Hill

Name Date

Centimeter Grid Paper

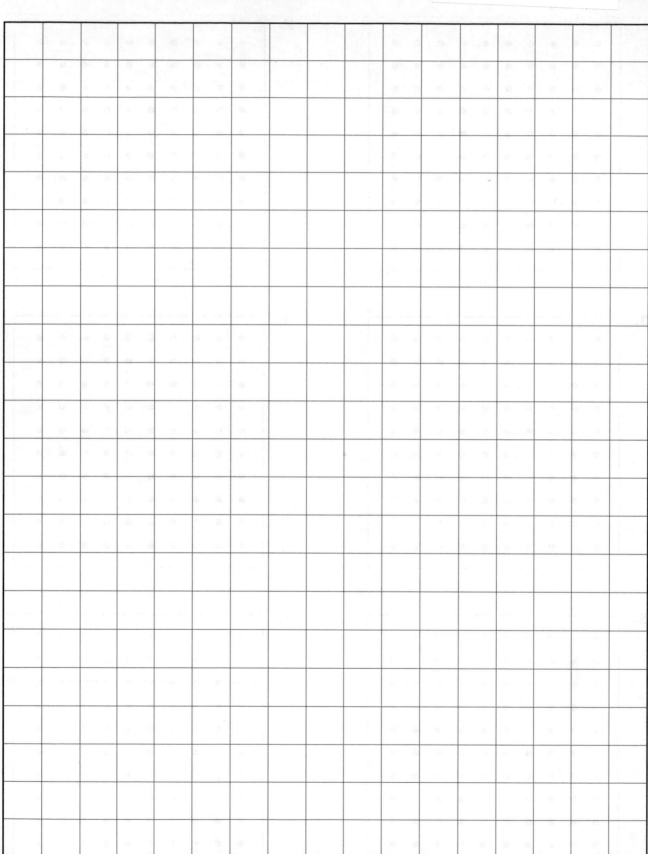

Copyright © Wright Group/McGraw-Hill

Name Date Time

10 × 10 Grid

Copyright © Wright Group/McGraw-Hill

Name Date Time

One-Inch Grid

Copyright © Wright Group/McGraw-Hill

Name Date Time

Multiplication/Division Diagram

________	________ per ________	________ in all

________	________ per ________	________ in all

________	________ per ________	________ in all

Copyright © Wright Group/McGraw-Hill

Name Date Time

4 × 3 Grid

Copyright © Wright Group/McGraw-Hill

Name Date Time

Multiplication/Division Fact Triangle

$\times, \div$

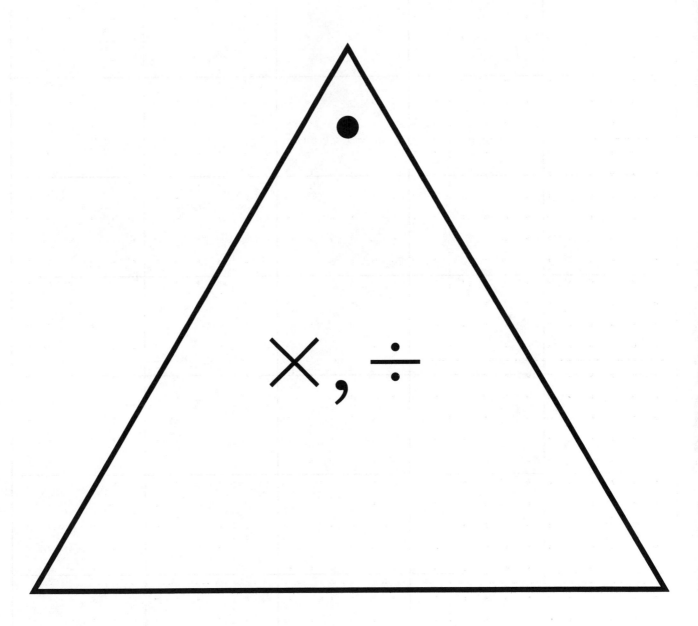

Copyright © Wright Group/McGraw-Hill

Name Date Time

5-Digit Place-Value Chart

Ten-Thousands	Thousands	Hundreds	Tens	Ones

Copyright © Wright Group/McGraw-Hill

Name Date Time

7-Digit Place-Value Mat

Millions

Hundred-Thousands

Ten-Thousands

Thous

Copyright © Wright Group/McGraw-Hill

Name Date Time

7-Digit Place-Value Mat *continued*

Ones

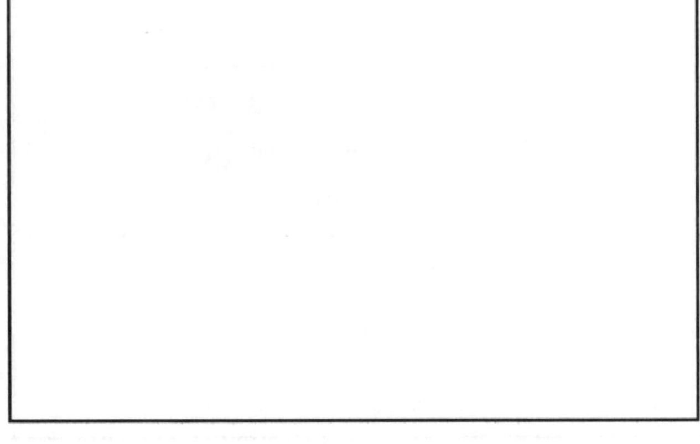

Tens

Hundreds

ands

Do not cut. Paste or tape to *Math Masters*, page 423.

Copyright © Wright Group/McGraw-Hill

Name Date Time

A Flat

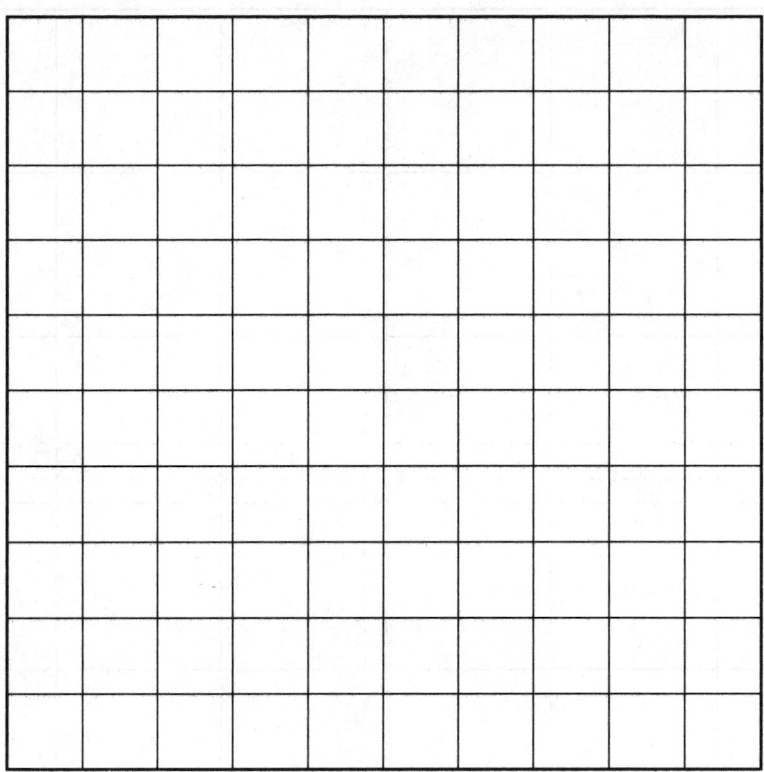

Copyright © Wright Group/McGraw-Hill

Name Date Time

10 × 10 Grid

TAB

Copyright © Wright Group/McGraw-Hill

Name Date Time

10 × 10 Grid *continued*

Copyright © Wright Group/McGraw-Hill

Name Date Time

Circles for Angle Measures

Cut the sheet into four parts along the dashed lines.

Share the circles with the members of your group. Each person will cut out his or her own circle.

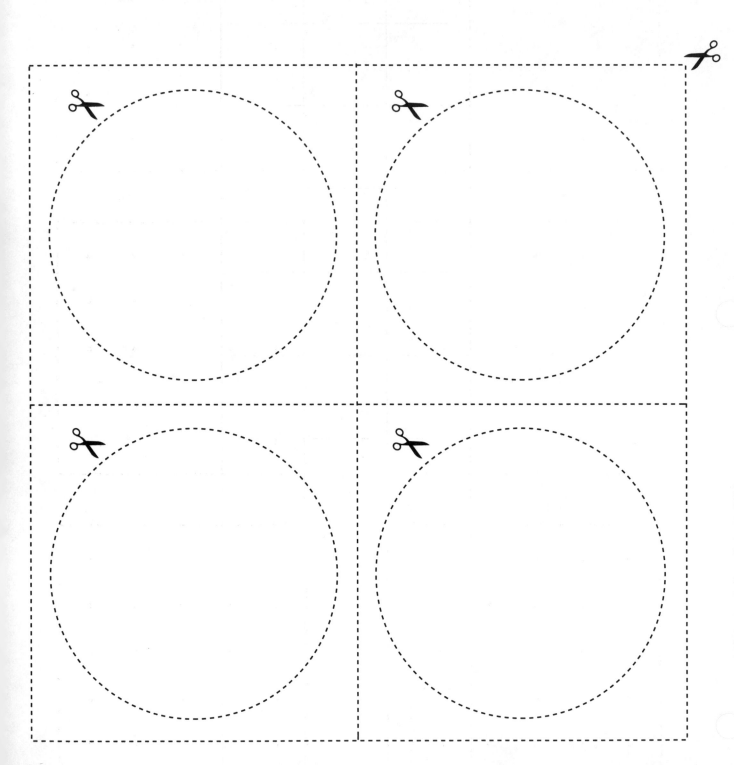

Copyright © Wright Group/McGraw-Hill

Name Date Time

Geoboard Dot Paper (5 × 5)

1.

2.

3.

4.

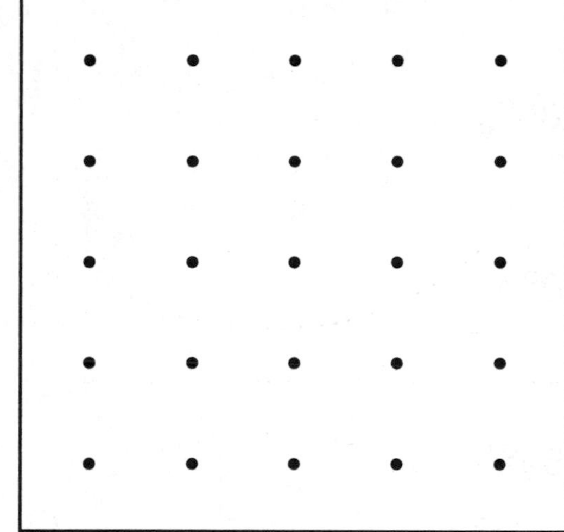

5.

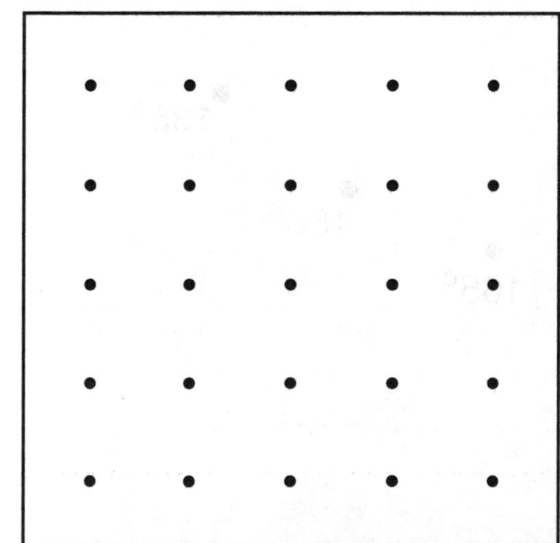

6.

Copyright © Wright Group/McGraw-Hill

Name Date Time

Circular Geoboard Paper

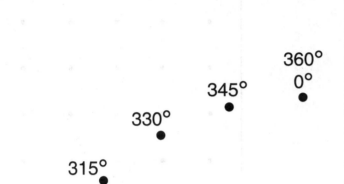

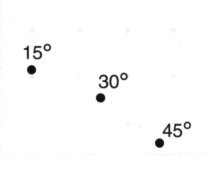

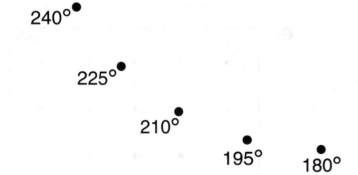

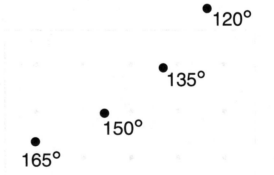

360°
0°
15°
30°
45°
60°
75°
90°
105°
120°
135°
150°
165°
180°
195°
210°
225°
240°
255°
270°
285°
300°
315°
330°
345°

Copyright © Wright Group/McGraw-Hill

Name Date Time

×, ÷ Fact Triangles 3

9 ×, ÷ 36 • 6 2

16 • ×, ÷ 2 8

45 • ×, ÷ 9 8 5

6 4 ×, ÷ 36 •

24 • ×, ÷ 3 8

32 • ×, ÷ 8 4

27 • ×, ÷ 3 9

40 • ×, ÷ 5 8

18 • ×, ÷ 9 2

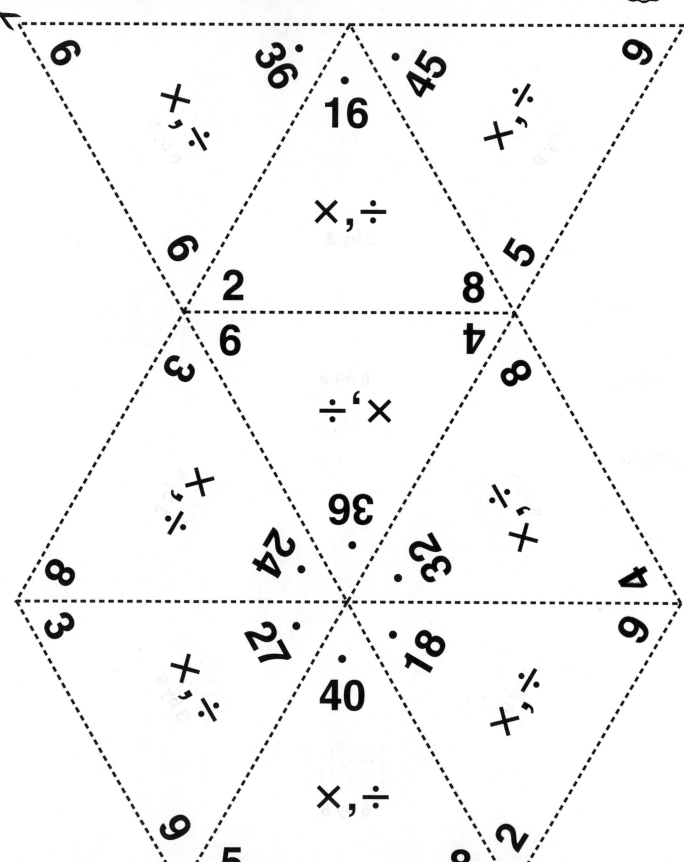

Copyright © Wright Group/McGraw-Hill

Name Date Time

×, ÷ Fact Triangles 3 *continued*

5 by 9

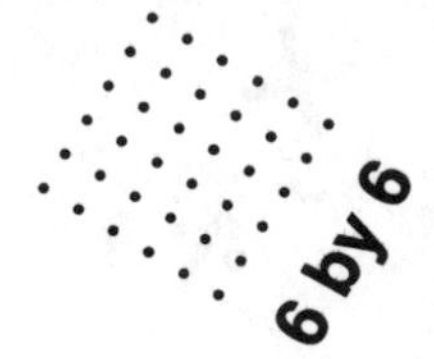

6 by 9

2 by 8

4 by 9

4 by 8

3 by 8

2 by 9

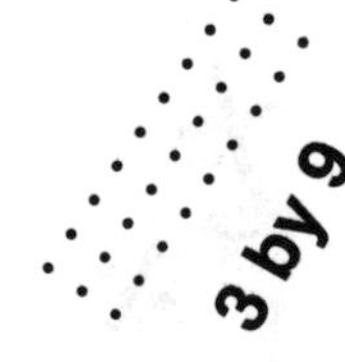

3 by 9

5 by 8

Copyright © Wright Group/McGraw-Hill

Name Date Time

×, ÷ Fact Triangles 4

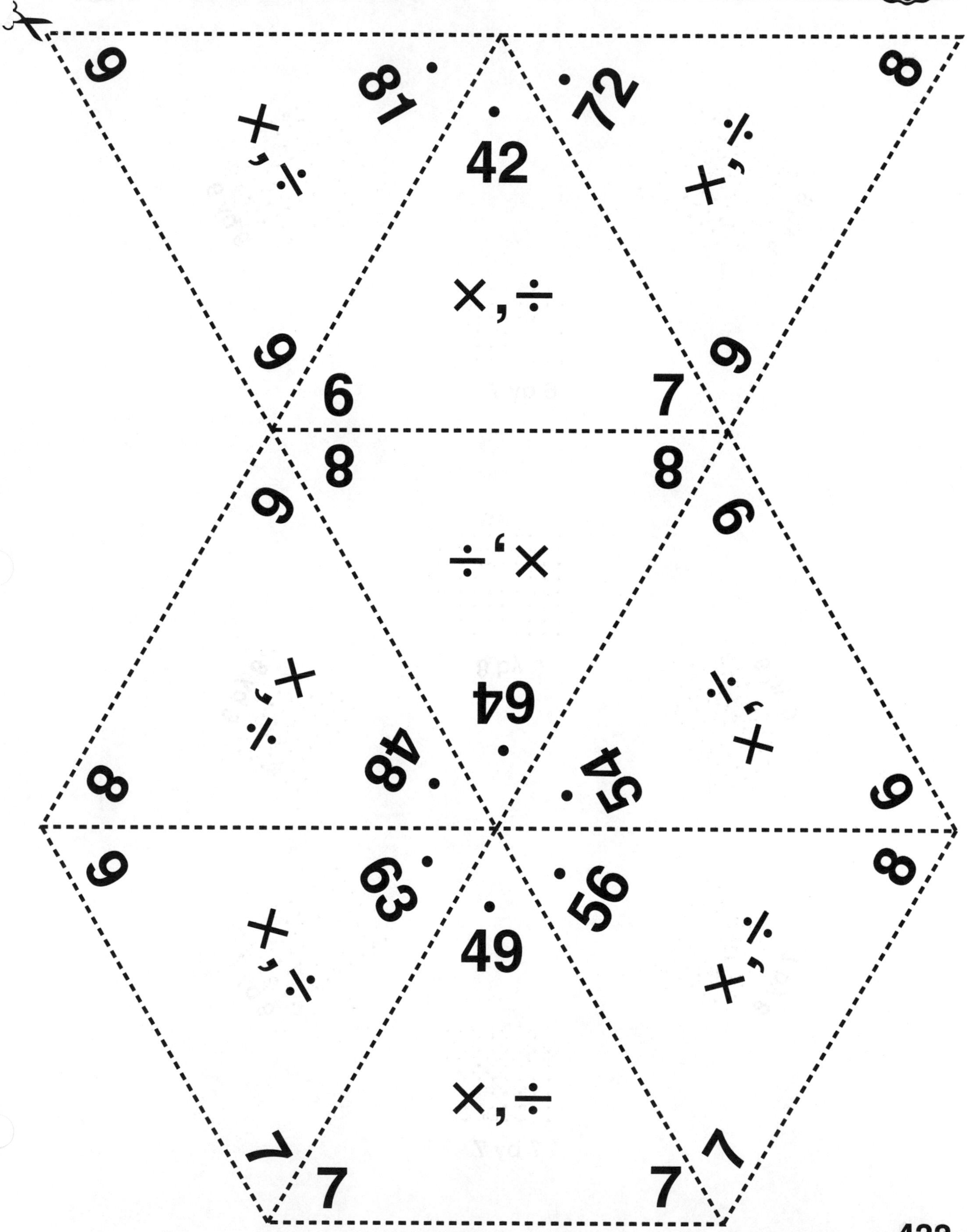

9

81 •

× , ÷

• 72

8

• 42

× , ÷

× , ÷

9

6

7

9

8

8

9

÷ , ×

9

× , ÷

64 •

× , ÷

48 •

• 54

8

9

9

63 •

• 56

8

• 49

× , ÷

× , ÷

× , ÷

7

7

7

7

Copyright © Wright Group/McGraw-Hill

Name Date Time

×, ÷ Fact Triangles 4 *continued*

9 by 8

9 by 9

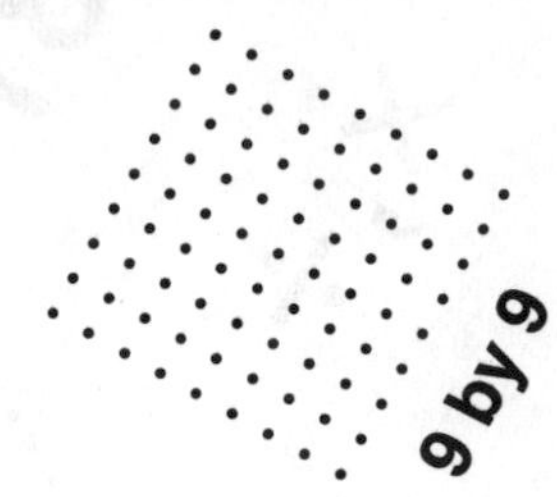

6 by 7

8 by 8

6 by 9

6 by 8

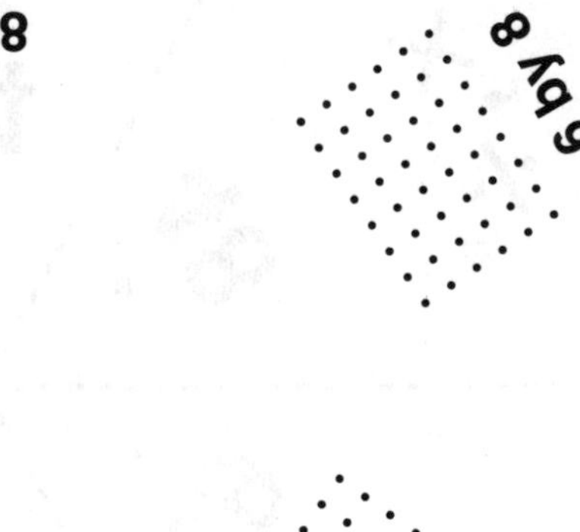

7 by 8

9 by 7

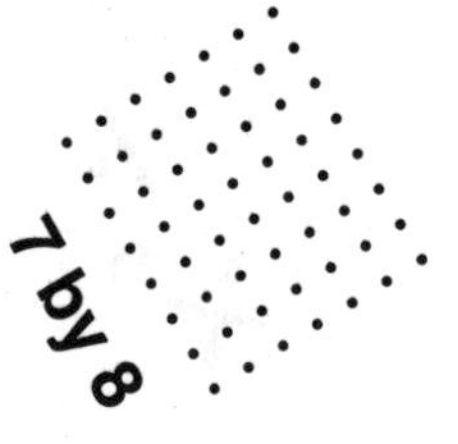

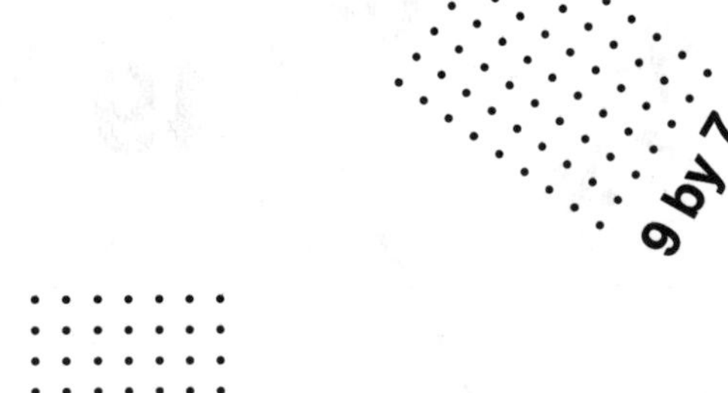

7 by 7

Copyright © Wright Group/McGraw-Hill

Name Date Time

Tangram Puzzles

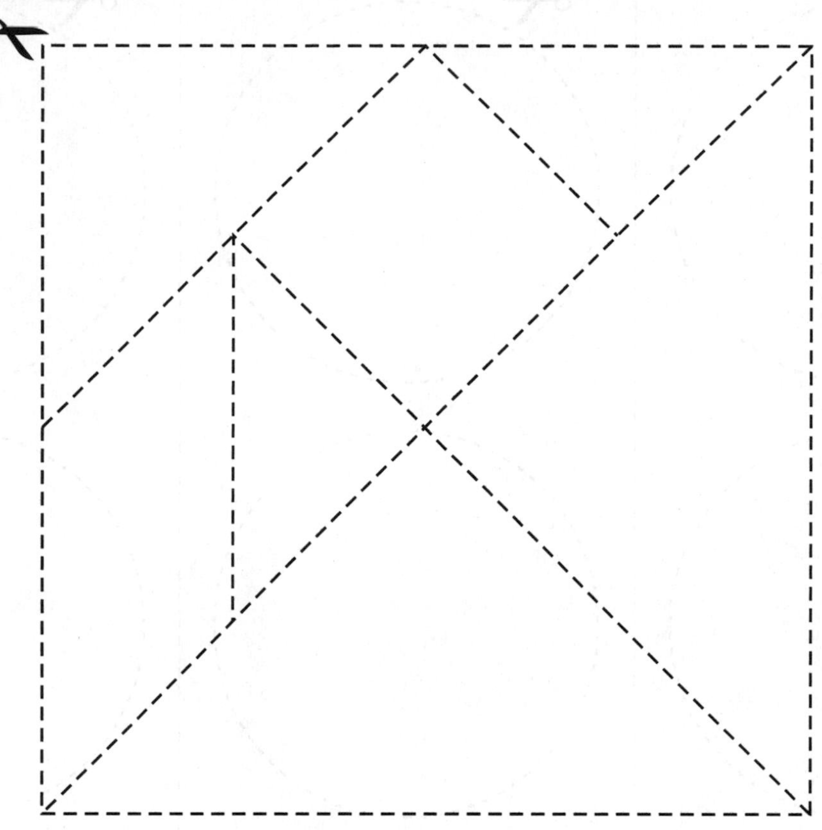

Copyright © Wright Group/McGraw-Hill

Name Date Time

Fractions Greater than One

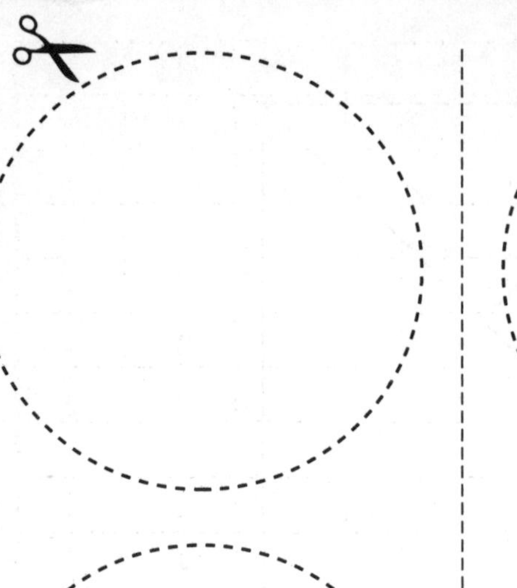

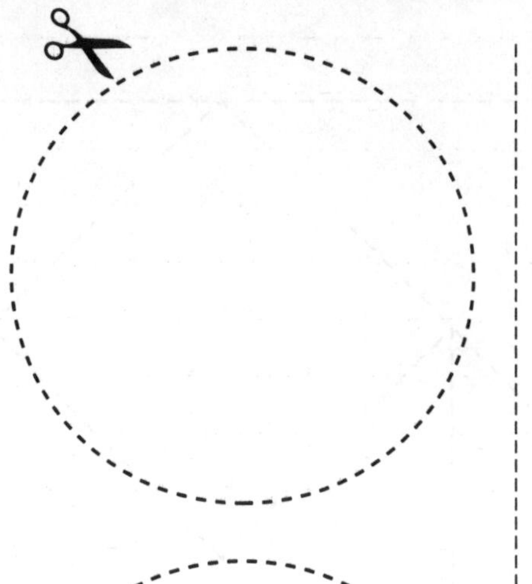

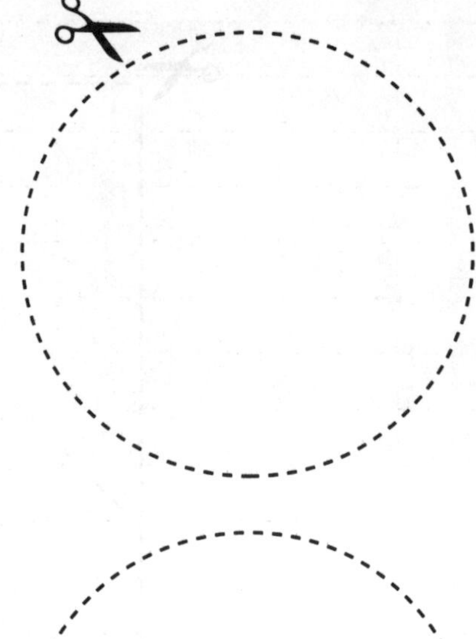

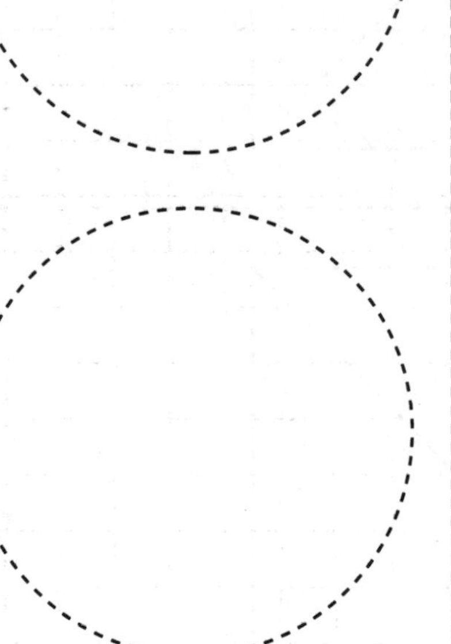

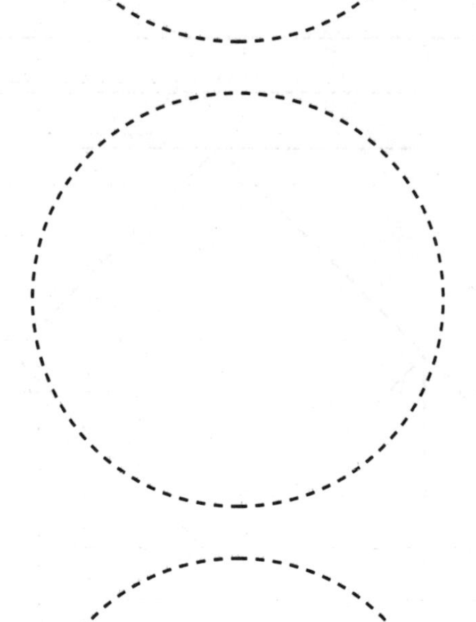

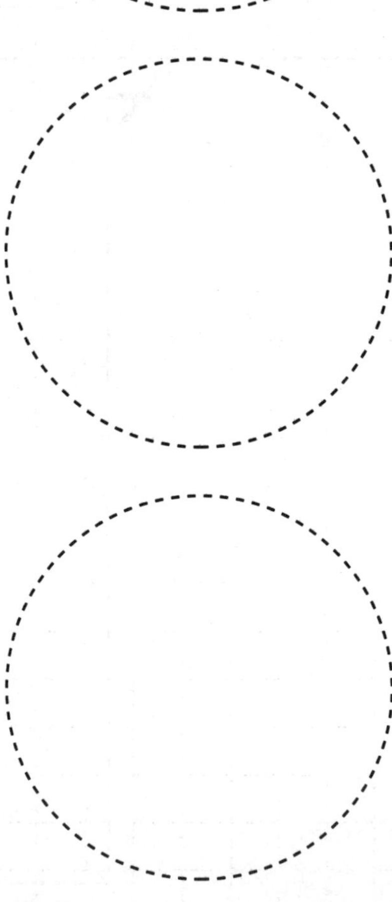

Copyright © Wright Group/McGraw-Hill

Name Date Time

$\frac{1}{4}$-inch Grid Paper

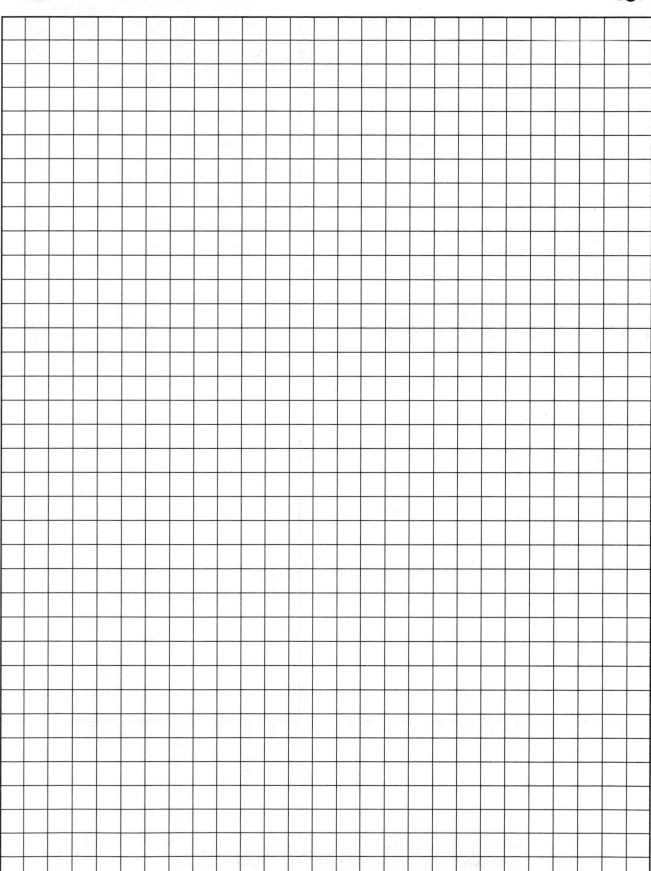

Copyright © Wright Group/McGraw-Hill

Name Date Time

Coordinate Grids

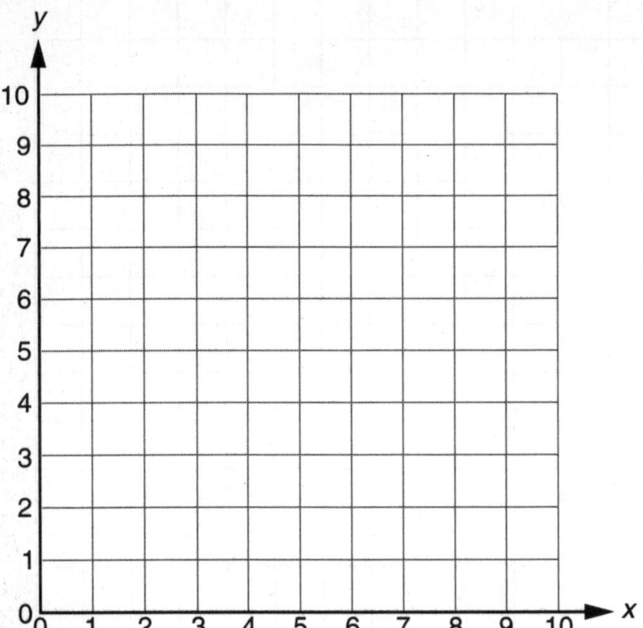

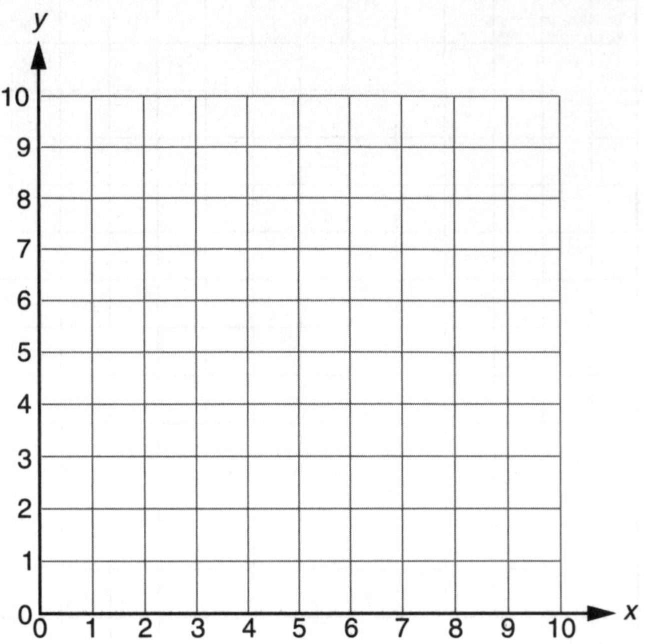

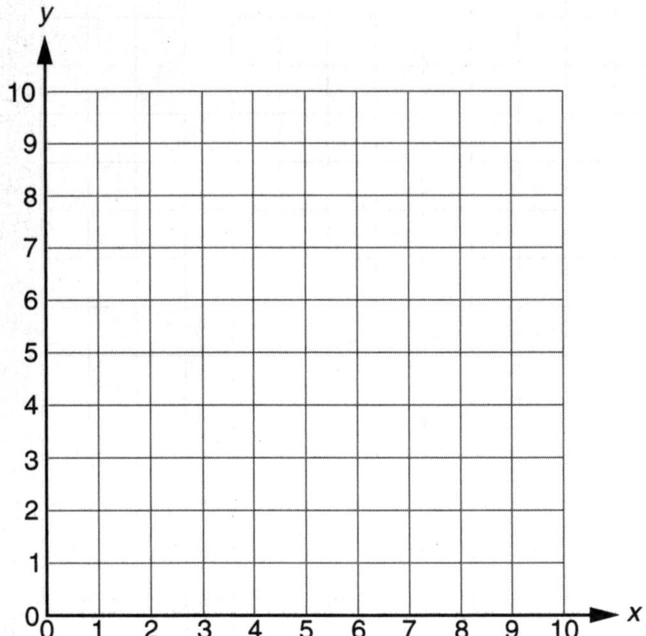

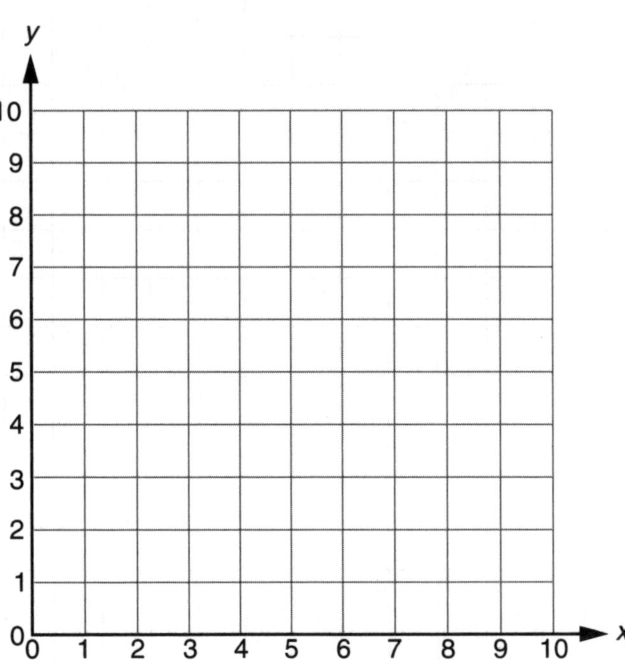

Copyright © Wright Group/McGraw-Hill

Game Masters

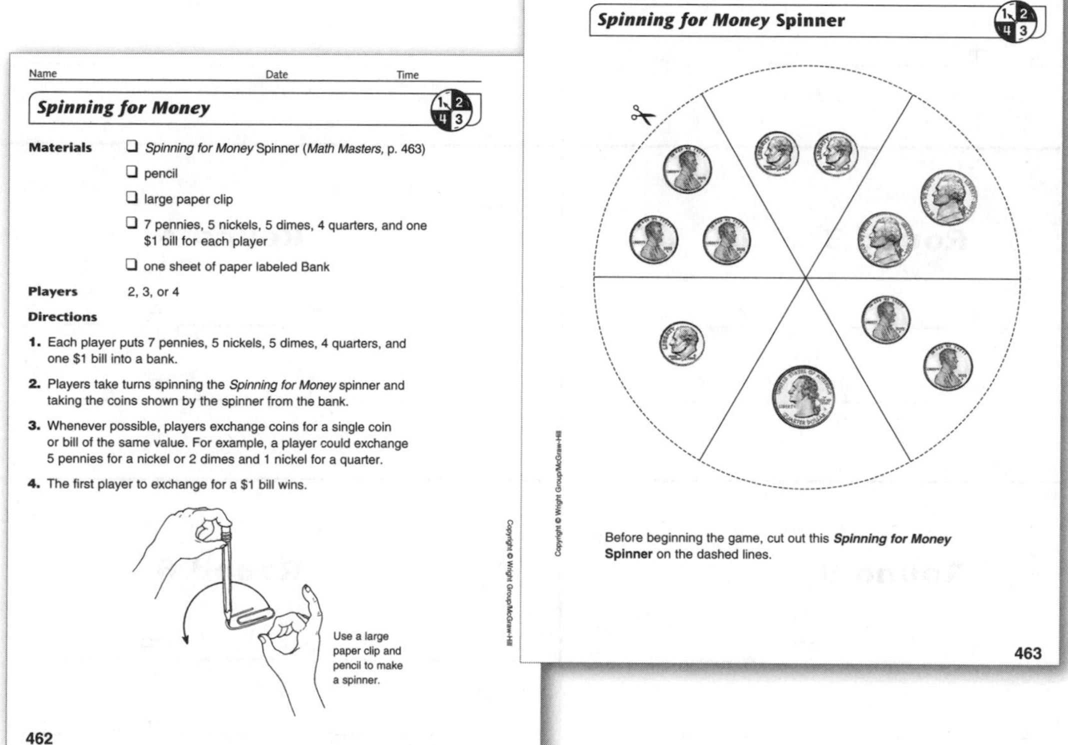

Name Date Time

Spinning for Money

Materials ❑ *Spinning for Money* Spinner (*Math Masters,* p. 463)
❑ pencil
❑ large paper clip
❑ 7 pennies, 5 nickels, 5 dimes, 4 quarters, and one $1 bill for each player
❑ one sheet of paper labeled Bank

Players 2, 3, or 4

Directions

1. Each player puts 7 pennies, 5 nickels, 5 dimes, 4 quarters, and one $1 bill into a bank.
2. Players take turns spinning the *Spinning for Money* spinner and taking the coins shown by the spinner from the bank.
3. Whenever possible, players exchange coins for a single coin or bill of the same value. For example, a player could exchange 5 pennies for a nickel or 2 dimes and 1 nickel for a quarter.
4. The first player to exchange for a $1 bill wins.

Use a large paper clip and pencil to make a spinner.

Copyright © Wright Group/McGraw-Hill

462

Name Date Time

Spinning for Money Spinner

Copyright © Wright Group/McGraw-Hill

Before beginning the game, cut out this ***Spinning for Money* Spinner** on the dashed lines.

463

Game Masters

Copyright © Wright Group/McGraw-Hill

Name Date Time

Addition Top-It Record Sheet

Players ______________ and ______________________

Write the number sentences for each round. Circle the winning sum.

Round 1	Round 2
_____ + _____ = _____ _____ + _____ = _____	_____ + _____ = _____ _____ + _____ = _____
Round 3	**Round 4**
_____ + _____ = _____ _____ + _____ = _____	_____ + _____ = _____ _____ + _____ = _____
Round 5	**Round 6**
_____ + _____ = _____ _____ + _____ = _____	_____ + _____ = _____ _____ + _____ = _____

Copyright © Wright Group/McGraw-Hill

Name Date Time

Angle Race Degree-Measure Cards

15°	15°	15°	15°	30°	30°
30°	30°	45°	45°	45°	45°
60°	60°	60°	75°	75°	75°
90°	90°	90°	120°	120°	150°
180°	210°	240°			

Copyright © Wright Group/McGraw-Hill

Name Date Time

Array Bingo Cards

2 × 2	2 × 3	2 × 4	4 × 4
2 × 5	2 × 6	3 × 5	6 × 3
3 × 3	1 × 7	4 × 3	3 × 6
5 × 3	6 × 1	4 × 5	5 × 4

Copyright © Wright Group/McGraw-Hill

Name Date Time

Baseball Multiplication Game Mat

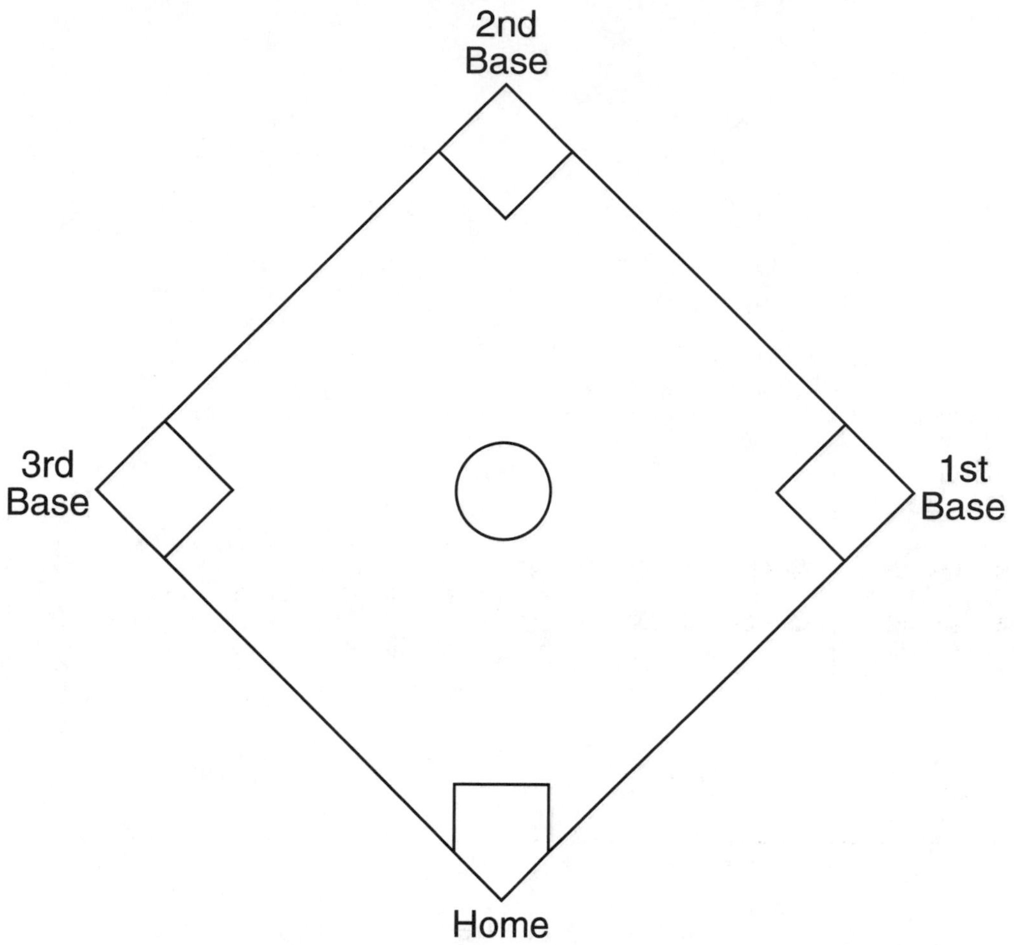

Scoreboard				
Inning	**1**	**2**	**3**	**Final**
Team 1				
Team 2				

Runs-and-Outs Tally			
Team 1		**Team 2**	
Runs	**Outs**	**Runs**	**Outs**

Scoring Chart (for 2 six-sided dice)	
36 = Home run (score a run)	6 to 15 = Single (go to 1st base)
25 to 35 = Triple (go to 3rd base)	5 or less = Out (record an out)
16 to 24 = Double (go to 2nd base)	

Copyright © Wright Group/McGraw-Hill

Name Date Time

Baseball Multiplication (Advanced)

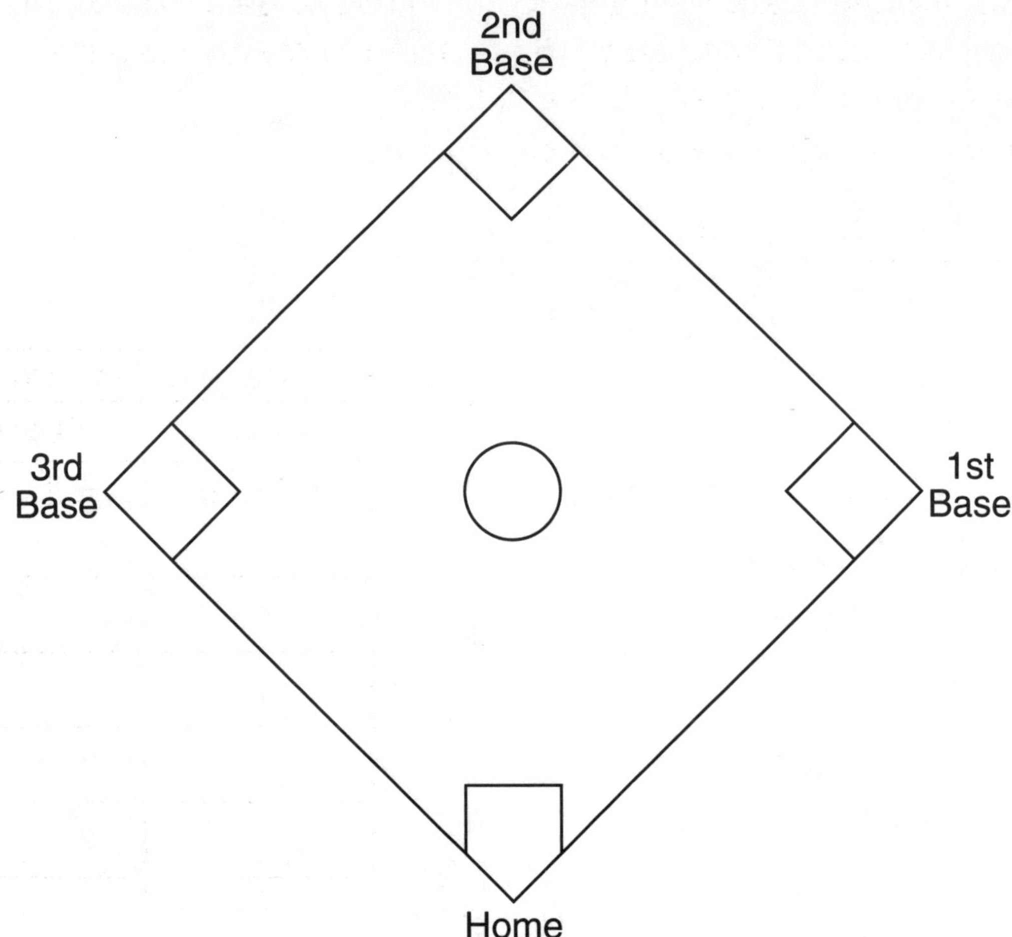

Scoreboard				
Inning	**1**	**2**	**3**	**Final**
Team 1				
Team 2				

Runs-and-Outs Tally			
Team 1		**Team 2**	
Runs	**Outs**	**Runs**	**Outs**

Scoring Chart (for 2 rolls of a 12-sided die)	
91 or more = Home run (score a run)	21 to 50 = Single (go to 1st base)
76 to 90 = Triple (go to 3rd base)	20 or less = Out (record an out)
51 to 75 = Double (go to 2nd base)	

Copyright © Wright Group/McGraw-Hill

Name Date Time

Baseball Multiplication with Tens

The rules for this game are the same as for the basic game except that a 1 is worth 10, a 2 is worth 20, and so on. If you need to review the rules, see the *Student Reference Book,* pages 274 and 275.

Example: If you roll a 4 and a 6, multiply 40 × 60.

Scoreboard

Inning	1	2	3	4	5	6	7
Team 1							
Team 2							

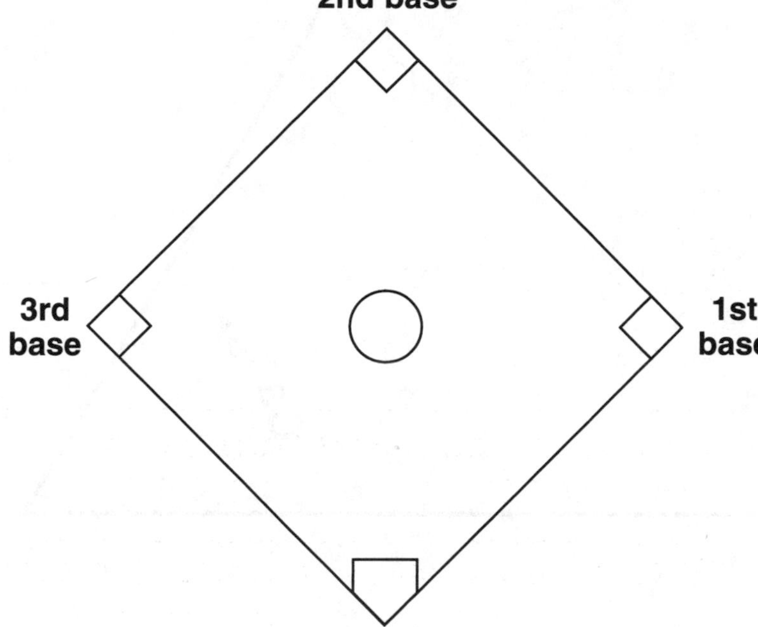

Runs and Outs Table			
Team 1		Team 2	
Runs	Outs	Runs	Outs

Scoring Chart
3,600 = Home run (score a run)
2,600–3,500 = Triple (go to 3rd base)
1,600–2,500 = Double (go to 2nd base)
600–1,500 = Single (go to 1st base)
500 or less = Out (record an out)

Copyright © Wright Group/McGraw-Hill

Name Date Time

Beat the Calculator Triangle

Calculator

Brain

Caller

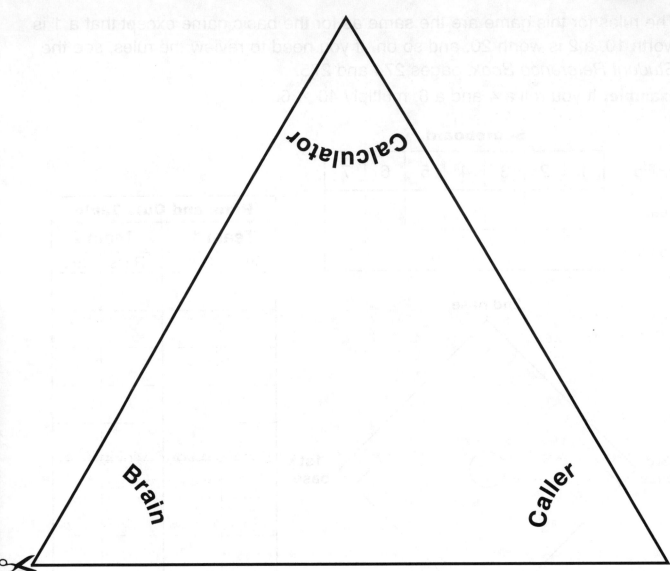

Copyright © Wright Group/McGraw-Hill

Name Date Time

Decimal Solitaire

To play this game, you need

- number cards 0–9 (1 of each)
- 2 pennies or counters to use as decimal points
- 1 index card labeled with ">" greater than
- half-sheet of paper

Directions:

1. Shuffle the number cards.
2. Draw 3 cards.
3. Make a number with 2 decimal places. Use the penny or counter as your decimal point.
4. Place the ">" greater than card next to your number.
5. Draw 3 more cards.
6. Make as many numbers as you can that are less than your original number. Put these numbers to the right of the ">" greater than card.
7. Read each number sentence, and record it on a half-sheet of paper.

Example:

Draw: 5 1 8

Make: 5 . 1 8

Draw: 3 2 4

Number Sentence: 5 . 1 8 > *greater than* . 4 2 3

Copyright © Wright Group/McGraw-Hill

Name Date Time

Factor Bingo Game Mat

Write any of the numbers 2 through 90 on the grid above.

You may use a number only once.

To help you keep track of the numbers you use, circle them in the list.

	2	3	4	5	6	7	8	9	10
11	12	13	14	15	16	17	18	19	20
21	22	23	24	25	26	27	28	29	30
31	32	33	34	35	36	37	38	39	40
41	42	43	44	45	46	47	48	49	50
51	52	53	54	55	56	57	58	59	60
61	62	63	64	65	66	67	68	69	70
71	72	73	74	75	76	77	78	79	80
81	82	83	84	85	86	87	88	89	90

Copyright © Wright Group/McGraw-Hill

Name Date Time

Multiplication Bingo Game Mat

Read the rules for *Multiplication Bingo* on pages 293–295 in the *Student Reference Book.*

For a game with easy facts, use these numbers:
1, 4, 6, 8, 9, 12, 15, 16, 18, 20, 24, 25, 30, 36, 50, 100

For a game with all facts, use these numbers:
24, 27, 28, 32, 35, 36, 42, 45, 48, 49, 54, 56, 63, 64, 72, 81

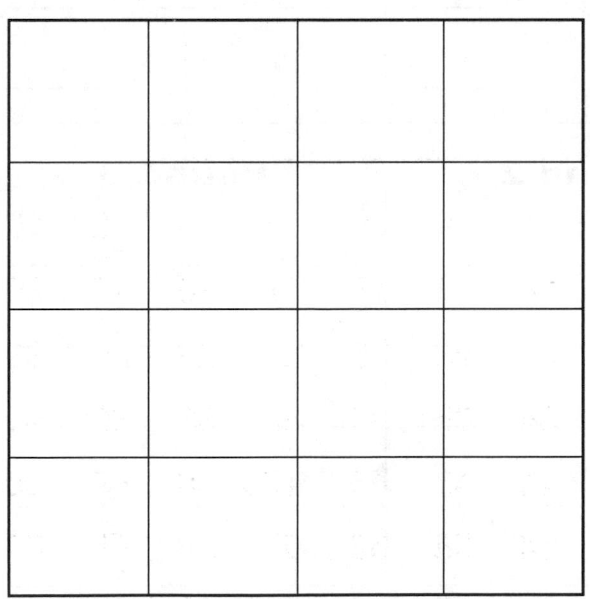

Record the facts you miss on the back of this page. Be sure to practice them!

Copyright © Wright Group/McGraw-Hill

Name Date Time

Multiplication Draw Record Sheet

	Round 1	Round 2	Round 3
1st draw:	____ × ____ = ____	____ × ____ = ____	____ × ____ = ____
2nd draw:	____ × ____ = ____	____ × ____ = ____	____ × ____ = ____
3rd draw:	____ × ____ = ____	____ × ____ = ____	____ × ____ = ____
4th draw:	____ × ____ = ____	____ × ____ = ____	____ × ____ = ____
5th draw:	____ × ____ = ____	____ × ____ = ____	____ × ____ = ____
Sum of products:	______	______	______

	Round 1	Round 2	Round 3
1st draw:	____ × ____ = ____	____ × ____ = ____	____ × ____ = ____
2nd draw:	____ × ____ = ____	____ × ____ = ____	____ × ____ = ____
3rd draw:	____ × ____ = ____	____ × ____ = ____	____ × ____ = ____
4th draw:	____ × ____ = ____	____ × ____ = ____	____ × ____ = ____
5th draw:	____ × ____ = ____	____ × ____ = ____	____ × ____ = ____
Sum of products:	______	______	______

	Round 1	Round 2	Round 3
1st draw:	____ × ____ = ____	____ × ____ = ____	____ × ____ = ____
2nd draw:	____ × ____ = ____	____ × ____ = ____	____ × ____ = ____
3rd draw:	____ × ____ = ____	____ × ____ = ____	____ × ____ = ____
4th draw:	____ × ____ = ____	____ × ____ = ____	____ × ____ = ____
5th draw:	____ × ____ = ____	____ × ____ = ____	____ × ____ = ____
Sum of products:	______	______	______

Copyright © Wright Group/McGraw-Hill

Name Date Time

Name That Number Record Sheet

  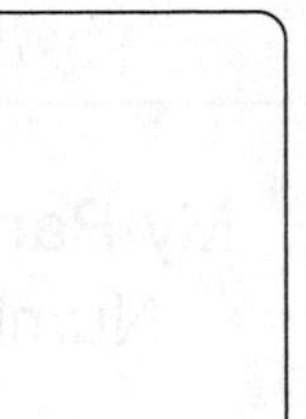 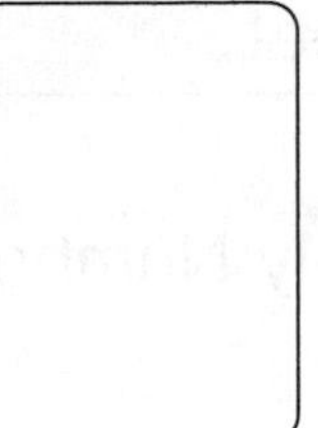

Target Number →

Number Sentence Solution

____

____

____

____

____

Reminder: Write each step separately!

Name Date Time

Name That Number Record Sheet

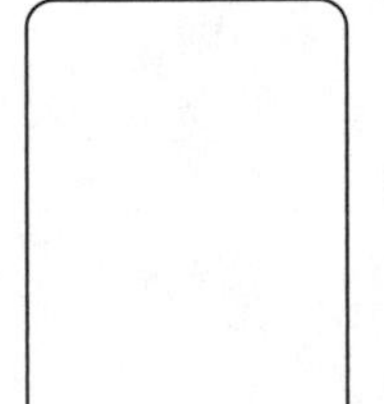   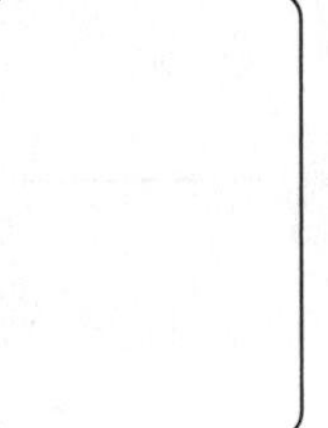 

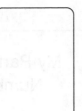

Target Number →

Number Sentence Solution

____

____

____

____

____

Reminder: Write each step separately!

Copyright © Wright Group/McGraw-Hill

Name Date Time

Number-Grid Difference Record Sheet

My Record Sheet

Round	My Number	My Partner's Number	Difference (Score)
1	______	______	______
2	______	______	______
3	______	______	______
4	______	______	______
5	______	______	______

Total: ______

Copyright © Wright Group/McGraw-Hill

Name Date Time

Number Top-It Mat (2-Place Decimals)

Hundredths

Tenths

Ones

0.   0.

Copyright © Wright Group/McGraw-Hill

Name Date Time

Number Top-It Mat (3-Place Decimals)

Ones

Tenths

Hundredths

Thousandths

Copyright © Wright Group/McGraw-Hill

Name Date Time

Pick-a-Coin Record Table

	Ⓟ	Ⓝ	Ⓓ	Ⓠ	$1	Total
1st turn						$____.____
2nd turn						$____.____
3rd turn						$____.____
4th turn						$____.____
					Total	$____.____

	Ⓟ	Ⓝ	Ⓓ	Ⓠ	$1	Total
1st turn						$____.____
2nd turn						$____.____
3rd turn						$____.____
4th turn						$____.____
					Total	$____.____

	Ⓟ	Ⓝ	Ⓓ	Ⓠ	$1	Total
1st turn						$____.____
2nd turn						$____.____
3rd turn						$____.____
4th turn						$____.____
					Total	$____.____

Copyright © Wright Group/McGraw-Hill

Name Date Time

Roll to 100 Record Sheet

Write your score at the end of each turn. The first player to reach or pass 100 wins.

Turn	Player 1 ________	Player 2 ________	Player 3 ________	Player 4 ________
1				
2				
3				
4				
5				
6				
7				
8				
9				
10				

Continue recording scores on the back of this page.

Copyright © Wright Group/McGraw-Hill

Name Date Time

Shading Shapes

Materials □ gameboard and *Shading Shapes* Reference Page (*Math Masters,* p. 458)

Object To claim the most quadrangles

Directions

Players take turns.

1. Shade one small triangle on the gameboard.
2. Players shade triangles to make quadrangles they see on the reference page.
3. When a player shades the final triangle of a quadrangle from the reference page, that player claims the quadrangle by tracing the shape with a finger and saying the name of the quadrangle. When a player claims a quadrangle, he or she scores a point and that quadrangle is no longer available to claim.
4. Finished quadrangles may overlap each other (the same small triangle may be colored twice), but no one can shade exactly the same quadrangle once it has been claimed.
5. The game ends when time runs out or when the gameboard is completely shaded. The winner is the player with the most points.

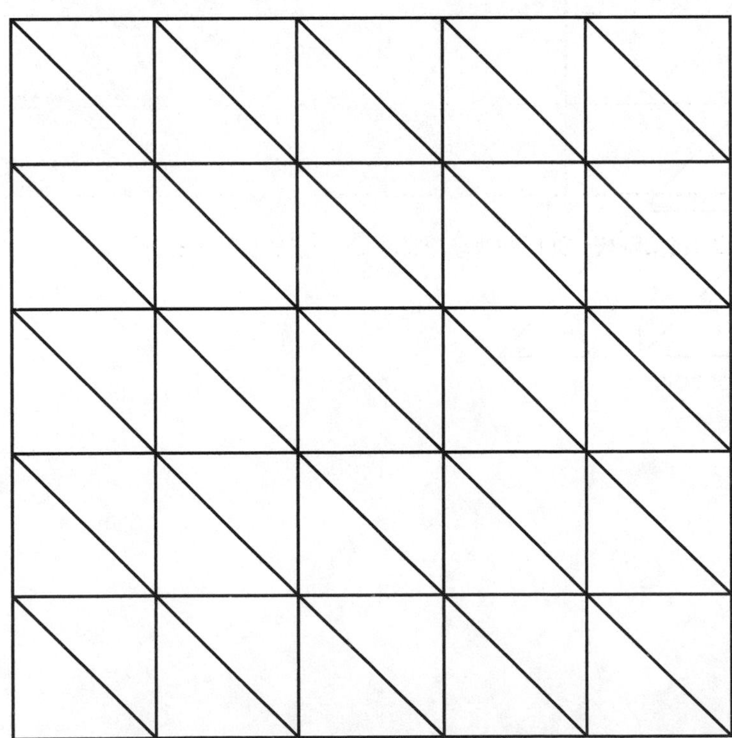

Copyright © Wright Group/McGraw-Hill

Name Date Time

Shading Shapes Reference Page

Shade triangles on the gameboard to make the following quadrangles:

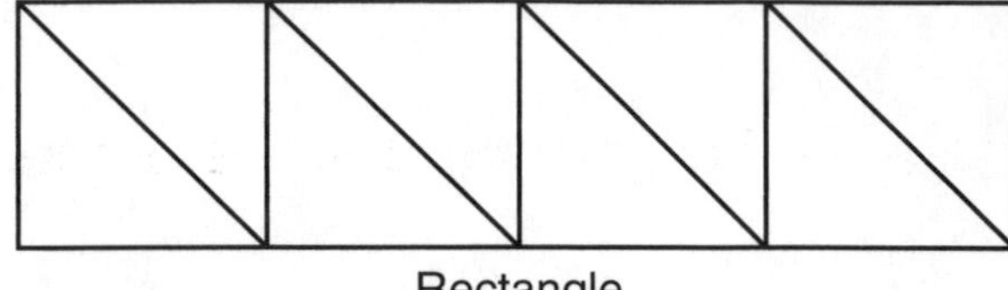

Rectangle

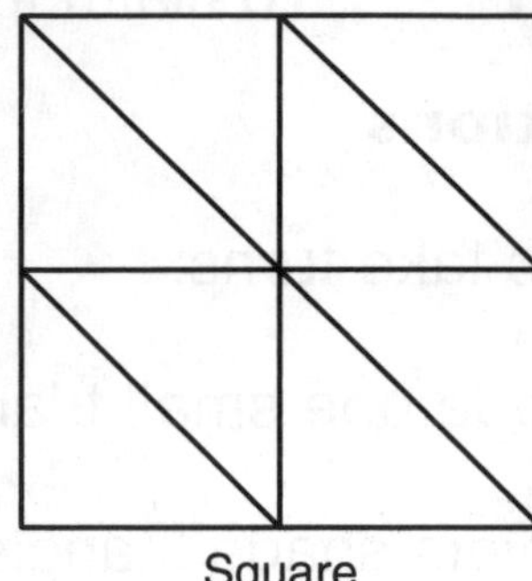

Square

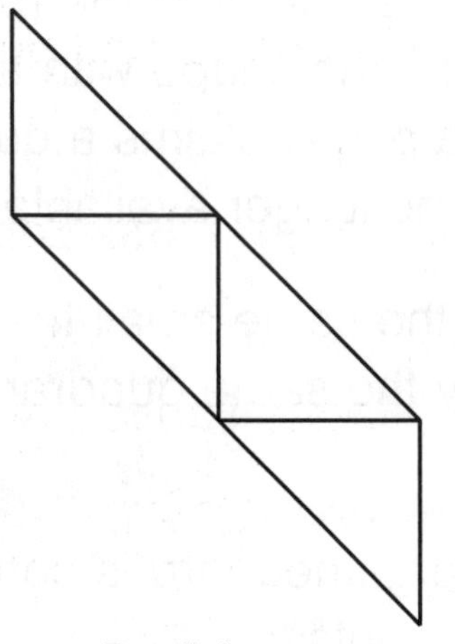

Parallelogram

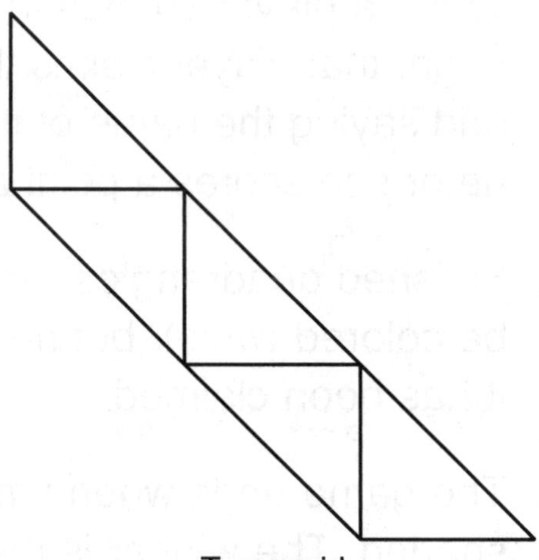

Trapezoid

Trapezoid

Copyright © Wright Group/McGraw-Hill

Name Date Time

Soccer Spin

Materials ☐ *Math Masters,* pp. 460 and 461 ☐ 1 large paper clip
☐ 1 counter per partnership ☐ 1 pencil

Players 2

Object of the game Test the prediction made at the beginning of the game.

Directions

1. Players choose a spinner on *Math Masters,* page 460 to use during the game.
2. Each player chooses a team to cheer for, **Checks** or **Stripes.** (Players can cheer for the same team.) They look at their spinner choice and predict which team will win the game.
3. The game begins with the counter (the ball) in the center of the *Soccer Spin* Game Mat (*Math Masters,* p. 461).
4. Players take turns spinning and moving the counter one space toward the team's goal that comes up on the spinner.
5. The game is over when the counter reaches a goal.
6. Players compare and discuss the results of their predictions.

Use a pencil and paper clip to make a spinner.

Play two more games using the other two spinners.

Copyright © Wright Group/McGraw-Hill

Name Date Time

Three Spinners

Copyright © Wright Group/McGraw-Hill

Name Date Time

Soccer Spin Game Mat

1 2 4 3

Stripes Win!

Checks Win!

Copyright © Wright Group/McGraw-Hill

Name Date Time

Spinning for Money

Materials

- ❑ *Spinning for Money* Spinner (*Math Masters,* p. 463)
- ❑ pencil
- ❑ large paper clip
- ❑ 7 pennies, 5 nickels, 5 dimes, 4 quarters, and one $1 bill for each player
- ❑ one sheet of paper labeled Bank

Players 2, 3, or 4

Directions

1. Each player puts 7 pennies, 5 nickels, 5 dimes, 4 quarters, and one $1 bill into a bank.
2. Players take turns spinning the *Spinning for Money* spinner and taking the coins shown by the spinner from the bank.
3. Whenever possible, players exchange coins for a single coin or bill of the same value. For example, a player could exchange 5 pennies for a nickel or 2 dimes and 1 nickel for a quarter.
4. The first player to exchange for a $1 bill wins.

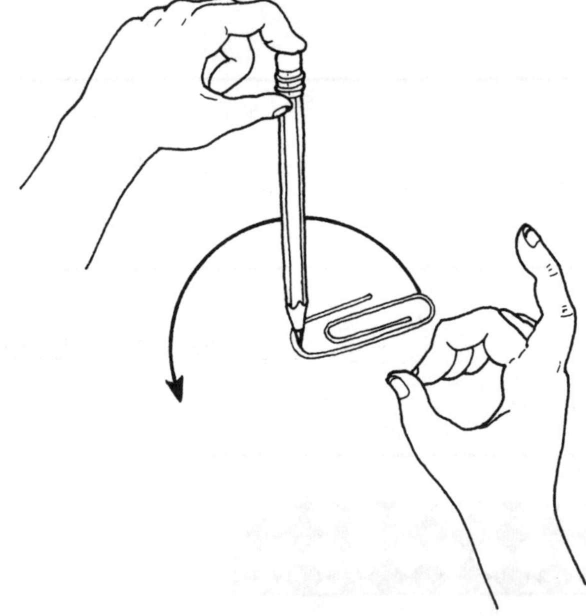

Use a large paper clip and pencil to make a spinner.

Copyright © Wright Group/McGraw-Hill

Name Date Time

Spinning for Money Spinner

Before beginning the game, cut out this ***Spinning for Money* Spinner** on the dashed lines.

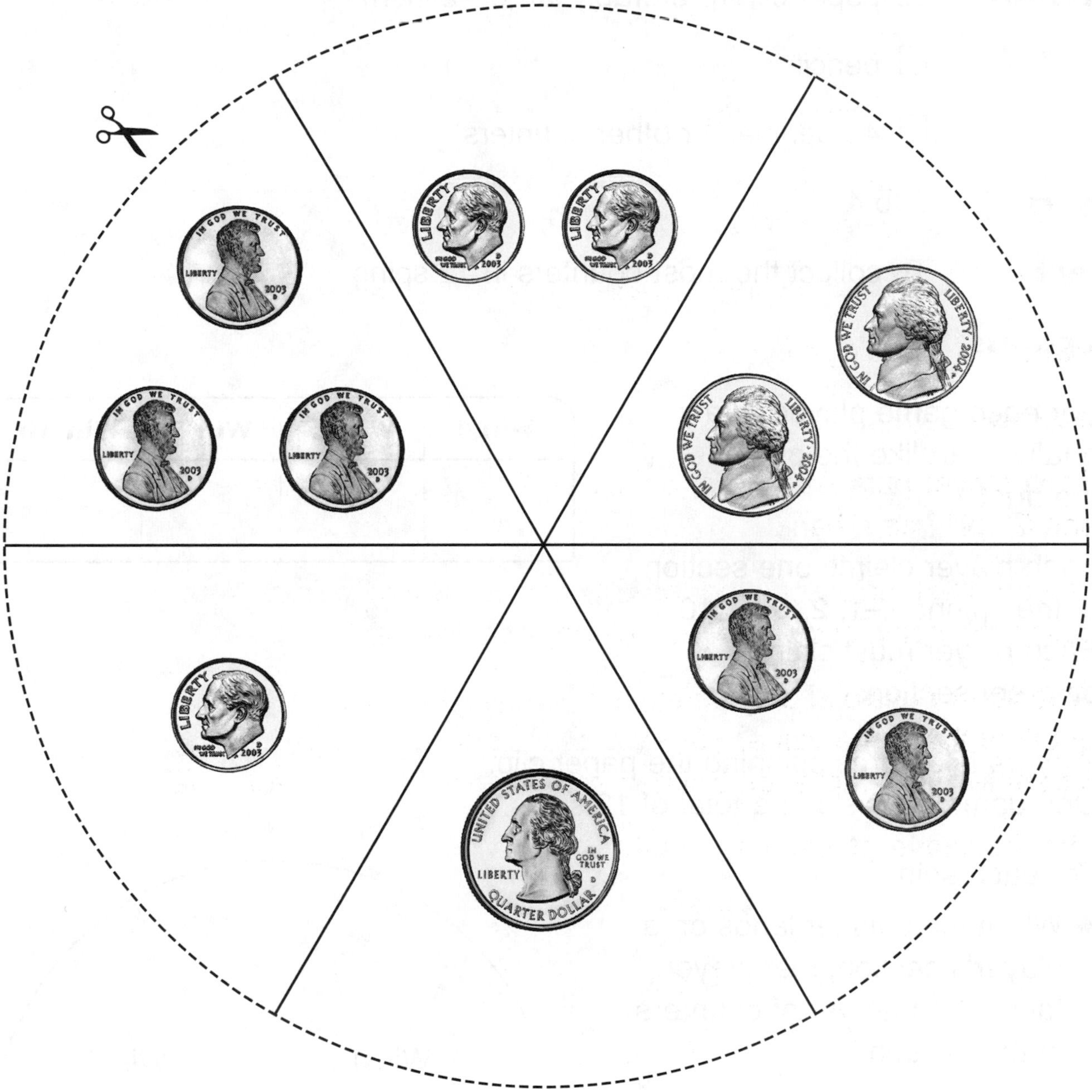

Copyright © Wright Group/McGraw-Hill

Name Date Time

Spinning to Win

Materials ☐ paper clip (preferably large—2 inch)

☐ pencil

☐ 40 pennies or other counters

Players 2 to 4

Object To collect the most counters in 12 spins

Directions

1. For each game played, draw a tally chart like the one at the right.

Win 1	Win 2	Win 5	Win 10

2. Each player claims one section of the spinner—1, 2, 5, or 10. Each player must claim a different section.
3. Players take turns spinning the paper clip. One game consists of a total of 12 spins.
4. For each spin:
    - ◆ When the spinner lands on a player's section, that player takes the number of counters in the section.
    - ◆ After each spin, make a tally mark in the table in the corresponding column to keep track of the spins.
5. The winner is the player with the most counters after 12 spins.

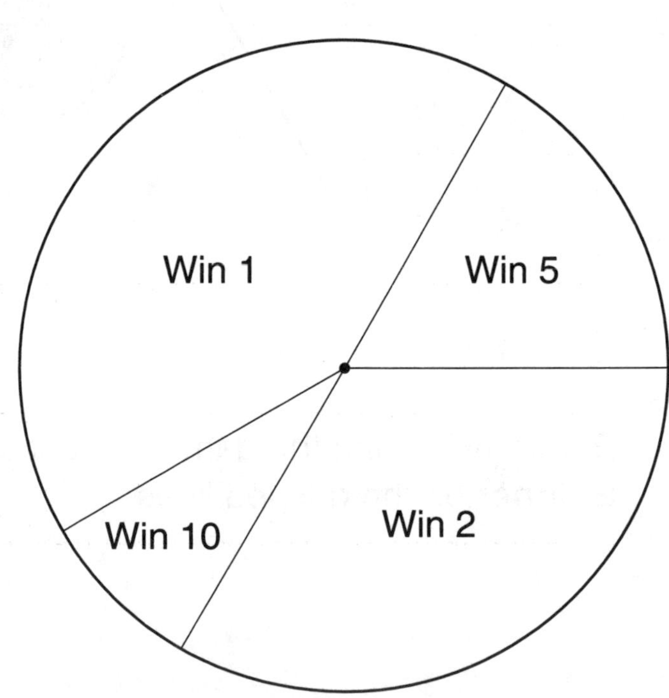

Copyright © Wright Group/McGraw-Hill

Name Date Time

Target: 50 Record Sheet

For each of your turns, record the number you make and the value you show with base-10 blocks on the Place-Value Mat.

Turns	Number You Made	Value on Place-Value Mat
1		
2		
3		
4		
5		
6		
7		
8		
9		
10		

Copyright © Wright Group/McGraw-Hill

Name Date Time

Three Addends Record Sheet

For each turn, write the numbers you picked. Then write a number model.

Unit

1. Numbers: _____, _____, _____

Number model:

_____ + _____ + _____ = _____

2. Numbers: _____, _____, _____

Number model:

_____ + _____ + _____ = _____

3. Numbers: _____, _____, _____

Number model:

_____ = _____ + _____ + _____

4. Numbers: _____, _____, _____

Number model:

_____ = _____ + _____ + _____

5. Numbers: _____, _____, _____

Number model:

_____ = _____ + _____ + _____

6. Numbers: _____, _____, _____

Number model:

_____ + _____ + _____ = _____

7. Numbers: _____, _____, _____

Number model:

_____ + _____ + _____ = _____

8. Numbers: _____, _____, _____

Number model:

_____ = _____ + _____ + _____

Copyright © Wright Group/McGraw-Hill

Name Date Time

Touch-and-Match Quadrangles

Copyright © Wright Group/McGraw-Hill